BUILDING CONTRACT CLAIMS

Second Edition

VINCENT POWELL-SMITH
LLB(Hons), LLM, DLitt, FCIArb

AND

JOHN SIMS
FRICS, FCIArb

BSP PROFESSIONAL BOOKS

OXFORD LONDON EDINBURGH

BOSTON PALO ALTO MELBOURNE

First Edition published in Great Britain by
Granada Publishing 1983
Reprinted 1984
Reprinted with minor amendments by
Collins Professional and Technical Books
1985
Second Edition published by
BSP Professional Books 1988

British Library
Cataloguing in Publication Data

Powell-Smith, Vincent
    Building contract claims.—2nd ed.
    1. Great Britain. Buildings. Construction.
    Contracts. Claims
    I. Title   II. Sims, John, *1929*–
    344.103′7869

ISBN 0–632–02079–2

BSP Professional Books
A division of Blackwell Scientific
    Publications Ltd
Editorial Offices:
Osney Mead, Oxford OX2 0EL
    (Orders: Tel. 0865 240201)
8 John Street, London WC1N 2ES
23 Ainslie Place, Edinburgh EH3 6AJ
3 Cambridge Center, Suite 208, Cambridge
    MA 02142, USA
667 Lytton Avenue, Palo Alto, California
    94301, USA
107 Barry Street, Carlton, Victoria 3053,
    Australia

Set by DP Photosetting, Aylesbury, Bucks
Printed and bound in Great Britain by
Mackays of Chatham plc, Chatham, Kent

Contents

References

The following books are referred to in various parts of the text. Full bibliographical details are therefore given here rather than throughout the text.

Bickford-Smith, S., Anderson, A. J., Freeth, E., Powell-Smith, V., (1980) *Emden's Building Contracts and Practice*, 8th edn., 3 vols., with supplement, London: Butterworth.

Hibberd, Peter R. (1986) *Variations in Construction Contracts*, London: Collins.

Keating, D., (1978) *Building Contracts*, 4th edn. with supplement, London: Sweet & Maxwell.

Parris, John, (1985) *The Standard Form of Building Contract: JCT 80,* 2nd edn. London: Blackwell Scientific Publications.

Wallace, I. N. Duncan, (1969) *Building and Civil Engineering Standard Forms*, with 1970 and 1973 supplements, London: Sweet & Maxwell.

Wallace, I. N. Duncan, (1973) *Further Building and Engineering Standard Forms*. London: Sweet & Maxwell.

Wallace, I. N. Duncan, (1979) *Hudson's Building and Engineering Contracts*, 10th edn. with supplement, London: Sweet & Maxwell.

Acknowledgements

Extracts from JCT 1980, JCT 1963, IFC 84 and the *JCT Guide* are reproduced by kind permission of RIBA Publications Ltd, the copyright holder.

Clauses from the 'Green Form' and DOM/1 and NSC/4 are reproduced with the permission of the Building Employers Confederation, the copyright holders.

Clauses from the ACA Form of Building Agreement and Sub-contract Form are reproduced by permission of the Association of Consultant Architects, Ltd., the copyright holders.

Form GC/Works/1, Crown copyright, is published by HM Stationery Office.

Preface

Building contract claims are a unique combination of law and practice. All contractual, as well as common law, claims must be founded in law – which does not necessarily imply justice let alone mercy – but the proper preparation and evaluation of building contract claims requires knowledge of building practice as much as of law.

This book attempts to set out some of the principles which underlie the whole subject and is the fruit of our joint and several experience of handling building contract claims over more years than we now care to remember. The subject is extremely complex and constantly evolving and, while the text deals essentially with claims arising from and under standard contract forms, readers must not assume that those forms are handbooks of rules sufficient to themselves; they are contracts and must be read and interpreted against the general background of law.

We have dealt with the principles because, in our experience, many claims made by contractors are ill-founded, often because the basic principles have been misunderstood. The mere fact that the contractor may be losing money or not making the profit he hoped is not a basis for a claim. On the other hand, we do not believe (as many architects seem to do) that 'claim' is a dirty word. The contractor's entitlement will be founded in the terms of the contract and in the general law to which it relates, and if a particular contract term confers on the contractor a right to reimbursement of direct loss and/or expense which he has suffered or incurred he is entitled to invoke the machinery laid down in the contract in order to obtain his proper due.

As this book progressed so did our ideas. For the most part, we were in agreement on all essential points; where we differed, or where the position is not clear – because, for example, there is conflicting case law or legal opinion – we have attempted to make our respective or joint views clear. On many points there is room for reasonable argument and opinions can and do differ. The opinions we put forward are based on practice and experience, but we do not claim infallibility.

We have generally avoided worked examples because in our experience these tend to be taken as holy writ and followed slavishly in circumstances quite different from those to which the examples actually relate. What we have endeavoured to provide is a guide through the claims labyrinth. Our book is addressed to all parties involved in the construction scheme. Sometimes we have hard words to say, but no particular criticism of any profession or arm of the construction industry is intended. There are reasonable and unreasonable architects, just as there are reasonable and unreasonable contractors. We accept, too, that lawyers and quantity surveyors can be unreasonable, though in our own cases we believe that our approach is that of the common law 'reasonable man'.

In this second edition we have taken the opportunity to update and expand the text in a number of areas to take account of many important judicial decisions and revisions to the standard forms which have appeared since the first edition was prepared. We have also included references to the JCT Intermediate Form of Building Contract (IFC 84) which is proving extremely popular. We unfortunately still find it necessary to include commentary on the 1963 Edition of the JCT Standard Form since its use, while mercifully declining, still continues among some misguided practitioners and their clients.

In our revisions we have also taken into account comments and criticisms, friendly and unfriendly, in public and in private. The first edition of this book was warmly welcomed not, we suspect, because of its intrinsic merits, but because it filled a need. Of the only two dissentient reviews, only one requires comment; that by an architect who expressed the view that it is 'the architect's duty to decide whether a right to an extension of time or additional payment exists and for the QS to quantify the payment. It is common practice for builders to seek to influence the decisions by the presentation of much supporting information – that is a claim' *RIBA Journal*: Mr Raymond Cecil. We are happy that one of Her Majesty's judges (Mr Justice Vinelott in *London Borough of Merton* v. *Stanley Hugh Leach Ltd* (1985)) agreed with our analysis of what the JCT contracts require since, *pace* Mr Cecil, a contractor's application for direct loss and/or expense cannot be ascertained in a vacuum, and neither the architect – nor the quantity surveyor if the duty of ascertainment is delegated to him – can perform his duty without seeking information from the contractor. The widespread ignorance of many architects about what the standard forms require has led to the growth of a substantial body of case law, all of which we have reviewed in so far as it is relevant to building contract claims. The law is stated as from sources available to us in March 1988, although it has been possible to incorporate certain additional material at proof stage.

The law is stated as from sources available to us in March 1988, although it has been possible to incorporate certain additional material at proof stage.

Once again, we thank Julia Burden of Blackwell Scientific Publications for doing far more than any commissioning editor should reasonably be expected to do. Quite apart from cajoling us, she roused us from our lethargy and then coped with our constant stream of excuses when we failed to deliver the revised text as promised. We should like to dedicate this book to her.

Sintra
London
August 1988

VINCENT POWELL-SMITH
JOHN SIMS

Chapter 1

Introduction

This book is about building contract claims.

DEFINITIONS

A dictionary definition of the word 'claim' is 'an assertion of a right to something'. For the purposes of this book the term may be defined as the assertion of a right to payment arising under the express or implied terms of a building contract, other than under the ordinary contract provisions for payment of the value of the work.

In the construction industry the word 'claim' is commonly used to describe *any* application by the contractor for payment which arises other than under the ordinary contract payment provisions. In this broader sense, a claim includes an application for an *ex gratia* payment, although this would not fall within the dictionary definition given above as it is not the assertion of a right. The word is also used to describe a contractor's application for extension of time under a building contract. In one sense, claims for loss and expense are regulated provisions for the payment of damages.

In fact, there are four types of claim that may be made by contractors against employers if the broader definition is accepted. They are:

(1) Contractual claims
These are claims that arise out of the express provisions of the particular contract, e.g. for 'direct loss and/or expense' under certain clauses of the Joint Contracts Tribunal (JCT) Standard Forms.

(2) Common law claims
Common law claims are usually and misleadingly called 'ex-contractual'

or 'extra-contractual' claims in the construction industry. (These terms should not be confused with the Latin term *ex contractu*, which is sometimes found in legal textbooks to refer to claims 'arising from the contract', i.e. contractual claims as already defined.)

Common law claims are claims for damages for breach of contract at common law and/or legally enforceable claims for breach of some other aspect of the law, e.g. in tort or for breach of copyright. Entitlement to such claims is expressly preserved to the contractor by the JCT Forms: see JCT 80, clause 26.6 and JCT 63, clause 24(2); it is also so preserved by most other standard forms, and a common law claim for breach may avoid some of the restrictions under the contract, as to the giving of notices and so on.

(3) *Quantum meruit* claims

A *quantum meruit* claim ('as much as he has earned') provides a remedy for a person who has carried out work where no price has been agreed or where the original contract has been replaced by a new one and payment is claimed for work done under the substituted contract.

A homely example is where a plumber has been called in by a householder to effect emergency repairs and no price has been agreed in advance. In that case, failing subsequent agreement as to price, the plumber would be entitled in law to 'reasonable' remuneration. A simple reported example of this kind of *quantum meruit* is *Powell* v. *Braun* (1954) where an employer wrote to his secretary saying that he was pleased with her past services and that he wished her to undertake added responsibility in the future. Instead of a salary increase, he offered to pay her a yearly bonus on the net trading profits of the business. She accepted this offer, but the manner in which the bonus was to be assessed was never agreed. The Court of Appeal held that the employer was bound to pay her a reasonable sum each year.

A recent example of a successful *quantum meruit* claim in the construction industry is *Amantilla Ltd* v. *Telefusion PLC* (1987), where the plaintiff carried out building and shop-fitting works for the defendant for an agreed lump sum price of £36,626. The plaintiff agreed to carry out extensive extra works on a daywork basis, but no price was actually agreed. The defendant made various interim payments amounting to £53,000 but the plaintiff's request for a further interim payment of £5000 was not met. Subsequently, correspondence and meetings took place between the parties, during which the plaintiff submitted a detailed breakdown of the cost of the extra works. At no time did the defendant make any complaint about the plaintiff's work and, during a lengthy meeting between the parties the defendant's representative expressed satisfaction with it and 'confirmed' that the defendant would shortly submit an offer of 'somewhere between' £10,000 and £132,000 to settle the account. After further correspondence, the defendant offered the sum of £2000 in full and final settlement, having made a further interim payment. The final offer was rejected and the plaintiff was held entitled to recover on a *quantum meruit* basis.

Similarly, in *British Steel Corporation* v. *Cleveland Bridge & Engineering Co. Ltd* (1981), contractors were held entitled to be paid on a *quantum meruit* in respect of work done on a letter of intent, the High Court finding that no contract had come into existence between the parties, although the plaintiffs had done work to the value of some £230,000 on the basis of a letter of intent from the defendants.

An interesting but rather special case in the field of building contracts is *Sir Lindsay Parkinson & Co. Ltd* v. *Commissioners of Works and Public Buildings* (1950). The plaintiffs contracted with the defendants to erect an ordnance factory at a cost of £3½ million. Under the contract the defendants were entitled to require the plaintiffs to perform additional work and at the date of the contract it was thought that this would cost a further £½ million. Later, the parties further agreed that, in order to complete the work by the date originally fixed, uneconomic methods should be employed which would add £1 million to the cost of the work, and that the plaintiffs should be allowed a net profit of at least £150,000 but not more than £300,000 on the actual cost of the works. It was clear from the evidence that at this time the total cost was estimated to be approximately £5 million. In fact, the total cost of the work exceeded £6½ million.

The Court of Appeal held that the plaintiffs were entitled to be paid a reasonable profit on the excess cost of £1½ million in addition to the maximum profit of £300,000 previously agreed. This was because the upper and lower limits of profit were based on an estimated cost of the works made at the time of the further agreement. It was because that estimate had been greatly exceeded, at the request of the employer, that the contractors were entitled to be paid the additional profit.

In fact, a reading of the full report of the case illustrates the difficulty of establishing such a claim and the facts were very special. Moreover, it is quite clear that 'in the absence of express provision, there is no principle ... that agreed fees under "cost-plus-fee" contracts should be raised if cost exceeds estimates': *Hudson's Building and Engineering Contracts*, 10th Edition, page 551.

However, what is in effect a *quantum meruit* approach to the contractor's claim for damages for disruption and delay has been adopted in Canada in the case of *Penvidic Contracting Co., Ltd* v. *International Nickel Co. of Canada, Ltd* (1975), where the contractor was held entitled to claim the price he would have charged for the job had he foreseen the problems caused by the employer's breaches of contract at the time he tendered. There was evidence that the figure claimed was a reasonable estimate, and Mr Justice Spence saw no objection to 'using the method suggested by the plaintiff ... rather than attempting to reach it by ascertaining items of expense from records which, by the very nature of the contract, had to be fragmentary and probably mere estimations'. In effect, the contractor there performed work which was substantially different from what he tendered for, and effectively the court adopted a 'broad brush' approach to the assessment of damages. The general principle is that damages are purely compensatory and, as will be seen, under JCT and allied forms, loss and expense claims can be equated to common law damages for breach of contract.

(4) *Ex gratia* claims

An *ex gratia* ('out of kindness') claim is one which the employer is under no legal obligation to meet. It is sometimes called a 'sympathetic' claim. *Ex gratia* claims are often put forward by contractors but are seldom met unless some benefit may accrue to the employer as a result. For example, an employer might agree to make an *ex gratia* payment to save a contractor from insolvency where the cost of employing another contractor to complete the work would be more than the amount of the *ex gratia* payment.

ARCHITECT'S POWERS

Under JCT contracts the architect's powers are limited. For example, JCT 80, clause 4.1.1 [JCT 63, clause 2(1)], obliges the contractor to comply only with instructions 'expressly empowered by the Conditions', and a later sub-clause provides a method whereby the contractor may challenge the architect's authority to issue a particular instruction.

In a claims situation, the architect can certify for payment only sums which the express terms of the contract authorise him to so certify. Under the JCT Standard Forms the architect has no power to certify amounts in respect of common law, *quantum meruit* or *ex gratia* claims. A contract may, of course, endow the architect with authority to do so.

All too often architects assume, incorrectly, that they enjoy inherent powers to act as the employer's agents in all respects. The same mistaken assumption is often made by contractors who consequently are disappointed when the architect correctly refuses to certify payment for such claims. Under the JCT Forms of Contract the powers of the architect as agent of the employer and to certify sums for payment are closely defined, and the architect may himself be at risk if he exceeds the powers so conferred upon him.

QUANTITY SURVEYOR'S POWERS

The powers of the quantity surveyor are similarly limited to those expressly conferred upon him by the terms of the contract. Under the JCT Standard Forms these powers generally consist of the valuation of variations, valuations of work done for interim payment (1980 Edition only), and the ascertainment of any direct loss and/or expense incurred by the contractor where, under the relevant clauses, the architect instructs him so to do.

The limited nature of the quantity surveyor's powers under JCT forms was confirmed by the decision of Mr Justice Webster in *County & District Properties, Ltd* v. *John Laing Construction, Ltd* (1982) where this question arose under a contract in JCT 63 form. His lordship said:

'His authority and function under the contract are confined to measuring and quantifying. The contract gives him authority, at least in certain instances, to decide quantum. It does not in any instance give him authority to determine any liability, or liability to make any payment or allowance.'

The judge then went on to deal specifically with the position under JCT 63, clause 11 (4), where it is provided that 'the valuation of variations ... *unless otherwise agreed* shall be made in accordance with the following rules'. His lordship said that it was suggested in argument that

'those words meant "agreed by or with the quantity surveyor". I reject that submission. In my view the words can only mean"agreed between the parties", although it may well be that on occasion a quantity surveyor may perhaps be given express authority by the employer to make such an agreement.'

This point does not arise, in any case, under JCT 80, since clause 13.4.1. uses the words 'unless otherwise agreed by the Employer and the Contractor', i.e. between the parties to the contract.

Mr Justice Webster added:

'The JCT contract does not give him that authority. There are few express references to him in the contract. He is identified in article 4 of the Articles of Agreement. By clause 11 (4), he is given the express duty of measuring and valuing variations. By clause 11 (6) he is given the duty of ascertaining loss and expense involved in a variation – but only if so instructed by the architect. By clause 24 (1), he is given a similar duty in respect of loss or expense caused by disturbance of the work etc – but only if instructed by the architect'.

The position is, in our view, the same under JCT 80 so far as the quantity surveyor's powers are concerned. The terms of the contract, express and implied, give the quantity surveyor no independent authority.

ORIGIN AND BASIS OF CLAIMS

Contractual claims as defined must originate from a particular clause in the contract. Under the JCT Standard Forms the following clauses may give rise to money claims:

JCT 63	JCT 80	IFC 84
Clause 11 (6) – Variations, provisional and prime cost sums		
Clause 24 (1) – Disturbance of regular progress of the works	Clause 26 – Matters materially affecting regular progress of the works	Clause 4.11 – Disturbance of regular progress
Clause 34 (3) – Antiquities	Clause 34.3 – Antiquities	Clause 4.12 – Matters referred to in Clause 8.12

The JCT Standard Forms also contain provisions enabling the architect to extend the time for completion of the contract (JCT 63, clause

23; JCT 80, clause 25; IFC 84, clauses 2.3–2.8). However, an extension of the contract time does not, of itself, give the contractor any right to make a money claim. Conversely, it is not necessary for the contract time to be extended in order for the contractor to have a right to make a money claim. There is considerable confusion in the construction industry on this point.

This confusion no doubt arises because under JCT Forms all of the grounds on which the contractor can make a money claim are also grounds that may entitle him to an extension of time. But it is not the granting of an extension of time that gives rise to the entitlement to money but the fact of delay and/or disruption of regular working. There is no necessary link between the grant or refusal of an extension of time and the success of a contractor's application for direct loss and/or expense: *H. Fairweather & Co. Ltd* v. *London Borough of Wandsworth* (1988).

Generally speaking, unexpected difficulty or expense in completing the contract does not entitle the contractor to refuse to carry out the work or to claim additional payment. This statement is well illustrated by the case of *Davis Contractors Ltd* v. *Fareham Urban District Council* heard by the House of Lords in 1956.

The plaintiffs agreed with the Fareham Council to build for them seventy-eight council houses within a period of 8 months for a firm price. There was a shortage of skilled labour, and the work of erecting the houses took 22 months to complete as a result. The contractors claimed that by reason of the scarcity of labour the contract has been brought to an end and that they were entitled to recover a sum in excess of the contract price on the basis of a *quantum meruit*.

The House of Lords found against the contractors. An unexpected turn of events that renders the performance of a contract more onerous than the parties contemplated does not release the party adversely affected from the contract. Here, the scarcity of labour, which was not due to the fault of either party, was not sufficient to justify a finding that the contract had been brought to an end when the expectations of the parties were not realised. Accordingly, the contractors had not been released from the terms of the contract as regards price and could not maintain a claim for payment on a *quantum meruit*.

In the Court of Appeal – which also ruled against the contractors – Lord Justice Denning, as he then was, put the matter in a nutshell when he said:

'We could seriously damage the sanctity of contracts if we allowed a builder to charge more, simply because, without anyone's fault, the work took him much longer than he thought.'

The *Davis* case may be contrasted with the *Parkinson* case quoted earlier in this chapter (see page 13). The distinguishing point being that in the latter case considerably more work was done than was originally contemplated in the contract.

Chapter 2

Extensions of time and liquidated damages

INTRODUCTION

All the standard forms of building contract contain provisions for the granting of extensions of time and for payment of liquidated damages by the contractor in the event of late completion. In the absence of express contractual power to extend the time for completion, the architect could not do so. In practice, the main relevance of claims for extension of time is in relation to the contractor's liability to pay liquidated damages.

Extension of time provisions and liquidated damages clauses are closely linked, and failure by the architect properly to exercise the power to extend time, where any delay is caused by the employer (or for which the employer is responsible in law), relieves the contractor from his liability to pay liquidated damages (*Dodd* v. *Churton* (1897)) and the time for completion may become 'at large'.

In the New Zealand case of *Fernbrook Trading Co. Ltd* v. *Taggart* (1979), Mr Justice Roper expressed the view that

'no one rule of construction to cover all the circumstances can be postulated, and the best that can be said on the present state of the authorities is that whether the completion date is set at large by a delay in granting an extension must depend upon the particular circumstances pertaining'.

It is submitted that this statement is an accurate expression of the position in English law as well, and so far as JCT contracts are concerned the position has been clarified by the House of Lords in *Percy Bilton Ltd* v. *Greater London Council* (1982), discussed later in this chapter.

The case of *Peak Construction (Liverpool) Ltd* v. *McKinney Foundations*

19

Ltd (1970) is modern authority for the view that if any part of the delay is caused by the employer, however slight and unless it falls within the *de minimis* rule, then the liquidated damages clause becomes inoperative. It may be, however, that this may be subject to some future qualification. In *The Rapid Building Group Ltd* v. *Ealing Family Housing Association Ltd* (1985), Lord Justice Lloyd said, *obiter*:

> 'I can well understand how that must necessarily be so in a case in which the delay is indivisible and there is a dispute as to the extent of the employer's responsibility for that delay. But where there are, as it were, two separate and distinct periods of delay, and where the dispute relates to only one of those two causes, then it would seem to me just and convenient that the employer should be able to claim liquidated damages in relation to the other period'.

This is a possible pointer to future developments.

Where the contract completion date ceases to be applicable because time has become 'at large' and the contractor's obligation is one to complete 'within a reasonable time', if the work is not so completed, the employer's remedy is to sue for damages on the basis of his actual proven loss. What is a reasonable time is a question of fact in each case, and the employer can serve notice on the contractor after a reasonable time for performance has elapsed requiring completion by a specified date: *Charles Rickards Ltd* v. *Oppenheim* (1950). In these circumstances, if the contractor fails to complete on time, the employer may treat the contract as being at an end: *Felton* v. *Wharrie* (1906).

In *The Rapid Building Group Ltd* v. *Ealing Family Housing Association Ltd* (1985), the Court of Appeal considered the situation where the employer is himself in breach of contract – in that case by failure to give possession of the site to the contractor as required by JCT 63, clause 21 – and has a counterclaim for damages for the contractor's alleged failure to complete on time. The court held that 'where the claim for liquidated damages has been lost or has gone ... the [employers] are not precluded from pursuing their counterclaim for unliquidated damages': *per* Lord Justice Stephenson. Lord Justice Lloyd agreed and emphasised that such a counterclaim for unliquidated damages 'can be set-off against the sum due to the contractors under the architect's certificates' on the basis of the decision of the House of Lords in *Modern Engineering (Bristol) Ltd* v. *Gilbert-Ash (Northern) Ltd* (1974).

An interesting point fell to be considered by the Court of Appeal in *Temloc Ltd* v. *Errill Properties Ltd* (1987), where the contract was in JCT

80 terms and the Appendix entry for liquidated damages had been completed as '£nil' and the period over which payment was to be made was left blank. The court ruled that where the parties completed the relevant part of the Appendix, either by stating a rate at which the sum was to be calculated or, as in this case, by stating that the sum was '£nil', this constituted an exhaustive agreement as to the damages which were or were not payable by the contractor in respect of his failure to complete on time. There was no scope for any claim for unliquidated damages or for breach of an implied term that work would be completed within a reasonable time which would give rise to a claim for unliquidated damages. The point was an important one from the employer's point of view because there were claims against the employer by third parties arising out of delay in completion.

The employer argued, unsuccessfully, that '£nil' meant that there was no effective clause for liquidated damages, and that it might therefore still sue for damages at large. The Court of Appeal said that '£nil' did not mean that there was no effective liquidated damages clause. There was, but the damages had been expressed in a negative way. Lord Justice Croom-Johnson put the matter thus:

'On the wording of clause 24 there is no choice available. Any such claim for damages at large would have to be based on an implied term in the contract. If clause 24 had been excluded from the contract altogether, as submitted by (the employer), it would have been necessary to imply such a term and give effect to it. But as clause 24 is tied to dates certified by the architect and a method of calculation is provided in the Appendix, there is no room for implying such a term. Clause 24 is headed "Damages for non-completion" and then lays down an agreed provision for calculating these by liquidated damages, which is covering all the damages for non-completion'.

LIQUIDATED DAMAGES

The JCT contracts contain provisions for the payment by the contractor of a fixed sum of money as 'liquidated and ascertained damages' at a specified rate per week or month in the event of late completion.

JCT 63, clause 22, provides as follows:

22 **Damages for non-completion**
'If the contractor fails to complete the Works by the Date for Completion stated in the Appendix to these Conditions or within any extended time fixed under

clause 23 or clause 33 (1)(c) of these Conditions and the Architect certifies in writing that in his opinion the same ought reasonably so to have been completed, then the Contractor shall pay or allow to the Employer a sum calculated at the rate stated in the said Appendix as Liquidated and Ascertained Damages for the period during which the Works shall so remain or have remained incomplete, and the Employer may deduct such sum from any monies due or to become due to the Contractor under this Contract.'

The corresponding provision in JCT 80 is clause 24, which reads:

24 Damages for non-completion
Certificate of architect
24.1 'If the Contractor fails to complete the Works by the Completion Date then the Architect shall issue a certificate to that effect.

Payment of allowance of liquidated damages

24.2 .1 Subject to the issue of a certificate under clause 24.1 the Contractor shall, as the Employer may require in writing not later than the date of the Final Certificate, pay or allow to the Employer the whole or such part as may be specified in writing by the Employer of a sum calculated at the rate stated in the Appendix as liquidated and ascertained damages for the period between the Completion Date and the date of Practical Completion and the Employer may deduct the same from any monies due or to become due to the Contractor under this Contract (including any balance stated as due to the Contractor in the Final Certificate) or the Employer may recover the same from the Contractor as a debt.
.2 If, under clause 25.3.3, the Architect fixes a later Completion Date the Employer shall pay or repay to the Contractor any amounts recovered allowed or paid under clause 24.2.1 for the period up to such later Completion Date.'

(The equivalent clauses, in IFC 84 are reviewed below. See page 33.)

A comparison of the wording shows that there are significant differences between the two provisions, but both clauses carefully refer to 'liquidated and ascertained damages'. To be enforceable a liquidated damages clause must represent a genuine pre-estimate of the loss that will be caused by the particular breach of contract – in this case, failure to complete by the agreed date – or a sum lower than that. Where the clause is valid, it is irrelevant that the actual loss is greater or less than the estimated amount, or even that there is no loss at all: *Clydebank Engineering and Shipbuilding Co. Ltd* v. *Don José Ramos Yzquierdo y Castaneda* (1905).

An agreed damages clause of this type is valid and enforceable provided the amount is a genuine pre-estimate of the loss that is likely to be caused to the employer by late completion or a lower sum. Where a lower sum is specified – and often the amount is purely nominal compared with the potential loss – the clause also operates as a limit on the contractor's liability. This is a point that is frequently overlooked.

A provision for liquidated damages thus defines the risk that the contractor is undertaking and also saves the employer the trouble and expense of proving his actual loss in litigation. It does not matter that the actual loss is hard to assess, for, as Lord Halsbury LC remarked in the *Clydebank Engineering Co. Ltd* case, 'the very reason why the parties agreed to such a stipulation was that, sometimes, the nature of the damage was such that proof would be extremely difficult, complex and expensive'. In that case, shipbuilders contracted to build four torpedo-boat destroyers for the Spanish Government at an agreed price, delivery to be within specified periods. The contract provided that liquidated damages for late delivery 'should be at the rate of £500 a week for each vessel not delivered by the contractors in the contract time'. The vessels were delivered late. The Spanish Government paid the full price, but claimed from the shipbuilders £500 for each week of late delivery.

The House of Lords held that the claim was enforceable, and summarily dismissed the shipbuilders' argument 'that there could be no measure of damages in the case of a warship which had no commercial value at all'. Lord Halsbury LC said,

'It is a strange and somewhat bold assertion to say that, in the case of a commercial ship, the damages could easily be ascertained, but that the same principle could not be applied to a warship as it earned nothing. The deprivation of a nation of its warships might mean very serious damage, although it might not be very easy to ascertain the amount. But is that a reason for saying they were to have no damages at all? It seems to me hopeless to advance such a contention. It is only necessary to state the assertion to show how absurd it is.'

These principles apply, with equal force, to the construction industry where, in some cases, such as those of educational buildings, ecclesiastical buildings, and housing association projects, the argument is sometimes put forward by contractors that the amount fixed for liquidated damages is such as to render it a penalty, either because – it is said – there is no loss or alternatively because the likely loss is impossible to estimate.

In fact, the converse is the case, and in such circumstances it is a common and sensible practice to use a simple formula, which gives an approximation to the detailed analysis of all individual costs. The best-known formula method of calculation is that suggested by the Society of

Chief Quantity Surveyors in Local Government. This formula gives three main headings under which the calculation should be made:

(1) Assume that at the anticipated completion date 80% of the total capital cost of the scheme (including fees) will have been advanced and that interest at the current rate is being paid. Assuming an interest rate of 12%, capitalised interest will be

$$\frac{80\% \times 12\%}{52} = 0.185\% \text{ of the contract sum per week.}$$

(2) Administrative costs are assessed as 2.75% of the contract sum per year.
(3) Exceptional costs, e.g. temporary classrooms.

The net result of (1) and (2) of the above formula reduces to 0.237% of the contract sum per week. It may well be that such a figure under-represents the losses, but it is thought that such a calculation is a fair and reasonable approach to use.

Another calculation is that recommended by the Housing Corporation for housing association work, under which it is suggested that 30% of the total capital cost of the scheme is multiplied by the current interest rate and then divided by 52 to give a weekly figure.

Such formulae are useful where the actual loss is difficult to assess; but in commercial contracts it is a fairly simple matter for the employer and his advisers to estimate the possible loss at the time the contract is made. If the figure is a genuine pre-estimate of the loss as reasonably envisaged at that time, the courts will not interfere with it, and that is the figure recoverable whether the actual loss be greater or less.

Liquidated damages must be distinguished from penalties, but the distinction is not always easy to appreciate, as Lord Cranworth LC recognised in *Ranger* v. *Great Western Railway Co.* (1854).

'The distinction between a penalty and a sum fixed as the conventional amount of damages is too well established to be now called into question, however difficult it may be to say in any particular case under which head the stipulation is to be classed.'

A penalty clause is unenforceable. A clause will be a penalty and not a genuine pre-estimate of loss (1) if the sum stipulated is extravagant in relation to the greatest possible loss that could be suffered, or (2) as a general rule, if a single sum is payable in relation to various breaches with widely differing consequences. This second principle is inapplicable to standard form contracts in the construction industry because the standard liquidated damages clauses are limited to the breach of late completion.

The principles applied by the courts to determine whether a clause is a provision for liquidated damages or a penalty were summarised by Lord Dunedin in *Dunlop Ltd* v. *New Garage Co. Ltd* (1915) in a speech that is regarded as a classic exposition of the position. He said that the following propositions are supported by the case law:

'(i) Though the parties to a contract who use the words penalty or liquidated damages may *prima facie* be supposed to mean what they say, yet the expression used is not conclusive. The court must find out whether the payment stipulated is in truth a penalty or liquidated damages.... (ii) The essence of a penalty is a payment of money stipulated as *in terrorem* of the offending party; the essence of liquidated damages is a genuine covenanted pre-estimate of damage. (iii) The question whether a sum stipulated is penalty or liquidated damages is a question of construction to be decided upon the terms and inherent circumstances of each particular contract, judged as at the time of the making of the contract, not as at the time of the breach. (iv) To assist this task of construction various tests have been suggested, which, if applicable to the case under consideration, may prove helpful or even conclusive. Such are: (a) It will be held to be a penalty if the sum stipulated for is extravagant and unconscionable in amount in comparison with the greatest loss which could conceivably be proved to have followed from the breach.... (b) It will be held to be a penalty if the breach consists only in not paying a sum of money, and the sum stipulated is a sum greater than the sum which ought to have been paid.... This ... is truly a corollary to the last test. (c) There is a presumption (but no more) that it is a penalty when "a single lump sum is made payable by way of compensation, on the occurrence of one or more or all of several events, some of which may occasion serious and others but trifling damages". On the other hand (d) it is no obstacle to the sum stipulated being a genuine pre-estimate of damage that the consequences of the breach are such as to make precise pre-estimation almost an impossibility. On the contrary, that is just the situation when it is probable that the pre-estimated damage was the true bargain between the parties.'

It is, of course, a defence to a claim for liquidated damages to establish that the specified sum is a penalty, the onus of showing that this is so lying on the party making the allegation. If it can be established that the sum is a penalty, that is a defence to any claim by way of action or deduction under the express terms of the contract. Conversely, the fact that the sum is in truth a penalty may be advantageous to the employer. In such a case, it is suggested by Donald Keating in *Building Contracts*, 4th Edition, page 60, that 'he may either rely on his claim for the penalty, in which case he cannot recover more than the actual loss which he proves up to the amount of the penalty, or he can ignore the penalty and sue for unliquidated damages: *Watts, Watts & Co Ltd* v. *Mitsui & Co. Ltd* (1917)'.

If the sum is found to be a penalty, this is not a complete bar to the employer's claim. He is merely left to prove his actual loss, which he recovers by way of unliquidated damages.

Liquidated damages clauses are, it is thought, caught by the provisions of the misnamed Unfair Contract Terms Act 1977, which was designed to limit the use of exclusion or exemption clauses. The Act follows Law Commission Report No. 69, which gave as an example of the type of exclusion clause contemplated by section 3(2)(a) of the Act one providing for liquidated damages. So far as liquidated damages clauses in standard form construction industry contracts are concerned, we take the view that if in truth a particular clause does provide for liquidated damages (as opposed to a penalty) it would be upheld as satisfying the test of reasonableness introduced by the Act, as being a genuine pre-estimate of loss.

It is often said that liquidated damages clauses must be construed *contra proferentem*, i.e. strictly against the person relying on the clause and, indeed, this is the general position as was made clear by Lord Justice Salmon in *Peak Construction (Liverpool) Ltd* v. *McKinney Foundations Ltd* (1970) in his observations both about extension of time provisions and about liquidated damages clauses. His lordship was there dealing with Liverpool Corporation's own form of contract, and he said:

'The liquidated damages and extension of time clauses in printed forms of contract must be construed strictly *contra proferentem*. If the employer wishes to recover liquidated damages for failure by the contractors to complete on time in spite of the fact that some of the delay is due to the employer's own fault or breach of contract, then the extension of time clause should provide, expressly or by necessary inference, for an extension on account of such a fault or breach on the part of the employer.'

These generalised observations most certainly apply to unilaterally drafted contracts but, in our view, they have no application at all to the extension of time and liquidated damages clauses under the JCT Forms of Contract nor, indeed, under any negotiated form of contract; they apply only where the form of contract is put forward by the employer so that it is his own contract. In our opinion, the rule does not apply to a negotiated standard form contract, such as the JCT Forms, and the generally accepted position was made plain by Lord Justice Pearson in *Tersons Ltd* v. *Stevenage Development Corporation* (1963) in considering the argument that the second edition ICE conditions (a similarly negotiated document) were to be construed *contra proferentem*. His lordship said:

> 'The maxim has little, if any, application in this case. The General Conditions are not a partisan document or an "imposed standard contract" as that phrase is sometimes used. It was not drawn up by one party in its own interests and imposed on the other party. It is a general form, evidently in common use, and prepared and revised jointly by several representative bodies .... It would naturally be incorporated in a contract of this kind, and should have the same meaning whether the one party or the other happens to have made the first mention of it in the negotiations.'

This statement applies equally to the JCT Form and we agree with Dr John Parris (*The Standard Form of Building Contract: JCT 80*; Section 7.01 on the provisions regarding liquidated damages) that the liquidated damages and extension of time clauses in JCT contracts 'are there for the benefit of both [parties]. It is a wholly incorrect approach to consider each clause and attribute each to one or other party. The contract must be taken as a whole'.

The liquidated damages clause in *Peak Construction (Liverpool) Ltd* v. *McKinney Foundations Ltd* was a very unusual one; and the terms of the contract as a whole were so one-sided as to be virtually unbelievable. The particular liquidated damages clause said that 'time shall be considered of the essence of the contract on the part of the contractor', and this is an unusual provision to find in any building contract.

Two further passages from the judgment of Lord Justice Salmon in that case are worthy of quotation, bearing in mind that they are general observations:

> 'A clause giving the employer liquidated damages at so much a week or month which elapses between the date fixed for completion and the

actual date of completion is usually coupled ... with an extension of time clause. The liquidated damages clause contemplates a failure to complete on time due to the fault of the contractor. It is inserted by the employer for his own protection; for it enables him to recover a fixed sum as compensation for delay instead of facing the difficulty and expense of proving the actual damage which the delay may have caused him. If the failure to complete on time is due to the fault of both the employer and the contractor, in my view, the clause does not bite. I cannot see how, in the ordinary course, the employer can insist on compliance with a condition if it is partly his own fault that it cannot be fulfilled.'

He later continued:

'I consider that unless the contract expresses a contrary intention, the employer, in the circumstances postulated, is left to his ordinary remedy; that is to say, to recover such damages as he can prove flow from the contractor's breach. No doubt if the extension of time clause provided for a postponement of the completion date on account of delay caused by some breach or fault on the part of the employer, the position would be different. This would mean that the parties had intended that the employer could recover liquidated damages notwithstanding that he was partly to blame for the failure to achieve the completion date. In such a case the architect would extend the date for completion and the contractor would then be liable to pay liquidated damages for delay as from the extended completion date.'

Substantial alterations made by the employer to a negotiated standard form contract might well cause any ambiguities in it to be interpreted *contra proferentem* the employer. The rule is one of last resort, dealing with the situation where there is an ambiguity in a document so that, after all other rules of construction have failed to resolve the problem, there are two possible meanings to certain words. In that event the court will construe the words against the party seeking to rely on them and give effect to the meaning more favourable to the other party.

It must also be said that, even as regards negotiated standard form contracts, different views have been expressed by the courts. For example, in *Monmouthshire County Council* v. *Costelloe & Kemple Ltd* (1965), and which arose under the second edition of the ICE Conditions, Lord Justice Harman said of the arbitration clause that:

'one must construe it with some strictness as having a forfeiting effect.

It is not a penal clause, but it must be construed against the party putting it forward who is, after all, trying to shut out the ordinary citizen's right to go to the courts to have his grievances ventilated'.

The better view, however, is generally taken to be that of Lord Justice Pearson in *Tersons Ltd* v. *Stevenage Development Corporation*.

On the other hand, in *Bramall & Ogden Ltd* v. *Sheffield City Council* (1985) the court did apply the *contra proferentem* rule to the liquidated damages provisions of a contract in JCT 63 form, but in rather special circumstances. The contract was for the construction of 123 houses, together with ancillary works. The date for completion was stated in the appendix as 6 December 1976, but the liquidated damages entry in the Appendix was '£20 per week for each uncompleted dwelling'. No sectional completion supplement was entered into, but by agreement houses were taken over by the employer as they were completed. On these facts, the Senior Official Referee, Judge Lewis Hawser QC, held that the employers were not entitled to claim or deduct liquidated damages in respect of the dwellings which were completed late. The provision was construed *contra proferentem* and was unenforceable because the appendix entry was expressed in a manner which was inconsistent with the contract provisions to which it related, specifically with clause 16 (a) dealing with the adjustment of liquidated damages in the event of 'partial possession' by the employer.

Position under JCT Forms
The text of the liquidated damages provisions in both JCT 63 and 80 (clauses 22 and 24, respectively) is printed on pages 21–22. There are important differences between the two versions.

JCT 63, clause 22
There are three conditions that must be met before the employer is entitled to liquidated damages. First, there must be a failure by the contractor to complete the works by the date for completion specified or within any extended time. Secondly, the architect must have performed his duties as regards adjudicating upon extensions of time under clauses 23 and 33(1)(c). *Token Construction Co. Ltd* v. *Charlton Estates Ltd* (1973), although a decision on a special form of contract, is relevant to JCT 63 because of the similar wording of the relevant clauses. There, an architect sent a somewhat jumbled letter to the employer some two years after contract completion in which he said 'with 13 weeks extension of time the adjusted completion date would have been 30.1.68 ... Details of

the 13 weeks' extension of time are being prepared and will be forwarded to you ... liquidated damages ought to be calculated from 30 January 1968 to 15 July 1968, a period of 24 weeks.' The Court of Appeal held that on the facts there was no valid certificate of delay or extension of time, and that the architect could not certify for delay until he had first adjudicated upon all the contractor's applications for extensions of time. It seems that the architect may continue his consideration of, and adjudications on, extensions of time even after the original completion date has passed, at least in respect of those causes of delay in clause 23 which are outside the control of the architect or employer. This follows from the case of *Amalgamated Building Contractors Ltd* v. *Waltham Holy Cross UDC* (1952), where an architect granted an extension of time after the works had been completed on grounds of shortage of labour and materials (clause 23(j), JCT 63), and the extension so granted was held valid. The contract was in the 1939 RIBA Form which contained a provision similar to clause 25.4.10 of JCT 80.

Lord Justice Denning, as he then was, commenting on the provision that 'the architect shall make a fair and reasonable extension of time for completion of the works' and the contractors' argument that this meant that the architect must give the contractors a date at which they can aim in the future, and that he cannot give a date which has passed, said:

'I do not agree with this contention. It is only necessary to take a few practical illustrations to see that the architect, as a matter of business, must be able to give an extension even though it is retrospective. Take a simple case where contractors, near the end of the work, have overrun the contract time for six months without legitimate excuse. They cannot get an extension for that period. Now suppose that the works are still uncompleted and a strike occurs and lasts a month. The contractors can get an extension of time for that month. The architect can clearly issue a certificate which will operate retrospectively. He extends the time by one month from the original completion date, and the extended time will obviously be a date which is already past. Or take a cause of delay, such as we have in this case, due to labour and materials not being available. That may cause a continuous delay operating partially, but not wholly, every day, until the works are completed. The works do not stop. They go on, but they go on more slowly right to the end of the works. In such a case, seeing that the cause of delay operates until the last moment, when the works are completed, it must follow that the architect can give a certificate after they are completed.'

His lordship added, however, that

> '... on principle there is a distinction between cases where the cause of delay is due to some act or default of the building owner, such as not giving possession of the site in due time, or ordering extras, or something of that kind. When such things happen the contract time may well cease to bind the contractors, because the building owner cannot insist on a condition if it is his own fault that the condition has not been fulfilled'.

The wording was altered in the 1963 Edition of the JCT Form, but Lord Justice Denning's views are still worthy of note. The wording introduced in 1963 was as follows:

> 'Upon it becoming reasonably apparent that the progress of the Works is delayed, the Contractor shall forthwith give written notice of the cause of the delay to the Architect, and if in the opinion of the Architect the completion of the works is likely to be or has been delayed *beyond the Date for Completion ...*'

then the architect shall grant a fair and reasonable extension of time.

This would suggest to us that if a delay occurs after the date for completion as currently fixed under the contract, the architect is under no obligation to grant an extension of time and, in all probability, cannot do so if the cause of delay is the 'fault' of the employer in law. If this view is correct, architects must clearly exercise great care in issuing instructions after the date for completion currently fixed under the contract, as otherwise they may find that they can grant no extension of time to the contractor and may therefore find that they have invalidated the provisions relating to the enforceability of the contract completion date, thus depriving the employer of his right to liquidated damages.

The foregoing caveat, if correct, would not in our view apply to architect's instructions made necessary by conditions which only become apparent when the works have reached a certain stage, e.g. when ground conditions discovered during the execution of external works make additional work necessary, and the conditions would have been discovered at an earlier date had the contractor himself not been in default with regard to time. In that event, in our view, the architect would be entitled to grant an appropriate extension of time retrospectively. This point has, to our knowledge, never been tested in the courts. In our view, there is no difference between the position under the 63 and 80 editions of the JCT

Contract as the wording is similar and in both cases is in contrast with that of the 1939 Form.

The third condition to be observed is that the architect must have certified 'in writing that in his opinion the same ought reasonably so to have been completed'. He can issue his clause 22 certificate at any time prior to the issue of the final certificate. However, once he has issued the final certificate under clause 30(6) then, if no notice of arbitration has been given by either party in accordance with clause 30(7), the architect becomes *functus officio* and is thereby excluded thereafter from issuing any valid certificate under clause 22: see *H. Fairweather Ltd* v. *Asden Securities Ltd* (1979).

The architect's certificate under clause 22 is not, it seems, a condition precedent to arbitration. Once a dispute arises, it can be referred to arbitration under clause 35, subject to the rights of parties to apply to the High Court for the action to be stayed: *Ramac Construction Co. Ltd* v. *J. E. Lesser (Properties) Ltd* (1975).

In *Percy Bilton Ltd* v. *Greater London Council* (1982), the House of Lords gave consideration to the question of whether or not time becomes at large under JCT 63 where, as in that case, a nominated sub-contractor failed, and there was a delay in re-nomination by the employer. At first instance, Judge William Stabb QC held that time had become 'at large' by reason of the employer's failure to re-nominate so as not to delay the main contractor, and in so deciding the judge relied upon the observations of Lord Justice Salmon in *Peak Construction (Liverpool) Ltd* v. *McKinney Foundations Ltd* (1970), that 'if the failure to complete in time is due to the fault of both the employer and the contractor ... the [liquidated damages] clause does not bite. I cannot see how, in the ordinary course, the employer can insist on compliance with a condition if it is partly his own fault it cannot be fulfilled...'.

The learned judge's view that the dropping out of the nominated sub-contractor was a fault or breach of contract by the employer was rejected by both the Court of Appeal and the House of Lords. Lord Fraser of Tullybelton summarised the true position in this way:

'The general rule is that the main contractor is bound to complete the work by the date for completion stated in the contract. If he fails to do so, he will be liable for liquidated damages to the employer. That is subject to the exception that the employer is not entitled to liquidated damages if by his acts or omissions he has prevented the main contractor from completing his work by the completion date: see for example *Holme* v. *Guppy* (1938) and *Wells* v. *Army and Navy Co-*

operative Society (1902). These general rules may be amended by the express terms of the contract. In this case, the express terms of clause 23 of the contract do affect the general rule.'

The position is the same under JCT 80.

JCT 80, clause 24

There are significant differences between JCT 80, clause 24, and the corresponding provision in JCT 63, which are not merely drafting changes.

Clause 24.1 makes it a condition precedent to the employer's right to liquidated damages that the architect issue a certificate that the contractor has failed to complete the works by the completion date. This certificate is a simple statement of fact and is merely confirmatory. It is issued after the architect has considered all claims for extension of time under clause 25 which have been presented by the contractor when the current completion date is reached. He must also issue a fresh certificate if he alters the completion date in his review under clause 25.3.3.

Clause 24.2.1 introduces a further condition precedent and makes it clear that the deduction of liquidated damages is a discretionary right of the employer. Liquidated damages are only payable if the employer gives written notice to the contractor of his intention to claim or deduct liquidated damages, and this he must do before the issue of the final certificate. The wording makes it plain that the employer may elect to claim the whole or part of the liquidated damages. The contractor is only bound to pay or allow 'to the employer the whole or part of such as may be specified in writing by the employer ...'. If the employer fails to give notice before the final certificate is issued then he loses his right to liquidated damages.

If the architect revises the completion date under clause 25.3.3 (see p. 58) after reviewing contract progress within 12 weeks of the date of practical completion and fixes a later completion date, clause 25.2.2 provides for the contractor to be reimbursed for any liquidated damages that have been deducted by the employer for the period up to the later completion date.

IFC 84, clauses 2.6, 2.7 and 2.8

These clauses read as follows:

Certificate of non-completion

2.6 If the Contractor fails to complete the Works by the Date for Completion or within any extended time fixed under clause 2.3 then the Architect/the Contract Administrator shall issue a certificate to that effect.

In the event of an extension of time being made after the issue of such a certificate the Architect/the Contract Administrator shall issue a written cancellation of that certificate and shall issue such further certificate under this clause as may be necessary.

Liquidated damages for non-completion

2.7 Subject to the issue of a certificate under clause 2.6 the Contractor shall, as the Employer may require in writing not later than the date of the final certificate for payment, pay or allow the Employer liquidated damages at the rate stated in the Appendix for the period during which the Works shall remain or have remained incomplete, and the Employer may deduct the same from any monies due or to become due to the Contractor under this Contract (including any balance stated as due to the Contractor in the final certificate for payment) or may recover the same from the Contractor as a debt.

Repayment of liquidated damages

2.8 If after the operation of clause 2.7 the relevant certificate under clause 2.6 is cancelled the Employer shall pay or repay to the Contractor any amounts deducted or recovered under clause 2.7 but taking into account the effect of a further certificate, if any, issued under clause 2.6.

The effect of these clauses is substantially the same as that of clause 24 in JCT 80. However, it should be noted that clause 2.6 provides that, if the architect grants a further extension of time after the completion date previously fixed has been passed he is to issue a written cancellation of the certificate issued in relation to the previous completion date and issue a new certificate. The employer's duty to repay any damages deducted is then related to the issue of the new certificate. This appears to us a useful and valuable improvement and we are puzzled by the JCT's failure to amend JCT 80 to the same effect in the set of amendments issued in July 1987.

Two final points should be made to clear up certain common misconceptions. First, the JCT liquidated damages clause in all three Forms is concerned only with liquidated damages for delay in completion, and is to be treated as dealing comprehensively with the employer's right to damages for late completion. His right to claim unliquidated damages for other breaches of contract by way of an action at common law remains intact. Secondly, if no figure for liquidated damages is inserted in the Appendix, whether through oversight or otherwise, then no liquidated damages are payable. In such a case the employer's remedy for delay in completion would be by way of an action for unliquidated damages at common law, with the necessity of proving loss, and it seems that the position would be the same if the liquidated damages clause is struck out: see *Temloc Ltd* v. *Errill Properties Ltd* (1987). Equally, should no completion date be inserted in the Appendix, then no liquidated damages will be payable (see *Kemp* v. *Rose* (1858)) since there must be a date from which liquidated damages may begin to run.

EXTENSIONS OF TIME

The express provisions for extension of time in JCT 63 and in JCT 80, are clause 23 and 25 respectively. The latter provision is a completely revised and extended version of the former, and the procedural aspects of each provision will be considered separately.

JCT 63, clause 23
The text of clause 23 reads:

23 'Upon it becoming reasonably apparent that the progress of the Works is delayed, the Contractor shall forthwith give written notice of the cause of the delay to the Architect, and if in the opinion of the Architect the completion of the Works is likely to be or has been delayed beyond the Date for Completion stated in the Appendix to these Conditions or beyond any extended time previously fixed under either this clause or clause 33 (1)(c) of these Conditions,

   (a) by *force majeure*, or
   (b) by reason of any exceptionally inclement weather, or
   (c) by reason of loss or damage occasioned by any one or more of the contingencies referred to in clause 20 [A], [B] or [C] of these Conditions, or
   (d) by reason of civil commotion, local combination of workmen, strike or lockout affecting any of the trades employed upon the Works or any of the trades engaged in the preparation manufacture or transportation of any of the goods or materials required for the Works, or
   (e) by reason of Architect's instructions issued under clauses 1 (2), 11 (1) or 21 (2) of these Conditions, or
   (f) by reason of the Contractor not having received in due time necessary instructions, drawings, details or levels from the Architect for which he specifically applied in writing on a date which having regard to the Date for Completion stated in the Appendix to these Conditions or to any extension of time then fixed under this clause or clause 33 (1) (c) of these Conditions was neither unreasonably distant from nor unreasonably close to the date on which it was necessary for him to receive the same, or

(g) by delay on the part of nominated sub-contractors or nominated suppliers which the Contractor has taken all practicable steps to avoid or reduce, or

(h) by delay on the part of artists tradesmen or others engaged by the Employer in executing work not forming part of this Contract, or

(i) by reason of the opening up for inspection of any work covered up or of the testing of any of the work materials or goods in accordance with clause 6 (3) of these Conditions (including making good in consequence of such opening up or testing), unless the inspection or test showed that the work materials or goods were not in accordance with this Contract, or

(j) (i) by the Contractor's inability for reasons beyond his control and which he could not reasonably have foreseen at the date of this Contract to secure such labour as is essential to the proper carrying out of the Works, or

   (ii) by the Contractor's inability for reasons beyond his control and which he could not reasonably have foreseen at the date of this Contract to secure such goods and/or materials as are essential to the proper carrying out of the Works, or

(k) by reason of compliance with the provisions of clause 34 of these Conditions or with Architect's instructions issued thereunder, or

(l) by a local authority or statutory undertaker in carrying out work in pursuance of its statutory obligations in relation to the Works, or in failing to carry out such work.

then the Architect shall so soon as he is able to estimate the length of the delay beyond the date or time aforesaid make in writing a fair and reasonable extension of time for completion of the Works. Provided always that the Contractor shall use constantly his best endeavours to prevent delay and shall do all that may reasonably be required to the satisfaction of the Architect to proceed with the Works.

Commentary

The wording of clause 23 is both important and widely misunderstood and we propose to examine it in detail, phrase by phrase.

'*Upon it becoming reasonably apparent*' – This means that, as soon as progress is delayed – not 'may be' or even 'will be' but 'is' – for whatever reason, irrespective of whether or not it is one of the reasons listed in clause 23 or even whether or not it is a reason for which the contractor may be responsible, such as plain inefficiency on his part, then the contractor *shall*, i.e. must, notify the architect in writing. The intention is that the architect should be informed immediately a delay occurs for whatever reason, so that he may be aware that the contract completion date may not be met. It has to be reasonably apparent that *the progress of the works is delayed*, and the initiative for taking action must come from the contractor when he realizes that the works are running behind time.

Clause 23 does not require the contractor to give notice of delay which will be caused by some unexpected future event. However, it does require him to give notice if there will be inevitable delay because of something that has already happened: *London Borough of Merton* v. *Stanley Hugh Leach Ltd* (1986).

'The Contractor shall forthwith give written notice' – As soon as it is reasonably apparent to the contractor that the progress of the works is delayed the contractor must give written notice to the architect. The notice must specify a cause of delay which has already started to affect progress, but the notice will be valid even if it does not contain sufficient detail to enable the architect to form the opinion whether the cause of delay comes under paragraphs (a) to (l): *London Borough of Merton* v. *Stanley Hugh Leach Ltd* (1986). This notice is not a condition precedent to granting an extension of time by the architect, and failure to give notice would not amount to more than a technical breach of contract although that breach can be taken into account by the architect when considering what extension to grant: *London Borough of Merton* v. *Stanley Hugh Leach Ltd* (1986). The situation was well put by Mr D. Keating (*Building Contracts*, 4th Edition, page 346) in a passage approved by the court:

'If the architect wrongly assumes that [the notice is a condition precedent] when it is not and in consequence refuses to perform such duties the employer loses his right to liquidated damages. It may therefore be against the employer's interest for the architect not to consider a cause of delay of which late notice is given, or of which he has knowledge despite lack of notice.'

'*... of the cause of the delay*' – The contractor is required to notify the architect only of the cause of the delay and not its extent. That is a matter for the architect to decide. However, the duty is not limited to notifying the causes of delay listed in paragraphs (a) to (l); it is a duty to give notice of delay which has occurred, howsoever caused. This is so even if it is uncertain whether the current completion date will be affected. We suggest that 'cause of the delay' is best interpreted in practice as meaning 'circumstances giving rise to the delay', although *London Borough of Merton* v. *Stanley Hugh Leach Ltd* (1986) emphasises that the purpose of the notice is simply to warn the architect of the situation, and it is then up to him to monitor the situation. The case also emphasises that it is the contractor's duty to give as much information as he can to the architect about the cause of the delay so as to help the architect in performing his duty. Mr Justice Vinelott ruled that a contractor might be in breach of his duty to give notice forthwith if the notice did not adequately explain the cause of the delay in light of the contractor's knowledge. This is so even if the contractor amplifies the notice by giving the information at a later date. The architect must know precisely why the delay has occurred if he is to make up his mind as to whether it is such as to justify an extension. It is the contractor's *actual* progress and not his planned or hoped-for progress that is relevant, as the plain words of the provision state. There is no right to an automatic extension of time.

'... *if in the opinion of the architect*' – It is entirely for the architect to decide whether, in his opinion, a delay in the contract completion date is likely to occur or has occurred and also whether the cause of delay is one of those listed in clause 23 and therefore one for which he should grant an extension.

Once the architect is notified by the contractor of delay, it is for him to monitor the position. In *Merton* v. *Leach*, Mr Justice Vinelott summarised the position neatly:

'Clause 23 imposes on the architect the duty of considering whether completion of the works is likely to be or has been delayed beyond the date for completion by way of the causes there set out and if it has whether any and if so what extension should be granted. That duty is owed both to the contractor and the building owner. The architect is entitled to rely on the contractor to play his part by giving notice when it has become apparent to him that the progress of the works is delayed. If the contractor fails to give notice forthwith upon it becoming so apparent he is in breach of contract and that breach can be taken into account by the architect in deciding whether he should be given an extension of time. But the architect is not relieved of his duty by the failure of the contractor to give notice or to give notice promptly, He must consider independently in light of his knowledge of the contractor's programme and the progress of the works and of his knowledge of other matters affecting or likely to affect the progress of the works ... whether completion is likely to be delayed by any of the stated causes. If necessary he must make his own inquiries, whether from the contractor or others.'

If the contractor feels that the architect has been unreasonable in reaching his opinion, his recourse is to arbitration. On receipt of the contractor's written notice the architect must decide if the cause of delay is covered by clause 23. If in his view it is not then, subject to the contractor's right to challenge that opinion by arbitration, that is the end of the matter.

'... *the completion of the works is likely to be or has been delayed*' – The architect must then decide whether or not the delay in progress is going to mean a failure or likely failure to complete by the date for completion. He may be required to make a prediction, unlike the contractor in relation to his written notice. This is because the contractor is required to give notice of circumstances that have already arisen, i.e. the cause of delay during the progress of the contract, whereas the architect is required to look at the matter with reference to what may be a future event (the contract completion date) and a prediction may therefore be necessary. In making up his mind on this point the architect is, in our view, entitled to consider the proviso to the clause, which begins 'provided always that the contractor shall constantly use his best endeavours to prevent delay'. The contractor's duty is to prevent delay, so far as he can reasonably do so, e.g. a delay in progress of the works at an early stage may be reduced or even eliminated by the contractor using his best endeavours.

'... *the architect shall so soon as he is able*' – In the view of Mr Duncan Wallace (*Building and Civil Engineering Standard Forms*, page 106) 'this sets a time limit for granting the extension and failure may have the effect of invalidating the liquidated damages clause altogether', but this appears to us to be overstating the position and is far too legalistic an approach. The words must be interpreted reasonably. It is not good enough for the architect to say 'I cannot estimate the length of any delays until the works have been completed and I can see the whole picture'. Delays may be said to fall into two classes: those that are a single definable cause of delay with a finite result, which is immediately apparent, and those that are a continuing cause of delay extending over a considerable period or even over the whole currency of the contract. An example of the first case may be a single major variation, which must be carried out before further work can commence; the architect must, in such a case, issue his extension of time, if not immediately, then within a reasonable time, and failure on his part to do so may lead to the contract being considered 'at large' as to time with the consequent forfeiture of the employer's right to deduct liquidated damages. An example of the second case might be delays on the part of a major nominated sub-contractor, which may extend up to, or nearly up to, completion of the works. In that case the architect would not be unreasonable in saying that he could not estimate the extent of the delay until at least the whole of the sub-contract work was completed.

The true position is, in our view, well summarised by Mr Justice Roper in *Fernbrook Trading Co. Ltd* v. *Taggart* (1979):

'I think it must be implicit in the normal extension clause that the contractor is to be informed of his new completion date as soon as reasonably practicable. If the sole cause is the ordering of extra work, then in the normal course extensions should be given at the time of ordering, so that the contractor has a target for which to aim. Where the cause of delay lies beyond the employer, and particularly where its duration is uncertain, then the extension order may be delayed, although even then it would be a reasonable inference to draw from the ordinary extension clause that the extension should be given a reasonable time after the factors which will govern the exercise of the [architect's] discretion have been established. Where there are multiple causes of delay, there may be no alternative but to leave the final decision until just before the issue of the final certificate.'

These principles are, in our opinion, sound common sense and good contract practice.

When the architect is considering the grant of an extension of time, the effect of the cause of delay is to be assessed at the time when the works are actually carried out and not when they were programmed to be carried out. This appears to be so even if the contractor is in culpable delay during the original or extended contract period: *Walter Lawrence & Son Ltd* v. *Commercial Union Properties (UK) Ltd* (1986).

'... *to estimate the length of the delay*' – The architect is required only to *estimate* the length of the delay and not to *ascertain* it; the architect must make an approximate judgement. The length of the delay is a matter solely for the architect's decision and the contractor is not required to give him any assistance in the matter. It is, of course, common practice for the contractor to give his opinion of what a proper extension would be. There is no harm in this and possibly a considerable advantage, provided that the contractor remembers that it is his own opinion that he is giving and that the decision is the architect's. Indeed, if the contractor does not give some indication of what he would consider to be a reasonable extension, he has only himself to blame if the architect subsequently grants an extension which, in the contractor's view, is totally inadequate. If the contractor is aggrieved by the architect's decision, his sole recourse is to arbitration.

'... *make in writing*' – The form in which the extension is to be made is not stated. The architect is not required to issue a certificate and disagreement by the contractor, whether with the architect's refusal to issue an extension or with the length of extension granted, is not a matter which can be taken to immediate arbitration under clause 35(2). Reference to arbitration must therefore wait upon practical completion of the works. It should be further noted that as the granting of an extension of time will not *in itself* involve an adjustment of the contract sum this is not a matter to which the time limit relating to the conclusiveness of the architect's final certificate in clause 30(7) will apply, and reference to arbitration may therefore be made at any time within the limitation period.

'... *a fair and reasonable extension of time*' – The architect's duty is to make a fair and reasonable extension of time in light of the contract conditions and, in the view of Mr Duncan Wallace (*Building and Civil Engineering Standard Forms*, page 107) these words 'mean nothing more than "reasonably accurate"'. We do not accept this interpretation; the 'fairness and reasonableness' of the extension of time granted must, in our view, relate to the effect upon contract progress and there is not necessarily any correlation between the actual length of the delaying event specified in clause 23 and the effect upon the contract works as a whole. For example, two weeks of 'exceptionally inclement weather' may or may not be likely to delay the completion of the works, dependent upon what stage the works have reached. If the 'exceptionally inclement weather' occurs at a critical stage, an extension of more than two weeks may, in fact, be fair and reasonable; if it occurs at a non-critical stage, then no extension may be justified.

It is important to remember that the only effect of the granting by the architect of an extension of time under clause 23 is to postpone the date for completion stated in the Appendix and therefore the date from which the contractor may be liable to pay liquidated damages; it has no other effect. The granting of an extension of time does not give the contractor an automatic right to claim reimbursement of loss and/or expense caused by the delay (for that is a separate matter) and, by the same token, refusal by the architect to grant an extension does not necessarily remove the contractor's right to reimbursement of loss and/or expense resulting from disruption of his working programme.

It is sometimes argued that 'loss of productivity' is not an acceptable claim under JCT 63, clause 24 and JCT 80, clause 26, and that there must be *delay* in progress so that the contractor's entitlement is limited to the effects of delayed completion. In our view, this is not the case at all and in our discussion of direct loss and/or expense claims we have taken the view that the contractor is entitled to recover the effects upon the cost of the work, such as labour and plant resources having been used less efficiently during the original contract period. Hence the final sentence of the preceding paragraph.

The *proviso* is important. *The contractor shall use constantly his best endeavours to prevent delay.* This seems to us to be no more than an express re-statement of the contractor's common law obligation and reinforcement of the express provisions of the contract relating to completion. This is a matter which the architect should take into account when deciding a claim under clause 23 and, if his decision is that the contractor has not *constantly* used his best endeavours, then the contractor's only recourse is to challenge that decision in arbitration. The contractor *shall do all that may reasonably be required to the satisfaction of the architect to proceed with the works.* This is the contractor's obligation in any case, but in our view the architect has no power to order that acceleration measures be taken (either under this provision or any other provision in the contract). The best legal view of the effect of the proviso is clearly set out by Mr Donald Keating in *Building Contracts*, 4th Edition, page 351:

> 'The proviso is an important qualification to the right to an extension of time. Thus, for example, in some cases it might be the contractor's duty to re-programme the works either to prevent or reduce delay. How far the contractor must take other steps depends upon the circumstances of each case, but it is thought that the proviso does not contemplate the expenditure of substantial sums of money.'

However, so far as the first part of the proviso is concerned – namely that 'the contractor shall use constantly his best endeavours to prevent delay' – John Parris (*The Standard Form of Building Contract: JCT 80*, Section 7.06 commenting on JCT 80 clause 25.4) says:

> '[The contractor] undertakes to use his *best endeavours*. In short, if it is within his power, *by any means* whatsoever, to prevent delay to the progress of the works, he has undertaken to exercise that power. And, if he has not done so, the architect is fully entitled to deny him an extension of time ... 'Best' means 'best'; it does not mean any steps which will not cause the contractor additional expense.'

Clearly, there is some justification for this point of view, particularly in light of the use of the phrase obligating the contractor to 'do all that may reasonably be required' in the second part of the proviso, which is in contrast with the 'best endeavours' obligation. There appears to be no construction industry case directly in point, but there are cases in relation to sale of goods where the phrase 'best efforts to secure delivery' have been judicially considered such as *Monkland* v. *Jack Barclay Ltd* (1951), and such authority as there is does not, with respect, support the view put forward by Parris. Whether or not a contractor has used his 'best endeavours' is a matter of fact, and a purposive interpretation of the obligation, considered in light of the contract as a whole does not support the very strict construction advanced by Dr Parris.

The actual grounds for extension of time are discussed in detail later in this chapter, as all of them are to be found (although sometimes worded slightly differently) in JCT 80: see pages 63–81.

JCT 80, clause 25

The provisions of JCT 80 regarding extensions of time are set out in clause 25. There are significant differences between JCT 80 provisions and clause 23 of JCT 63. Clause 25, as amended in 1987, provides as follows:

'25 Extension of time

25.1.1   In clause 25 any reference to delay, notice or extension of time includes further delay, further notice or further extension of time.

23.1 .2   Where clause 23.1.2 is stated in the Appendix to apply the Employer may defer the giving of posession for a period not exceeding six weeks or such lesser period stated in the Appendix calculated from the Date of Possession.

25.2 .1 .1   If and whenever it becomes reasonably apparent that the progress of the Works is being or is likely to be delayed the Contractor shall forthwith give written notice to the Architect of the material circumstances including the cause or causes of the delay and identify in such notice any event which in his opinion is a Relevant Event.

.1 .2   Where the material circumstances of which written notice has been given under clause 25.2.1.1 include reference to a Nominated Sub-Contractor, the Contractor shall forthwith send a copy of such written notice to the Nominated Sub-Contractor concerned.

25.2 .2   In respect of each and every Relevant Event identified in the notice given in accordance with clause 25.2.1.1 the Contractor shall, if practicable in such notice, or otherwise in writing as soon as possible after such notice:

.2 .1   give particulars of the expected effects thereof; and

.2 .2   estimate the extent, if any, of the expected delay in the completion of the Works beyond and Completion Date resulting therefrom whether or not concurrently with delay resulting from any other Relevant Event and shall give such particulars and estimate to any Nominated Sub-Contractor to whom a copy of any written notice has been given under clause 25.2.1.2.

.3   The Contractor shall give such further written notices to the Architect and send a copy to any Nominated Sub-Contractor to whom a copy of any written notice has been given under clause 25.2.1.2, as may be reasonably necessary or as the Architect may reasonably require for keeping up-to-date the particulars and estimate referred to in clauses 25.2.2.1 and 25.2.2.2 including any material change in such particulars or estimate.

25.3 .1 If, in the opinion of the Architect, upon receipt of any notice, particulars and estimate under clauses 25.2.1.1 and 25.2.2,

.1 .1 any of the events which are stated by the Contractor to be the cause of the delay is a Relevant Event and

.1 .2 the completion of the Works is likely to be delayed thereby beyond the Completion Date

the Architect shall in writing to the Contractor give an extension of time by fixing such later date as the Completion Date as he then estimates to be fair and reasonable. The Architect shall, in fixing such new Completion Date, state,

.1 .3 which of the Relevant Events he has taken into account and

.1 .4 the extent, if any, to which he has had regard to any instruction under clause 13.2 requiring as a Variation the omission of any work issued since the fixing of the previous Completion Date,

and shall, if reasonably practicable having regard to the sufficiency of the aforesaid notice, particulars and estimates, fix such new Completion Date not later than 12 weeks from receipt of the notice and of reasonably sufficient particulars and estimate, or, where the period between receipt thereof and the Completion Date is less than 12 weeks, not later than the Completion Date.

If, in the opinion of the Architect, upon receipt of any such notice, particulars and estimate it is not fair and reasonable to fix a later date as a new Completion Date, the Architect shall if reasonably practicable having regard to the sufficiency of the aforesaid notice, particulars and estimate so notify the Contractor in writing not later than 12 weeks from receipt of the notice, particulars and estimate, or, where the period between receipt thereof and the Completion Date is less than 12 weeks, not later than the Completion Date.

25.3 .2 After the first exercise by the Architect of his duty under clause 25.3.1 the Architect may fix a Completion Date earlier than that previously fixed under clause 25 if in his opinion the fixing of such earlier Completion Date is fair and reasonable have regard to the omission of any work or obligation instructed or sanctioned by the Architect under clause 13 after the last occasion on which the Architect made an extension of time.

25.3 .3 After the Completion Date, if this occurs before the date of Practical Completion, the Architect may, and not later than the expiry of 12 weeks after the date of Practical Completion shall, in writing to the Contractor either

.3 .1 fix a Completion Date later than that previously fixed if in his opinion the fixing of such later Completion Date is fair and reasonable having regard to any of the Relevant Events, whether upon reviewing a previous decision or otherwise and whether or not the Relevant Event has been specifically notified by the Contractor under clause 25.2.1.1; or

.3 .2 fix a Completion Date earlier than that previously fixed under clause 25 if in his opinion the fixing of such earlier Completion Date is fair and reasonable having regard to the omission of any work or obligation instructed or sanctioned by the Architect under clause 13 after the last occasion on which the Architect made an extension of time; or

.3 .3 confirm to the Contractor the Completion Date previously fixed.

25.3 .4 Provided always

.4 .1 the Contractor shall use constantly his best endeavours to prevent delay in the progress of the Works, howsoever caused, and to prevent the completion of the Works being delayed or further delayed beyond the Completion Date;

.4 .2 the Contractor shall do all that may reasonably be required to the satisfaction of the Architect to proceed with the Works.

25.3 .5 The Architect shall notify in writing to every Nominated Sub-Contractor each decision of the Architect under clause 25.3 fixing a Completion Date.

25.3 .6 No decision of the Architect under clause 25.3 shall fix a Completion Date earlier than the Date for Completion stated in the Appendix.

25.4 The following are the Relevant Events referred to in clause 25:

25.4 .1 force majeure;

25.4 .2 exceptionally adverse weather conditions;

25.4 .3 loss or damage occasioned by any one or more of the specified perils;

25.4 .4 civil commotion, local combination of workmen, strike or lock-out affecting any of the trades employed upon the Works or any of the trades engaged in the preparation, manufacture or transportation of any of the goods or materials required for the Works;

25.4 .5 compliance with the Architect's instructions

.5 .1 under clauses 2.3, 13.2, 13.3, 23.2, 34, 35 or 36; or

.5 .2 in regard to the opening up for inspection of any work covered up or the testing of any of the work, materials or goods in accordance with clause 8.3 (including making good in consequence of such opening up or testing) unless the inspection or test showed that the work, materials or goods were not in accordance with this Contract;

25.4 .6 the Contractor not having received in due time necessary instructions, drawings, details or levels from the Architect for which he specifically applied in writing provided that such application was made on a date which having regard to the Completion Date was neither unreasonably distant from nor unreasonably close to the date on which it was necessary for him to receive the same;

25.4 .7 delay on the part of Nominated Sub-Contractors or Nominated Suppliers which the Contractor has taken all practicable steps to avoid or reduce;

25.4 .8 .1 the execution of work not forming part of this Contract by the Employer himself or by persons employed or otherwise engaged by the Employer as referred to in clause 29 or the failure to execute such work;

.8 .2 the supply by the Employer of materials and goods which the Employer has agreed to provide for the Works or the failure so to supply.

25.4 .9 the exercise after the Base Date by the United Kingdom Government of any statutory power which directly affects the execution of the Works by restricting the availability or use of labour which is essential to the proper carrying out of the Works or preventing the Contractor from, or delaying the Contractor in, securing such goods or materials or such fuel or energy as are essential to the proper carrying out of the Works;

25.4 .10 .1 the Contractor's inability for reasons beyond his control and which he could not reasonably have foreseen at the Base Date to secure such labour as is essential to the proper carrying out of the Works; or

.10 .2 the Contractor's inability for reasons beyond his control and which he could not reasonably have foreseen at the Base Date to secure such goods or materials as are essential to the proper carrying out of the Works;

25.4 .11 the carrying out by a local authority or statutory undertaker of work in pursuance of its statutory obligations in relation to the Works, or the failure to carry out such work;

25.4 .12 failure of the Employer to give in due time ingress to or egress from the site of the Works or any part thereof through or over any land, buildings, way or passages adjoining or connected with the site and in the possession and control of the Employer, in accordance with the Contract Bills and/or the Contract Drawings, after receipt by the Architect of such notice, if any, as the Contractor is required to give, or failure of the Employer to give such ingress or egress as otherwise agreed between the Architect and the Contractor.'

25.4 .13 Where clause 23.1.2 is stated in the Appendix to apply, the deferment by the Employer of giving possession of the site under clause 23.1.2.

Commentary

Clause 25 is a revised version of its predecessor and it extends the provisions of JCT 63 relating to extension of time. As under JCT 63, this clause has no bearing on any claim that the contractor may have for direct loss and/or expense; this is a separate matter, which, under JCT 80, is covered by clauses 26 and 34.3 (discussed in chapter 5). Unfortunately, loss and expense under JCT Forms have traditionally been linked – by the construction industry, if not by the lawyers – to extensions of time, and in 1980 the Joint Contracts Tribunal compounded this erroneous view by the introduction of clause 26.3, which we discuss later. Moreover, as under JCT 63, JCT 80 allows additional or alternative claims for breach of contract, based on the same facts: see JCT 80, clause 26.6, and the discussion of common law claims in chapter 10. We must emphasise, however, that the contractor can only recover his loss once – he cannot recover under the express terms of the contract and then again at common law on the same facts. Moreover, under JCT terms the architect has no power at all to assess and quantify claims at common law; his powers, like those of the quantity surveyor, are very limited: see, for example, *County and District Properties Ltd* v. *John Laing Construction Ltd* (1982).

Under clause 25, the causes of delay for which an extension of time may be granted are called 'relevant events' and they are discussed later in this chapter. The revised wording of the contract provision overcomes some of the difficulties encountered when dealing with claims for extension of time under JCT 63, clause 23. By way of example, as we have seen, clause 23 merely required the architect to 'make in writing a fair and reasonable extension of time'; it did not require him actually to state the new date for completion of the works, though many architects did in fact do so. Under clause 25 of JCT 80, the architect is required to fix a new completion date and to inform the contractor of it.

In our view, the JCT Guide, issued in 1980 contemporaneously with the new contract, was misleading in its description of the effect of the changes, which it summarised (pages 11 and 12) in the following terms:

'**Extension of Time and Liquidated Damages**
14   The provisions on **extension of time** now appear in a completely revised and extended version of clause 23 of the 1963 Edition: see clause 25. The main changes are:
14.1 The Contractor must now give notice, particulars and estimates of likely delay to completion in respect of any matter which the Contractor has identified as a Relevant Event (see paragraph 14.3) in his written notice of delay to the progress of the Works and which is causing or is likely to cause delay to completion; and he must ensure that this information is kept reasonably up-to-date;
14.2 The Architect is obliged, if reasonably practicable having regard to the sufficiency of the Contractor's particulars and estimates,

within 12 weeks of receipt of the Contractor's notice, reasonable particulars and estimates but, in any case, not later than the Completion Date, to give his decision on extension, if any, of the "Completion Date" (which is now defined as the Date for Completion fixed and stated in the Appendix or any later date fixed and stated – by a decision of the Architect – under clause 25 or clause 33.1.3);

14.3 In reaching his decision the Architect must state which of the causes of delay (now called in clause 25.4 "Relevant Events") he has taken into account in reaching his decision;

14.4 The Architect is permitted after his first decision on extending time to take account of any Variations requiring an omission which have been issued since the date of his last decision on extending the Completion Date;

14.5 The Architect must give his decision on each notice given by the Contractor not later than the Completion Date then current, but within 12 weeks from the Date of Practical Completion of the Works the Architect must review the progress of the contract and may fix a revised Completion Date; such revised Completion Date can take account of any Relevant Event whether or not notified by the Contractor and can take account of any Variations requiring an omission which have been issued since the date of his last decision on extending the Completion Date;

14.6 No decision of the Architect under clause 25 can substitute an earlier date for the Date for Completion inserted in the Appendix;

14.7 The relevant events in clause 25.4 in general repeat, subject to drafting changes, the matters dealt with in the 1963 edition in clause 23(a) to (1) but have been varied, or increased in number, as follows:

.1 The provisions in clause 23(j) (i) and (ii) of the 1963 edition appear in clause 25.4.1 and the footnote is omitted. In its place is a new footnote to clause 25 as a whole which refers to new provisions (see below) which permit fluctuations under clause 39 (formerly 31A, C, D and E) or clause 38 (formerly 31B, C, D and E) to be "frozen" during the period when the Contractor becomes in default over completion provided clause 25 is not amended; and also refers to the similar provisions in clause 40 (formerly 31F) which have been repeated in the new editions:

.2 Clauses 25.4.9 (exercise of statutory powers by the UK Government) and 25.4.12 (failure of the Employer to give ingress to or egress from the site) are new.'

We feel it best to deal with the position by way of a phrase-by-phrase analysis of the procedural aspects of the clause because a reading of the wording of clause 25 does not support the interpretation placed upon it in the foregoing passage from the JCT Guide. The procedural aspects are found in clause 25.2, clause 25.1 merely being interpretive and saying that any reference to delay, notice or extension of time in clause 25 includes further delay, further notice or further extension of time.

'*If and whenever it becomes reasonably apparent*' – This is a key phrase, and it should be noted that the contractor is to give notice not only when the progress of the works is being delayed, but also when it becomes reasonably apparent that it is likely to be delayed in the future. This is an important difference between clause 25 and the corresponding JCT 63 provision. The phrasing is 'if and whenever' and not 'upon'. It has to be reasonably apparent that the progress of the works *is being or is likely to be delayed*. It is the *actual* progress and not the contractor's planned-for or hoped-for progress which is relevant, as the wording makes clear. Apparent means 'manifest' and once it becomes reasonably apparent that the progress is actually being delayed or is likely to be delayed, the contractor must notify the architect in writing.

'There is now direct authority for the view that it is actual progress and the Appendix completion date which is relevant. In *Glenlion Construction Ltd* v. *The Guiness Trust* (1988), the question of whether in a JCT contract where the contractor was required to provide a programme there was an implied term that the employer should so perform the contract as to enable the contractor to carry out the work in accordance with the programme and complete the works on the completion date appearing in the programme was answered in the negative.

The dispute arose under a contract in JCT 63 form but the position is the same under JCT 80. A programme was required by the Bills, which said that the contractor must provide the architect 'within 1 week from the date of possession, a programme chart of the whole of the works ... showing a completion date no later than the date for completion'. Judge James Fox-Andrews QC, sitting on Official Referees' Business, found that this was a contract requirement. Glenlion's programme as submitted showed a completion date earlier than that stated in the Appendix.

The judge ruled that, in light of the wording of clause 21 (JCT 80, clause 23.1.) requiring the contractor to complete the Works 'on or before' the completion date, Glenlion was entitled to complete before the stated date, whether or not it had produced a programme with an earlier date and whether or not it was contractually bound to produce a programme. It follows from this that if the contractor is entitled to complete early, he is also entitled to carry out the works in such a way as to enable him to achieve the earlier completion date whether or not the works were so programmed.

However, there was no implied term imposing an obligation on the employer to perform the contract so as to enable completion to be achieved by the programmed date. As the judge pointed out, the extension of time clause operates in relation to the completion date stated in the Appendix:

> 'A fair and reasonable extension of time for completion of the works beyond the date for completion stated in the Appendix might be an unfair and unreasonable extension from an earlier date'.

The purpose of this provision is not merely to entitle the contractor to an extension of time but also to notify the architect so that he may, if necessary, take remedial action and forwarn the employer. In other words, the contractor must give prior notice of delays which it is reasonable for him to anticipate. This gives the architect the opportunity, once he has been notified of any impending delay, to take steps to rectify the situation and bring the contract back on schedule. One of the things the architect can do so as to reduce the time needed to complete the project is to omit work under clause 13.2, e.g. he might omit landscaping from the contract. Further, if the contractor fails to give notice of a delay which he clearly should have been able to anticipate, the architect can in fact say that the contractor has not used his best endeavours to prevent delay in progress, which he is bound to do by the terms of clause 25.3.4.1.

Indeed, in the absence of express contractual power to extend time for completion, the architect would have no power to extend time. This clause confers express power to extend time, and it should be remembered that in some cases where there is such power and it is not properly exercised, e.g. on account of delay caused by the employer or for which the employer is responsible in law, then time for completion may become 'at large' and the contractor's obligation is then to complete within a reasonable time; in any event, he would be exonerated from liability for liquidated damages for delay: see *Miller* v. *London County Council* (1934), a decision of Mr Justice du Parcq, and the discussion on pp. 19–21, above.

In *Percy Bilton Ltd* v. *Greater London Council* (1982), Lord Fraser of Tullybelton, delivering the unanimous decision of the House of Lords, dealt with the question of time being 'at large' and the relationship between the extension of time clause and liquidated damages provisions in JCT contracts. His lordship said:

> 'The general rule is that the main contractor is bound to complete the

work by the date for completion stated in the contract. If he fails to do so, he will be liable for liquidated damages to the employer. That is subject to the exception that the employer is not entitled to liquidated damages if by his acts or omissions he has prevented the main contractor from completing his work by the completion date: see, for example, *Holme* v. *Guppy* (1838) and *Wells* v. *Army and Navy Co-operative Society* (1902). These general rules may be amended by the express terms of the contract. In this case [which involved a contract in terms identical to JCT 63] the express terms of clause 23 of the contract do affect the general rule ...'

The position is exactly the same under clause 25, JCT 80, which is, of course, quite specific and particular in its terms as to when the architect is to exercise his duty and, indeed, as will be seen, clause 25.3.3 provides for the architect to review the completion date not later than the expiry of 12 weeks from the date of practical completion, whether or not the contractor has specifically notified the delaying events and, in general terms, the architect must act not later than 12 weeks from receipt of the contractor's notice, etc.: see clause 25.3.1 and our commentary later.

Contractors often seek to argue that time has become 'at large' because of delay or alleged delay by the architect in granting an extension. Whether time is 'at large' must always depend on the particular facts and circumstances, and a New Zealand court has expressed the general position in this way:

'It must be implicit in the normal extension clause that the contractor is to be informed of his new completion date as soon as reasonably practicable. If the sole cause is the ordering of extra work, then in the normal course extensions should be given at the time of ordering, so that the contractor has a target at which to aim. Where the cause of the delay lies beyond the control of the employer, and particularly where its duration is uncertain, then the extension order may be delayed, although even then it would be a reasonable inference to draw from the ordinary extension clause that the extension should be given within a reasonable time after the factors which will govern the exercise of the architect's discretion have been established. Where there are multiple causes of delay, there may be no alternative but to leave the final decision until just before the issue of the final certificate.'

Under JCT 80 terms, provided the architect correctly operates the provisions of clause 25.3.3. it is virtually impossible for the contractor to argue that time has become at large.

'*The Contractor shall forthwith give written notice to the Architect*' – This is not a condition precedent to the contractor's right to an extension of time, and the statement in paragraph 14.1 of the JCT Guide, which suggests otherwise, is incorrect. The architect has power to grant an extension even in the absence of such written notice; failure by the contractor to give written notice merely means that the architect does not need to make a decision on extensions until a later date, i.e. on his review of the completion date not later than the expiry of 12 weeks from the date of practical completion 'whether or not the Relevant Event has been specifically notified by the Contractor': clause 25.3.3.

'*... of the material circumstances including the cause or causes of the delay*' – The contractor's notice is to state not just the 'cause or causes' of the delay; it must also state 'the material circumstances'. The notice should, in our view, go into some detail as to why and how the delay is occurring or is likely to occur; the 'material circumstances' will include, for example, the stage the contract has reached, the proposed order of works, and so on. The fact that the delay is likely to make a summer contract into a winter one, with consequent likely further disruption, would also be a 'material circumstance'.

'*... identify in such notice any event which in his opinion is a Relevant Event*' – The notice must state those listed causes of delay (or cause of delay) which, in the contractor's opinion, entitle him to an extension of time. The 'Relevant Event' so identified must be one (or more) of those listed in clause 25.4 and it is for the contractor to specify those causes of delay.

'*... notice to the nominated sub-contractor concerned*' – Clause 25.2.1.2 introduces a further and important requirement, and that is that a copy of the contractor's original notice must be sent to any nominated sub-contractor to whom reference is made in it. One of the 'Relevant Events' listed is 'delay on the part of nominated sub-contractors or nominated suppliers which the contractor has taken all practicable steps to avoid or reduce': see clause 25.4.7. 'Delay on the part of' a nominated sub-contractor has a very limited meaning as will be seen later. Delay by the employer in making a timely nomination of a new sub-contractor to replace a failed nominated sub-contractor is within clause 25.4.6 and the main contractor is entitled to an extension of time to cover such delay: *Percy Bilton Ltd* v. *Greater London Council* (1982). The purpose of giving a copy of the notice to affected nominated sub-contractors is to forewarn the nominated sub-contractor so that he may in turn, if necessary, make application for extension of time to the main contractor under clause 13 of the Nominated Sub-Contract Form (NSC/4 or NSC/4a, as appropriate).

'*The Contractor shall ... give particulars of the expected effects*' – Clause 25.2.2.1 imposes an additional obligation on the contractor. Either in his original notice or, where that is not practicable, as soon as possible after the notice, the contractor must state in writing to the architect *particulars of the expected effects* of each and every relevant event identified in the notice, i.e. particulars of the expected effects on progress, and each and every relevant event must, for this purpose, be considered in isolation. In our view, the contractor must go into sufficient detail to enable the architect to make a judgment.

'*... estimate the extent*' – This is a provision of vital significance. The contractor must give his own estimate of the expected delay in completion of the works beyond the completion date 'whether or not concurrently with delay resulting from any other Relevant Event'. The particulars and estimate must be 'reasonably sufficient' to enable the architect to form a judgment: see clause 25.3.1.

'*... give such particulars and estimate to any Nominated Sub-Contractor*' – A copy of the contractor's particulars and estimate must be given to any nominated sub-contractor to whom a copy of the original notice was given under clause 25.2.1.2.

'*... shall give such further written notices*' – The contractor must, by the terms of clause 25.2.3, keep each notice of delay under review and revise his statement of particulars and estimate and/or give whatever further notices *may reasonably be necessary or as the architect may reasonably require*. Notice that the duty extends to *any material change* in the particulars, etc. The contractor must keep the architect up to date with developments as they occur. The architect's time limit for dealing with applications for delay only starts to run when he has received 'reasonably sufficient particulars and estimates' from the contractor: see clause 25.3.1, page 56. The clear intention of these provisions is to provide the architect with sufficient information reasonably to form his own judgment on the matter, remembering that he has not been on the site, in all probability, at the time of the delay, though he must use his own records as well: *Stanley Hugh Leach Ltd* v. *London Borough of Merton* (1985).

'*... copy to any Nominated Sub-Contractor*' – This is self-explanatory: affected nominated sub-contractors must also be kept informed.

'*If, in the opinion of the architect*' – See our comments on the same phrase in clause 23, JCT 63: page 38.

'*Upon receipt of any notice, particulars and estimate*' – It is when, and only when he has received the notice, particulars and estimate from the contractor that the architect must consider them. The initiative then passes to the architect who must then decide: (1) Whether any of the causes of delay specified by the contractor in the notice is in fact a relevant event, i.e. he may disagree that the particular cause specified by the contractor is a relevant event, in which case the architect need not consider the next point. The contractor may, for example, have specified, 'exceptionally adverse weather conditions' and gone on to give the necessary detail, and yet the architect may say 'adverse weather conditions', not *'exceptionally* adverse weather conditions'. (2) Whether completion of the works is in fact likely to be delayed *thereby* (i.e. by the specified relevant event) beyond the completion date. Then, and only then, does his duty to grant an extension of time arise.

'...*shall in writing*...*give an extension of time*' – The architect must give an extension of time to the contractor if his conclusions are positive, i.e. if in his opinion there is a relevant event and that relevant event is likely to delay the completion of the works. However, in deciding what extension of time to give, if any, the architect will take into account any overlapping of delays resulting from different relevant events and, presumably, he will do so after study of the contractor's 'master programme' if this has, in fact, been provided under clause 5.3.1.2. Where there is such a 'master programme' we consider that it should be one of the 'reasonably sufficient particulars' to be provided by the contractor in support of his original notice. The architect's obligation is to grant an extension of time by fixing such later date as the completion date as he then estimates to be fair and reasonable, and there is no doubt in our minds that where the contractor is in advance of planned progress, or does not at that time actually need the extension, the architect is not bound to so grant it: see *Hounslow Borough Council* v. *Twickenham Garden Developments Ltd* (1970), *per* Mr Justice Megarry, quoted in full on page 64, and *Glenlion Construction Co. Ltd* v. *The Guiness Trust* (1988), discussed on p.49.

Having received from the contractor all the requisite information, the architect's duty is to consider the information provided and to make his own assessment of the situation as to whether or not an extension should be granted at that time and, if so, what extension should be granted.

The Aqua Group in *Contract Administration for Architects and Quantity Surveyors*, 6th Edition, page 79, put the problem squarely:

'Perhaps the greatest difficulty which may be encountered in the new procedure will be in deciding whether or not the notice, particulars and estimates which the contractor is required to provide are sufficient for the architect to make his decision on extending the completion date. This will require close co-operation between contractor and architect and it is hoped that architects will be decisive in the matter and will not use alleged insufficiency of particulars and estimates as an excuse for delaying the issue of extensions of time'.

We agree.

In considering this question, the architect will have to take into account any overlapping of delays resulting from different relevant events and, as the Aqua Group point out (*ibid.*) 'in the normal course of events the architect will be assisted by the new contractual obligations on the contractor to provide and keep up to date a master programme for the execution of the works'. In fact, there is no *contractual obligation* to provide a master programme: see John Parris, *The Standard Form of Building Contract: JCT 1980*, Section 4.07 on contractor's master programme, who adds 'it may be unlikely in modern conditions that the contractor has no master programme. He is not contractually obliged to have one, nor does the contract specify what it should comprise'. It is common and sensible practice for the architect to include such a requirement, and specify the type of programme required, in the Bills or Specification, in which case the requirement will become a contractual provision: *Glenlion Construction Co. Ltd* v. *The Guiness Trust* (1988).

Under clause 25 the architect is required to grant the extension of time by fixing as a new completion date for the works '*such later date ... as he then estimates to be fair and reasonable*'. In our view, this differs from JCT 63, clause 23, which simply required the architect to 'make in writing a fair and reasonable extension of time', i.e. simply to state the period of extension without actually stating the new date for completion of the works resulting from the extension. (The old RIBA Form for extensions of time did provide for the new completion date to be inserted, though this was not specifically required by the contract.) The position now is that the architect *must* state the new completion date.

'*The Architect shall, in fixing such new Completion Date, state*' – The architect must inform the contractor in writing of the new completion date, and he must state two things, first, which of the relevant events he has taken into account, and secondly, *the extent, if any, to which he has had regard to any omission instruction issued since the fixing of the previous completion date*. In our view, and contrary to the suggestion in the JCT Guide, paragraph 14.4, page 11, it is clear that the architect may take account of omissions when he decides on the first extension application that he grants because the definition of completion date in clause 1.3 is 'the Date for Completion as fixed and stated in the Appendix or any later date fixed' under the relevant provisions, and date for completion includes the original date. It follows that there is always a 'previous completion date' for the purposes of clause 25.3 and, indeed, it would be absurd if any other interpretation were to be placed upon this provision. The only proviso is that the architect cannot thereby fix a completion date earlier than the date for completion stated originally in the Appendix – something which is forbidden by clause 25.3.6. If he takes account of omissions, the architect must inform the contractor in writing when fixing the new completion date.

'... *shall, if reasonably practicable ... not later than 12 weeks*' – The architect is given a time limit of 12 weeks from receipt of the contractor's notice of delay and of 'reasonably sufficient particulars and estimate' from the contractor in which to reach a decision and, if he considers it appropriate, to grant an extension of time. This is qualified by 'reasonably practicable'. The correct operation of these provisions really depends upon both architect and contractor being of one mind as to whether the information supplied by the contractor is 'reasonably sufficient' to enable the architect to adjudicate. From the employer's point of view it is important that the architect should decide quickly because of the fluctuations provisions: see clauses 38.4.8.2; 39.5.8.2; and 40.7.2.2, the effect of which is that, unless the architect adjudicates timeously, the right of the employer to freeze the contractor's fluctuations on the due date for completion is lost.

However, if there are less than 12 weeks left between receipt of the contractor's notice, particulars and estimate and the currently fixed completion date, the architect must reach his decision and grant any extension no later than that date. The intention clearly is that the contractor should always have a date before him to work to.

Some architects have adopted the practice of amending clause 25 so as to do away with the time limits. This is, in our view, a most unwise practice, if only because of the fluctuations provisions. Fluctuations are only to be frozen at completion date 'if the printed text of clause 35 is unamended and forms part of the Conditions': see clause 38.4.7; 39.5.7; and 40.7.1.1. The situation is in contrast to that under JCT 63 (except where formula method fluctuations are employed under that form): see the observations of Lord Justice Salmon in *Peak Construction Ltd* v. *McKinney Foundations (Liverpool) Ltd* (1970), where he pointed out that fluctuations continued to be payable 'right up to the moment that [the Works are] completed'. In the same case Lord Justice Edmund Davies emphasised that 'the operation of the fluctuations clause is not to be regarded as impliedly restricted [to the completion date] but it extended throughout the whole period until the construction work was completed'.

'... *not fair and reasonable to fix a later date as a new Completion Date*' – The final paragraph of clause 25.3.1 was inserted by Amendment 4 issued by the Joints Contracts Tribunal in July 1987. It is important and its effect is that in respect of each application for an extension of time under clause 25.2 after the provision of any further particulars and estimates required, the architect must notify the contractor in writing where his decision is not to fix a later completion date as a new completion date. This corrects a drafting error in the original version of clause 25.3.1 and the amendment is an important one because the architect's decisions are required before the provisions restricting the level of fluctions or formula adjustment (clauses 38.4.7, 39.5.7 and 40.7) can be operated if the contractor is in default over completion, a point which should not escape those using JCT 80 without this amendment.

'... *after the first exercise*' – Clause 25.3.2 is much misunderstood. After the first extension of time that he grants, the architect can use his powers under the clause. He cannot, in any case, fix any earlier date than the original completion date: clause 25.3.6. But if he has issued instructions omitting work or obligations under clause 13, he is entitled to take this into account and 'fix a Completion Date earlier than that previously fixed under clause 25 if in his opinion the fixing of such earlier completion date is fair and reasonable' having regard to those instructions. Some commentators take the view that this is in conflict with clause 25.3.1.4, already discussed. The architect can, under this provision, reduce extensions previously granted and even extinguish them completely so as to return to the original date for completion but he can fix no earlier date than that, no matter how much work or obligations he omits. Under this provision he can only reduce extensions of time granted already on account of omissions of work, etc. instructed since he last granted an extension. Each extension is deemed to take into account all omissions instructed up to the date of the extension.

Before Amendment 4 (July 1987), clause 25.3.2 restricted the architect's right to fix an earlier completion date to those situations where he had issued variation instructions omitting *work*, so that variation instructions requiring the omission of obligations or restrictions (see clause 13.1.2) and provisional sum instructions under clause 13.3 requiring omissions of work, obligations or restrictions gave no grounds for the operation of clause 25.3.2. This lacuna was unintentional and the original wording which referred to 'any instructions of the architect requiring as a variation the omission of any work issued under clause 13.2.' has been replaced by 'the omission of any work or obligation instructed or sanctioned by the architect under clause 13'. In fact, despite this amendment, it is at least arguable that this does not extend to *restrictions* imposed by the employer and referred to in clause 13.1.2, but it is our view that on a purposive interpretation of the clause they are covered.

If architects wish to take advantage of this power to reduce extensions previously granted on account of omissions of work or obligations, we suggest that they should take the decision and notify the contractor at the earliest possible moment – preferably when issuing the instruction – and not leave it until they next grant an extension of time. The reason for this is that, in our experience, architects have tended to be conservative in granting extensions of time, knowing that they can, at the end of the day, grant a little more time: see below. To err too much in the direction of parsimony – and to be unrealistic in considering the effect of omissions – is not in our view good contract practice.

'... *not later than then expiry of 12 weeks from the date of Practical Completion*' – Clause 25.3.3 gives the architect the final opportunity to make a final decision on extensions of time. In the first edition of this book, we expressed the view that 'this clause imposes a mandatory obligation on the architect to review the completion date in any event' because the clause then read 'not later than the expiry of 12 weeks from the date of practical completion the architect *shall* in writing to the contractor' make a final decision on extensions of time. In *Temloc Ltd* v. *Errill Properties Ltd* (1988) the Court of Appeal held that the requirement is not mandatory. In that case the contractors had argued, *inter alia*, that since the architect had not issued his decision by the stipulated date, the liquidated damages clause was inapplicable. They submitted that the 12 week requirement was a condition precedent to the operation of clause 24.2. The Court of Appeal rejected this contention, pointing out that the certificate referred to in clauses 24.1 and 24.2.1 was not the architect's written decision or certificate under clause 25.3.3.1 fixing a later completion date. It was the certificate of delay referred to in clause 24 telling the contractor that his liability to pay liquidated damages at the agreed rate began. Quite clearly this is correct.

However, Lord Justice Croom-Johnson went further and said:

> 'Even if the provision in clause 25.3.3 is applicable *it is directory only as to time* and is not something which would invalidate the calculation and payment of liquidated damages. The whole right of recovery of liquidated damages does not depend on whether the architect, over whom the contractor has no control, has given his certificate by the stipulated day'. (*Italics supplied*)

With great respect to the learned Lord Justice we find the view that the wording of clause 25.3.3 is merely directory as opposed to mandatory to be surprising. 'Shall' indicates compulsion and is not the same as 'may'. It may well be that the last word has not been said on this subject.

Clause 25.3.3 requires the architect to review the completion date in any event; and he must do this in light of any relevant events whether or not specifically notified to him by the contractor. In its original wording, the architect was required to do this not more than 12 weeks after the actual practical completion of the works and so finally to fix the completion date. That wording, arguably, meant that the provision was inoperable where practical completion had not been achieved by the completion date and *prima facie* the contractor was in default over completion. The wording was revised by Amendment 4 (July 1987) and the opening sentence makes it clear that the architect can operate clause 25.3.2 in these circumstances and take account of any relevant events which occur during that period, which is intended to be the architect's final opportunity to consider extensions of time.

'... *shall in writing to the Contractor*' – Despite the views expressed by Lord Justice Croom-Johnson in *Temloc Ltd* v. *Errill Properties Ltd* (1988), and referred to above, the wording indicates the architect has no discretion; he must write to the contractor and do one of three things:

(1) *Fix a completion date later than that previously fixed* – He must do this if in his opinion so to do is 'fair and reasonable having regard to any of the Relevant Events', i.e. those listed in clause 25.4, '*whether upon reviewing a previous decision or otherwise*' and 'whether or not the Relevant Event has been specifically notified by the Contractor.'

(2) *Fix a completion date earlier than that previously fixed* – He must do this if 'in his opinion ... [it] is fair and reasonable having regard to' any omission instructions issued since he last granted an extension of time.

(3) *Confirm to the contractor the completion date previously fixed.*

'*The Contractor shall use constantly his best endeavours*' – The proviso is important and governs the whole of the preceding sub-clauses. See our commentary on the similar words in JCT 63, clause 23: pages 41–43.

'... *shall notify in writing every Nominated Sub-Contractor*' – Every nominated sub-contractor must be notified by the architect of each decision of his fixing a completion date under clause 25.3. It is not merely those nominated sub-contractors referred to in the contractor's notice of delay. Each time he fixes a new completion date under the main contract the architect must notify all nominated sub-contractors of the new date so fixed. This is obviously highly relevant information for sub-contractors as it will affect their own obligations under their nominated sub-contracts or could, potentially, do so. This is so even if a nominated sub-contractor has finished his work and left site – even after he may have been paid for his work in full – because each change in the main contract completion date affects the period for which the nominated sub-contractor remains liable for defects in his work.

'*No decision of the architect*' – Clause 25.3.6 makes plain that no decision of the architect under clause 25.3 can fix a completion date earlier than that stated in the Appendix. That date is sacrosanct, no matter how much work is omitted or otherwise.

IFC 84 clauses 2.3, 2.4 and 2.5

The provisions of IFC 84 concerning extensions of time are as follows:

Extension of time

2.3 Upon it becoming reasonably apparent that the progress of the Works is being or is likely to be delayed, the Contractor shall forthwith give written notice of the cause of the delay to the Architect/the Contract Administrator, and if in the opinion of the Architect/the Contract Administrator the completion of the Works is likely to be or has been delayed beyond the Date for Completion stated in the Appendix or beyond any extended time previously fixed under this clause, by any of the events in clause 2.4 then the Architect/the Contract Administrator shall so soon as he is able to estimate the length of delay beyond that date or time make in writing a fair and reasonable extension of time for completion of the Works.

If an event referred to in clause 2.4.5, 2.4.6, 2.4.7, 2.4.8, 2.4.9 or 2.4.12 occurs after the Date for Completion (or after the expiry of any extended time previously fixed under this clause) but before Practical Completion is achieved the Architect/ the Contract Administrator shall so soon as he is able to estimate the length of the delay, if any, to the Works resulting from that event make in writing a fair and reasonable extension of the time for completion of the Works.

At any time up to 12 weeks after the date of Practical Completion, the Architect/the Contract Administrator may make an extension of time in accordance with the provisions of this clause 2.3, whether upon reviewing a previous decision or otherwise and whether or not the Contractor has given notice as referred to in the first paragraph hereof. Such an extension of time shall not reduce any previously made.

Provided always that the Contractor shall use constantly his best endeavours to prevent delay and shall do all that may be reasonably required to the satisfaction of the Architect/the Contract Administrator to proceed with the Works.

The Contractor shall provide such information required by the Architect/the Contract Administrator as is reasonably necessary for the purposes of clause 2.3.

Events referred to in 2.3

2.4 The following are the events referred to in clause 2.3:

2.4.1 force majeure;

2.4.2 exceptionally adverse weather conditions;

2.4.3 loss or damage caused by any one or more of the Specified Perils;

2.4.4 civil commotion, local combination of workmen, strike or lock-out affecting any of the trades employed upon the Works or any trade engaged in the preparation, manufacture of transportation of any of the goods or materials required for the Works;

2.4.5 compliance with the Architect's/the Contract Administrator's instructions under clauses

1.4 *(Inconsistencies)*, or

3.6 *(Variations)*, or

3.8 *(Provisional sums)*, or

3.15 *(Postponement)*,

or, to the extent provided therein, under clause

3.3 *(Named sub-contractors)*;

2.4.6 compliance with the Architect's/the Contractor Administrator's instructions requiring the opening up or the testing of any of the work, materials or goods in accordance with clauses 3.12 or 3.13.1 (including making good in consequence of such opening up or testing), unless the inspection or test showed that the work, materials or goods were not in accordance with this Contract;

2.4.7 the Contractor not having received in due time necessary instructions, drawings, details or levels from the Architect/the Contract Administrator for which he specifically applied in writing provided that such application was made on a date which having regard to the Date for Completion stated in the Appendix or any extended time then fixed was neither unreasonably distant from nor unreasonably close to the date on which it was necessary for him to receive the same;

2.4.8 the execution of work not forming part of this Contract by the Employer himself or by persons employed or otherwise engaged by the Employer as referred to in clause 3.11 or the failure to execute such work;

2.4.9 the supply by the Employer of materials and goods which the Employer has agreed to supply for the Works or the failure so to supply;

2.4.10 where this clause is stated in the Appendix to apply, the Contractor's inability for reasons beyond his control and which he could not reasonably have foreseen at the Date of Tender to secure such labour as is essential to the proper carrying out of the Works;

2.4.11 where this clause is stated in the Appendix to apply, the Contractor's inability for reasons beyond his control and which he could not reasonably have foreseen at the Date of Tender to secure such goods or materials as are essential to the proper carrying out of the Works;

2.4.12 failure of the Employer to give in due time ingress to or egress from the site of the Works or any part thereof through or over any land, buildings, way or passage adjoining or connected with the site and in the possession and control of the Employer, in accordance with the Contract Documents, after receipt by the Architect/the Contract Administrator of such notice, if any, as the Contractor is required to give, or failure of the Employer to give such ingress or egress as otherwise agreed between the Architect/the Contract Administrator and the Contractor;

2.4.13 the carrying out by a local authority or statutory undertaker of work in pursuance of its statutory obligations in relation to the Works, or the failure to carry out such work;

2.4.14 where clause 2.2 is stated in the Appendix to apply, the deferment of the Employer giving possession of the site under that clause.

Further delay or extension of time

2.5 In clauses 2.3, 2.6 and 2.8 any references to delay, notice, extension of time or certificate include further delay, further notice, further extension of time, or further certificate as appropriate.

It will be seen that these provisions are essentially a cut-down version of clause 25 in JCT 80, but there are some significant differences which should be highlighted.

Firstly, the mandatory requirement for the contractor to provide particulars of the expected effects of delays and his own estimate of the resulting delay in completion has been omitted. Instead there is an obligation to provide 'such information required by the Architect/Contract Administrator as is reasonably necessary'. There is still therefore an obligation upon the contractor to provide the architect with the information he will need in order to grant a proper extension of time, but there is no obligation on the contractor to provide his own estimate of the extension he will need. In our view the word 'required' does not place an obligation on the architect to ask for the information or to specify what he needs; if that had been intended the word would have been 'requested'.

Secondly, the time limit for the architect to deal with extensions of time is omitted and IFC 84 reverts to the JCT 63 requirement that any extension is to be granted 'so soon as he is able to estimate the length of the delay'. Our comments on this phrase in JCT 63 therefore also apply to IFC 84 (see page 39 above).

Thirdly, the form of the architect's decision reverts to that required under JCT 63, i.e. he is not required to 'fix a completion date' but simply to grant in writing an extension of time, i.e. to specify a period of extension and not a date for completion.

Fourthly, the requirement for the architect to notify the contractor if he decides not to grant an extension of time, inserted into JCT 80 in July 1987, is not repeated here.

Fifthly, the power of the architect to reduce extensions previously granted if he has omitted work in the interim does not appear. In our view this would not affect his right to take such omissions into account when next granting an extension of time, but he will not be able actually to withdraw or reduce an extension already granted.

Sixthly, the provision for review of extensions following practical completion of the works has been made discretionary and not mandatory by the use of the word 'may' instead of 'shall' in the paragraph equivalent to JCT 80 clause 25.3.3. As to the effect of this, see our commentary on the case of *Temloc Ltd* v. *Errill Properties Ltd* (1988) on page 58–59 above.

While these provisions are in general a simplification of the JCT 80 provisions, it seems to us regrettable that IFC 84 has returned in some respects to the old unsatisfactory wording of JCT 63, particularly the use of the words 'so soon as he is able to estimate the length of the delay' in relation to the architect's time for granting extensions. This has frequently been used by architects as an excuse for leaving matters until the end of the contract, and we would have preferred to see some firmer wording used. However, if the contractor fulfills his obligation to provide the architect with 'such information ... as is reasonably necessary' in order for the architect to make a decision there will be no reason why the architect cannot estimate the length of the delay in completion and make his decision immediately.

Grounds for extension of time

JCT 63, clause 23 lists the grounds on which the architect is entitled to retard the date of completion by the contractor. The corresponding provision in JCT 80 is clause 25.4, which uses the term 'relevant event' to describe such a ground, and in IFC 84 is clause 2.4 and many of these grounds are common to all three editions of the contract.

They divide into two groups:

- *Those which are the fault of neither party*:
  JCT 1963, paragraphs (a) to (d), (g), (j), (l)
  JCT 1980 clauses 25.4.1, 25.4.2, 25.4.3, 25.4.4, 25.4.9, 25.4.10, 25.4.11
  IFC 84 clauses 2.4.1, 2.4.2, 2.4.3, 2.4.4, 2.4.10, 2.4.11, 2.4.13.
- *Those which are the responsibility of the employer or his architect or those for whom the employer is responsible in law*:
  JCT 1963, clause 23 paragraphs (e), (f), (h), (i) and (k)
  JCT 1980, clauses 25.4.5, 25.4.6, 25.4.7, 25.4.8, 25.4.10, 25.4.12, 25.4.13
  IFC 84 clauses 2.4.5, 2.4.6, 2.4.7, 2.4.8, 2.4.9, 2.4.12, 2.4.14.

Each of these grounds will be commented upon in turn, but it is seldom in practice that a 'relevant event' occurs in isolation. This raises the question of whether the architect is bound to take the cumulative or 'roll-on' effect into account in reaching his decision and, in our view, the answer to that question is unhesitatingly in the affirmative.

The same situation raises another problem, namely where the different causes of delay overlap and one is an event justifying an extension and the other is not. For example, the contractor is already behind programme due to his own fault, and then there is a spell of very bad weather. The problem arises in its most acute form, of course, where one of the grounds is also, and independently, a ground for claiming direct loss and/or expense. In *H. Fairweather & Co Ltd* v. *Wandsworth LBC* (1988), Judge James Fox-Andrews QC held that, where an event occurs on site which causes delay to completion, but which can be ascribed to more than one of the reasons set out in JCT 63, clause 23, it is incorrect to grant the extension to the dominant cause of the delay, because the grant of an extension of time is not a condition precedent to the right of reimbursement for direct loss and/or expense, even though JCT 63 contains no mechanism for allocating any extension between different heads. In contrast, JCT 80, clause 26.3 does require the architect to state in writing to the contractor what extension of time, if any, he has granted under clause 25 in respect of those events which are also, and independently, grounds for monetary reimbursement under clause 26 'if and to the extent that it is necessary for ascertainment under clause 26 of loss and/or expense'. Another common situation is where the contractor is in advance of this programme, and a delaying event occurs. There is no clear legal answer, but in *Hounslow Borough Council* v. *Twickenham Garden Developments Ltd* (1970), Mr Justice Megarry (as he then was) expressed certain views as to the effect of the JCT wording. He said:

'Provided the contractor has given written notice of the cause of delay, the obligation to make an extension appears to rest on the architect without the necessity of any formal request for it by the contractor. Yet he is required to do this only if the completion of the works "is likely to be or has been delayed beyond the Date for Completion", or any extended time for completion previously fixed. If a contractor is well ahead with his works and is then delayed by a strike, the architect may nevertheless reach the conclusion that completion of the works is not likely to be delayed beyond the date of completion. Under condition 21 (1), the contractor is under a double obligation: on being given possession of the site, he must "thereupon begin the works and regularly and diligently proceed with the same", and he must also complete the works "on or before the Date for Completion", subject to any extension of time. If a strike occurs when two-thirds of the work has been completed in half the contract time, I do not think that on resuming work a few weeks later the contractor is then entitled to slow down the work so as to last out the time until the date for completion (or beyond, if an extension of time is granted) if thereby he is failing to proceed with the work "regularly and diligently".'

These observations were purely *obiter* but, in our view, the analysis is impeccable, and the consequence is that the architect is entitled to take into account the fact that the contractor is in advance of programme when considering what extension to grant; and he may also make use of the contractor's 'float' element in the contract programme. Where there are overlapping causes of delay, the architect must consider each cause separately, so that if there is one ground justifying an extension and another not, the architect cannot deprive the contractor of any reasonable extension for the relevant event merely because there is an overlapping cause; but the cumulative effect on progress must be taken into account: it is delay to progress which is the important factor.

It is also unclear whether, under JCT terms, the extension of time clause is intended to operate during a period of delay for which the contractor in responsible in law. The point is an important one, and the only relevant reported case appears to be *Walter Lawrence & Son Ltd* v. *Commercial Union Properties (UK) Ltd* (1986), where on an application for summary judgment under Order 14 of the Rules of the Supreme Court, Judge Lewis Hawser QC, the very experienced Senior Official Referee, held that the effect of the delaying cause was to be assessed at the time when the works are actually carried out, *even if the contractor is in culpable delay during the original or extended contract period.* But this point turned on the employer's argument that the effect of the delaying event – in that case exceptionally inclement weather – had to be considered at the time when the works were programmed to be carried out and not when the works were actually carried out. Not surprisingly, the learned judge rejected this curious argument since there was no contractual obligation to programme express or implied. The contract in that case was in JCT 63 form, but the position would be the same under a JCT 80 or IFC 84 contract. If the works as carried out are actually delayed by one of the stated events during the original or extended contract period the contractor is entitled to an extension of time. However, attention is drawn to the short but useful discussion in *Hudson's Building Contracts*, supplement to 10th Edition, page 653, published in 1979.

The grounds on which an extension of time may be granted are as follows:
Force majeure: JCT 63, clause 23(a); JCT 80, clause 25.4.1; IFC 84, clause 2.4.1. Force majeure is a French law term which is wider in its meaning than the common law term 'Act of God', which is an overwhelming superhuman event: *Oakley* v. *Portsmouth & Ryde Steam Packet Co.* (1856). In fact, under JCT contracts the term *force majeure* has a restricted meaning because many matters such as war, strikes, fire and exceptional weather are expressly dealt with later in the contract. There appear to be no reported cases dealing with the matter in the context of JCT contracts, and the English authority usually quoted is *Lebeaupin* v. *Crispin* (1920), where Mr Justice McCardie accepted that

> 'This term is used with reference to all circumstances independent of the will of man, and which it is not in his power to control .... Thus war, inundations and epidemics are cases of *force majeure*; it has even been decided that a strike of workmen constitutes a case of *force majeure* ... [But] a *force majeure* clause should be construed in each case with a close attention to the words which precede or follow it and with due

regard to the nature and general terms of the contract. The effect of the clause may vary with each instrument.'

In fact, it seems that the term *force majeure* as used in JCT contracts is of limited effect, and decisions on the meaning of the word when used in other forms of contract are of little assistance. The only really helpful decision is *Matsoukis* v. *Priestman & Co.* (1915) where the dislocation of business caused by the general coal strike of 1912 was held to be covered by the term and also, in the same case, covered the breakdown of machinery. Mr Justice Bailhache also held there that it did not cover delay caused by bad weather, football matches or a funeral. 'These are the usual incidents interrupting work and the defendants, in making their contract, no doubt took them into account.' The best that can be said is that the event relied upon as *force majeure* must make the performance of the contract wholly impossible and, in this sense, the term is somewhat akin to the English law doctrine of frustration of contract.

Exceptionally inclement weather: JCT 63, clause 23(b);
Exceptionally adverse weather conditions: JCT 80, clause 25.4.2; IFC 84 clause 2.4.2.

These phrases are a frequent source of argument between architects and contractors and the change in wording in the 1980 Form is intended to make it clear that the ground is intended to cover adverse conditions caused by exceptional drought. The emphasis is on the word *exceptionally* and the meaning of the phrase is to be found by considering two factors. First, the kind of weather that may be expected at the site at the particular time when the delay occurs. Second, the stage which the works have reached. In regard to the first factor reference to local weather records may be helpful in showing that the adverse weather was 'exceptional' for that area, i.e. exceeding what may on the evidence of past years be reasonably expected. The dictionary meaning of adverse is 'contrary' or 'hostile', while 'exceptionally' means 'unusual'. In regard to the second factor even if the weather is exceptionally adverse for the time of year it must be such that it interferes with the works at the particular stage they have reached when the exceptionally adverse weather occurs. If despite the weather internal works could continue then the works have not been delayed by the exceptionally adverse weather. The contractor is expected to programme the works making due allowance for normal adverse weather, i.e. the sort of weather which is to be expected in the area and at the time of year during the course of the works. His programme for those parts of the work which may be affected by rain, wind or frost should acknowledge the fact that interruption is likely to occur, and should allow minimum and maximum target periods for the operations concerned.

This view is supported by The Aqua Group in *Contract Administration for Architects and Quantity Surveyors*, 6th Edition, page 76, who give the following example:

'If it were known at the time that a contract was let that the work was to be carried out during the winter months, and if that work is delayed by a fortnight of snow and frost during January, such a delay could not be regarded as due to exceptionally inclement weather. If, however, such work was held up by a continuous period of snow or frost, from early January until the end of March, an extension of time would clearly be justified ...'

Loss or damage occasioned by any one or more of the contingencies referred to in clause 20 [A], [B] or [C]: JCT 63, clause 23(c);
Loss or damage occasioned by one or more of the specified perils: JCT 80, clause 25.4.3; IFC 84 clause 2.4.3.
This simply gives the contractor the necessary time to fulfil his obligations to repair damage caused by fire, lightning, explosion, storm, tempest, flood, bursting or overflowing of water tanks, apparatus or pipes, earthquake, aircraft or other aerial devices, or articles dropped therefrom, riot and civil commotion, but (in JCT 80) excluding what are called the 'Excepted Risks': These are defined in clause 1.3. Although the JCT 80 and IFC 84 insurance clauses were amended in November 1986 clause 25.4.3 was only amended to the extent that the term 'Specified Perils' was substituted for the 1980 phrase 'Clause 22 Perils'.

The only important practical question arising under this heading is whether or not the contractor is entitled to an extension of time where the events are caused by the default or negligence of the contractor's own employees. On the plain reading of the wording it would appear that the contractor is still entitled to an extension: see Mr I.N. Duncan Wallace, *Building and Civil Engineering Standard Forms*, page 108 and Dr John Parris, *The Standard Form of Building Contract: JCT 1980*, Section 7.15 loss or damage by clause 22 perils: JCT 80 clause 25.4.3. However, we agree with the caveat entered by Dr Parris:

'... if the contractor burns down the works, the architect would be ill-advised to give him an extension of time, in spite of the indemnity in JCT 80 clause 20.2, since it is not wide enough to cover the loss of liquidated damages which are intended to compensate the employer for his loss of rent or loss of use of the premises. The plain tenor of the whole of JCT 80 clause 25 is that the contractor should not have an extension of time for anything that is in any way his fault'.

The only qualification to this statement is that there is now an optional provision (clause 22D) under which the employer can require the contractor to obtain insurance for the loss of liquidated damages as a result of an extension of time being granted on this ground, and entries in the Appendix are provided for the employer to state whether this insurance is required and the period of cover. This option was introduced by Amendment 2 in November 1986, and by it the Joint Contracts Tribunal has accepted that the position is as set out above. In those contracts incorporating clause 22D, the architect must clearly grant an extension of time.

Strikes and similar events: JCT 63, clause 23(d);
JCT 80, clause 25.4.4
IFC 84 clause 2.4.4
The full list of events is 'civil commotion, local combination of workmen, strike or lock-out affecting any of the trades employed upon the Works or any of the trades engaged in the preparation, manufacture or transportation of any of the goods or materials required for the Works'.

'Civil commotion' means, for insurance purposes, 'a stage between a riot and civil war': *per* Lord Justice Luxmoore in *Levy* v. *Assicurazioni Generali* (1940), where the following definition from Welford and Otter-Barry's *Fire Insurance*, 3rd Edition, at page 64, was approved:

'Civil commotion. This phrase is used to indicate a stage between a riot and civil war. It has been defined as meaning an insurrection of the people for general purposes, though not amounting to rebellion; but it is probably not capable of definition. The element of turbulence or tumult is essential; an organised conspiracy to commit criminal acts, where there is no tumult or disturbance until after the acts, does not amount to civil commotion. It is not, however, necessary to show the existence of any outside organisation at whose instigation the acts were done.'

So far as strikes are concerned, it should be noted that extension may be granted, not only for such circumstances affecting the contractor himself and his work on the site, but also those engaged in preparing or transporting any goods and materials required for the works. The wording covers both official and unofficial strikes, but it does not cover 'working to rule' or other obstructive activities which fall short of a strike. In *Boskalis Westminster Construction Ltd* v. *Liverpool City Council* (1983), it was held that a strike by workers employed by statutory undertakers directly engaged by the employer to execute work not forming part of the works was not covered by clause 23(d). A strike or other event referred to in the sub-clause must be one in which the trades mentioned in it are directly involved.

'Local combination of workmen' is an antiquated phrase beloved of the draftsmen of insurance policies. Possibly today it might be held to cover obstructive activities falling short of a strike provided they were confined to one area or site, but the true position is far from clear.

Architect's instructions: JCT 63, clause 23(e)
JCT 80, clause 25.4.5.1
IFC 84 clause 2.4.5.

Under JCT 63 the instructions referred to are:

(a) Clause 1   (2) – Instructions regarding discrepancies in or divergences between drawings and/or bills.
(b) Clause 11(1) – Instructions requiring a variation as defined in clause 11(2). These include, it is suggested, correction of errors in the bills which are deemed to be variations under the terms of the clause 12(2).
(c) Clause 21(2) – Instructions regarding the postponement of any work to be executed under the contract.

Under JCT 80 the instructions referred to are:

(i) Clause 2.3   – Discrepancies in contract bills, etc.
(ii) Clause 13.2 – Variations.
(iii) Clause 13.3 – Expenditure of provisional sums in bills and sub-contracts.
(iv) Clause 23.2 – Postponement of any work to be executed under the contract.
(v) Clause 34   – Antiquities.
(vi) Clause 35   – Nominated sub-contractors.
(vii) Clause 36   – Nominated suppliers.

Under IFC 84 the instructions referred to are:

(i) Clause 1.4   – Discrepancies in contract documents etc.
(ii) Clause 3.6   – Variations.
(iii) Clause 3.8   – Expenditure of provisional sums.
(iv) Clause 3.15 – Postponement of any work to be executed under the contract.
(v) Clause 3.3   – Named sub-contractors, but only to the extent permitted by the terms of the clause.

It should be noted that JCT 80, clause 25.4.5 is more extensive than JCT 63, clause 23(e), since under the latter provision extensions may be granted only for delays caused by architect's instructions relating to discrepancies between the contract drawings and/or the contract bills (clause 1(2)); variations (clause 11(2) – but not for instructions for the expenditure of PC sums or provisional sums under clause 11(3)); and postponement of work to be executed under the contract (clause 21(2)).

Under JCT 80, it is our view that if there is a failure of a nominated sub-contractor, and there is unreasonable delay by the architect in making a re-nomination, the contractor might be entitled to an extension of time under clause 25.4.5.1, with its specific reference to clause 35; he is certainly so entitled under clause 25.4.6 and under JCT 63, clause 23(f) which empowers the architect to extend time in such circumstances, as was emphasised by the House of Lords in *Percy Bilton Ltd* v. *Greater London Council* (1982) holding that delay by the employer in re-nomination of a nominated sub-contractor fell within the scope of JCT 63, clause 23(f): See also *Fairclough Building Ltd* v. *Rhuddlan Borough Council* (1985).

Under IFC 84 there is no provision for the nomination of sub-contractors. Instead sub-contractors may be 'named', either in the contract documents or by instructions for the expenditure of provisional sums. Except that the sub-contract must be on a prescribed standard form entered into after specified procedures, such sub-contractors become virtually domestic sub-contractors. There are no provisions for the certification of payments by the architect or for direct payment by the employer if the contractor defaults and there is no provision entitling the contractor to an extension of time for delay on their part. However, if the sub-contractor defaults in the performance of his work to the extent that his employment is determined the contractor is to notify the architect who must then issue instructions either, (a) naming a replacement sub-contractor, or (b) instructing the contractor to make his own arrangements for the completion of the work, or (c) omitting the remaining work, in which event the employer may make his own arrangements for completion. Whichever instruction the architect issues, the contractor will be entitled to an extension of time for the delaying effect of the instruction. If the sub-contractor determines his own employment because of the contractor's default the architect is still to issue an instruction, but such an instruction will not entitle the contractor to an extension of time.

Similarly, if the contractor finds that he cannot enter into a sub-contract with a sub-contractor named in the contract documents because of some problem over the particulars of the sub-contract as set out in those documents, the architect is to issue instructions either changing the particulars so as to remove the problem, or omitting the work or by substituting a provisional sum. In the last event, any sub-contractor subsequently named would be regarded as having been named in an instruction for the expenditure of that sum.

Where a sub-contractor is named in an instruction for the expenditure of a provisional sum, such an instruction will have been issued under clause 3.8 of the contract. If the instruction causes delay for any reason, therefore, the contractor will be entitled to an extension of time.

Opening up for inspection and testing: JCT 63, clause 23(i);
JCT 80, clause 25.4.5.2
IFC 84, clause 2.4.6.

The contractor may be entitled to an extension of time if delay has been caused by work being opened up for inspection or materials and goods being tested in accordance with architect's instructions (under clause 6(3), JCT 63; clause 8.3 JCT 80; clause 3.12, IFC 84) if, and only if, the work inspected or the materials or goods tested prove to be in accordance with the contract. There can thus only be an entitlement to an extension of time if the inspection, etc. is favourable to the contractor, which is a point sometimes overlooked by architects.

IFC 84 clause 3.13 has elaborate provisions for repeated testing in the event of a defect being shown in repetitive work. Here, again, an extension of time may only be granted if the tests of other items of similar work are favourable to the contractor.

Late instructions and drawings: JCT 63, clause 23(f);
JCT 80, clause 25.4.6;
IFC 84, clause 2.4.7

This is the heading which causes more dispute and difficulty than any other and the exact wording of the paragraph is vitally important. The 'instructions' referred to are any instructions under the contract which the contract empowers the architect to give, but the limitations should be noted. The contractor must have 'specifically applied in writing' to the architect for the 'necessary instructions, drawings, details or levels'; and, moreover, his written application must be made at the correct time. It must not be made to early or too late or, to use the wording of the contract form itself, the application must have been made 'on a date which having regard to the Completion Date was neither unreasonably distant from nor unreasonably close to the date on which it was necessary for him to receive the same' (JCT 80, clause 25.4.6).

There is much room for argument as to whether a contractor's application has been made at the right time, but in our view a blanket application at contract commencement, or the giving of an 'information supply chart' or programme to the architect is not sufficient, unless it is very detailed and is updated in light of contract progress. *Specific* application is required, but this does not mean that the contractor must make a separate written application for each item of information. It is common and acceptable practice for the contractor to apply for more than one item of information at a time, and this is clearly a specific application, but the submission of a programme or like request for all information for the whole of the contract period at the outset can in no sense be regarded as a 'continuing application' as is often alleged.

This was one of the many points at issue in *London Borough of Merton* v. *Stanley Hugh Leach Ltd* (1985) where the contractor submitted a programme for the whole of the works about a month after possession of the site had been given by the employer. The programme was in diagrammatic form and indicated by conventional signs the dates by which information was required. It was common ground that the programme was 'in writing'. Mr Justice Vinelott came to the conclusion that the contractor's submission of the programme with its symbols met the contractual requirement of being a 'specific application', provided that the dates set out in it met the requirements of being neither unreasonably close to nor unreasonably distant from the dates when the information was in fact required.

The intention of this very cumbersome phrasing is to prevent the contractor from requesting information on a date so close to the date on which he requires it that the architect is deprived of any proper opportunity of preparing the necessary drawings, etc., in time or, at the other extreme, of requesting the information so far in advance of his actual needs that the architect's compliance with the timing requirements (JCT 63, clause 3 (4); JCT 80, clause 5.4, IFC 84, clause 1.7) would result in the information being received unrealistically early. It is easy to define these extreme positions, but the words used are '... neither *unreasonably* distant from nor *unreasonably* close to ...' These words introduce the concept of reason and mean that the interpretation of the requirement must be a question of fact having regard to all the circumstances of the case.

There are some helpful observations in the civil engineering case of *Neodox* v. *Borough of Swinton & Pendlebury* (1958), where Mr Justice Diplock (as he then was) considered fully the question of terms to be applied as to the time within which further drawings, details or instructions are to be given. He started off by stating that such information must be given within a reasonable time, but he made it clear that this is a limited duty.

Mr Justice Diplock said:

'What is a reasonable time does not depend solely upon the convenience and financial interests of the [contractors]. No doubt it is in their interest to have every detail cut and dried on the day the contract is signed, but the contract does not contemplate that. It contemplates further drawings and details being provided, and the engineer is to have a time to provide them which is reasonable having regard to the point of view of him and his staff and the point of view of the employer as well as the point of view of the contractor.'

This is a common-sense business approach and is broadly applicable to the JCT wording. Under JCT contracts the architect does not control the order of the works, and the phrase 'the date on which it was necessary for him to receive the same' must primarily be interpreted from the contractor's point of view. Factors to be taken into account will include the time necessary for the contractor to organise adequate supplies of labour, materials and plant and to execute any prefabrication or prepare materials in such time as to ensure that these things are available on site having regard to his obligation to complete the works in accordance with the contract.

In *Merton* v. *Leach* Mr Justice Vinelott held that the contractor's written application could be made at the start of the contract for all the information, provided that the dates specified for delivery of each item of information then met the requirements of being neither unreasonably distant from or unreasonably close to the relevant date. The time constraints are, of course, to be determined with regard to the current date for completion. Because of the controversy which surrounds this issue, part of Mr Justice Vinelott's judgment must be quoted at length:

'What the parties contemplated by these provisions was first that the architect was not to be required to furnish instructions, drawings, etc., unreasonably far in advance from the date when the contractor would require them in order to carry out the work efficiently nor to be asked for them at a time which did not give him a reasonable opportunity to meet the request. It is true that the words "on a date" grammatically govern the date on which the application is made. But they are ... capable of being read as referring to the date on which the application is to be met. That construction seems to me to give effect to the purpose of the provision – merely to ensure that the architect is not troubled with applications too far in advance of the time when they will be actually needed by the contractor ... and to ensure that he is not left with insufficient time to prepare them. If that is right then there seems ... to be no reason why an application should not be made at the commencement of the work for all the instructions etc which the contractor can foresee will be required in the course of the works provided the date specified for delivery of each set of instructions meets these two requirements. *Of course if he does so and the works do not progress strictly in accordance with this plan some modification may be required to the prescribed timetable and the subsequent furnishing of instructions and the like ... It does not follow that [the programme] was a sufficiently specific application made at an appropriate time in relation to every item of information required, more particularly in light of the delays and the rearrangement of the programme for the work'.* (Italics supplied).

The reservation which is emphasised in our quotation should be noted.

Where extensions of time have already been granted, the completion date referred to in the clause is, of course, the revised completion date, and this is the point on which many 'late instructions' claims founder.

It is, of course, clear that apart from the express terms of the contract there is an implied term that the contractor will receive decisions, drawings, details, etc. from the architect in time to avoid disruption of the contract. But this is conditioned by the JCT wording as regards extensions of time: the contractor must have made a specific application in writing for them, and he must have done this at the right time. 'Specific' means 'definite or distinctly formulated' according to the dictionary, and thus merely presenting the architect with a general request is not sufficient.

Dr John Parris (*The Standard Form of Building Contract: JCT 80*, Section 7.08 Instructions, drawings not in time: JCT 80, clause 25.4.6, states that where the contractor has not made a specific application in due time, there is no power in the architect to extend time, although he adds, for the purposes of JCT 80, that 'it is perhaps possible that he may subsequently have power to entertain it in his review' under clause 25.3.3. We think that this is the best that can be said; but the architect certainly has no such power under JCT 63.

Delay on the part of nominated sub-contractors or nominated suppliers: JCT 63, clause 23(g); JCT 80, clause 25.4.7

A very limited meaning is to be given to this provision in light of the decision of the House of Lords in *City of Westminster* v. *J. Jarvis & Sons Ltd* (1970), as explained (again by the House of Lords) in *Percy Bilton Ltd* v. *Greater London Council* (1982). The effect of the *Jarvis* case is that 'delay on the part of nominated sub-contractors' only means delay by the nominated sub-contractor during the execution of the sub-contract works, and the net result of the decision is if a nominated sub-contractor (or, for that matter, a nominated supplier) ostensibly completes his sub-contract work or his supply contract but later is found to be in breach, e.g. because defects appear in the work, and has to return to remedy the breach, that is not a 'delay' within the meaning of this sub-clause.

In *Bilton's* case, the original nominated mechanical services sub-contractor withdrew from site and subsequently went into liquidation. The sub-contractor nominated as a replacement withdrew before starting work and ultimately a substituted nominated sub-contractor was named some 4 months after the main contractor had requested a re-nomination. The House of Lords held that 'when a nominated sub-contractor withdrew, the duty of the employer ... was ... limited to giving instruction for nomination of a replacement within a reasonable time after receiving a specific application in writing from the main contractor'. It follows that, if a nominated sub-contractor drops out, 'the result is not that time becomes at large but that ... the date for completion remains unaffected by the delay'.

The delay referred to by the sub-clause must, it is noted, be delay which the contractor has taken all practicable steps to avoid or reduce, and perhaps the observations of Viscount Dilhorne in *Bickerton* v. *North West Metropolitan Regional Hospital Board* (1970) as to the general legal situation will serve as a warning to main contractors. He said:

'I cannot myself see that the extent of the contractor's obligation ... is in any respect limited or affected by the right of the architect to nominate the sub-contractors. He has accepted responsibility for the carrying out and completion of all the contract works including those to be carried out by the nominated sub-contractor. Once the sub-contractor has been nominated and entered into the sub-contract, the contractor is as responsible for his work as he is for the works of other sub-contractors employed by him with the leave of the architect.'

Equally, however, *Percy Bilton Ltd* v. *Greater London Council* makes it clear that 'delay by the employer in making the timeous nomination of a new sub-contractor is within the express terms of clause 23(f)' of JCT 63 and, of course, within JCT 80, clause 25.4.6. Under JCT 63 and JCT 80 it is for the contractor to make application to the architect for a re-nomination in respect of failure by a nominated sub-contractor or nominated supplier.

IFC 84 contains no similar provision in respect of 'named' sub-contractors; see page 70–71 above.

Delay by artists, tradesmen or others: JCT 63, clause 23(h);
Work not forming part of the contract: JCT 80, clause 25.4.8;
IFC 84, clauses 2.4.8 and 2.4.9.

JCT 63, clause 23(h) refers to delay 'by artists, tradesmen or others engaged by the employer in executing work not forming part of this contract' and the employer's power to so engage independent contractors is contained in JCT 63, clause 29. Following the views expressed by the House of Lords in *City of Westminster* v. *J. Jarvis & Sons Ltd* (1970), it is suggested that clause 23(h) is restricted to delay by them in the execution of their work and does not include, for example, delay caused by their returning to carry out remedial work.

Under JCT 63, the correct interpretation of clause 23(h) was considered by Judge Edgar Fay QC in *Henry Boot Construction Ltd* v. *Central Lancashire New Town Development Corporation* (1980) and he held that the words 'or others' were not to be construed *ejusdem generis*, with the result that statutory undertakers engaged under contract with the employer (and *not* carrying out their statutory functions) fell within the description of 'work being done by ... others engaged by the employer'.

This decision is irrelevant to JCT 80, clause 25.4.8, except for the judge's observations on the meaning of 'work not forming part of this contract' because clause 25.4.8 has now been completely re-drafted, and there are two separate situations.

The first situation is covered by clause 25.4.8.1, which refers to:

'The execution of work not forming part of this contract by the employer himself or by persons employed, or otherwise engaged by the employer as referred to in clause 29 or the failure to execute such work.'

This is clearly a more extensive provision than JCT 63, clause 23(h), and it should be noted in particular that there is no reference to 'delay on the part of'. We suggest, therefore, that the limitation indicated above does not apply to JCT 80.

The second situation is a new ground for extension of time and is found in clause 25.4.8.2, which reads:

'the supply by the employer of materials and goods which the employer has agreed to provide for the works or failure so to supply.'

Government action: JCT 80, clause 25.4.9
JCT 80, clause 25.4.9, introduces a new ground for extension of time; there is no corresponding provision in JCT 63 or in IFC 84. The clause reads:

> 'the exercise after the Base Date by the United Kingdom Government of any statutory power which directly affects the execution of the Works by restricting the availability or use of labour which is essential to the proper carrying out of the works or preventing the Contractor from, or delaying the Contractor in, securing such goods or material or such fuel or energy as are essential to the proper carrying out of the Works'.

The Base Date is that date written into the Appendix. In the case of JCT 80 before its amendment in July 1987, the reference was to the 'Date of Tender', meaning '10 days before the date fixed for receipt of tenders by the employer' (clauses 38.6.1 and 39.7.1 in their original form), which did not always in practice provide a firm date.

This provision might, for example, be relied upon in a 'three-day-week' situation or wherever the British Government exercises any statutory power in the sense described in the clause, e.g. under the Defence of the Realm Regulations. The real significance of this is that it is no longer to be covered by *force majeure*, and such action would prevent the contract being brought to an end by frustration. A prolonged stoppage of work for this reason would not, therefore, be grounds for the contractor to determine his own employment under clause 28.1.

Inability to obtain labour and goods: JCT 63, clause 23 (j);
JCT 80, clause 25.4.10.1.2
IFC 84 clauses 2.4.10 and 2.4.11
In JCT 63, clause 23(j) was an optional provision and contains two paragraphs dealing separately with labour and materials. Despite JCT Practice Note No. 2, many architects consistently and unfairly deleted both parts of the sub-clause. Practice Note No. 2 advised that the sub-clause should be deleted, in whole or in part, 'only if it is reasonable in all the relevant circumstances to expect contractors tendering for the work to take the risk of either labour or materials or both not being available'.

Under JCT 80 the clause is mandatory and not merely an optional ground for extension. Moreover, the date at which any shortage is to be unforeseeable has been changed from 'the Date of this Contract' (JCT 63) to 'the Base Date' (JCT 80 as amended in July 1987.)

Prior to July 1987, clause 25.4.10.1.2. JCT 80 referred to 'the Date of Tender' which led to an apparent difficulty, both in this clause and under clause 25.4.9 (above). The 'Date of Tender' was defined in clause 1.3 by reference to the fluctuations clauses 38, 39 and 40. Those clauses, however, apparently defined 'Date of Tender' for the purposes of fluctuations only, e.g. clause 38.6: '*In clause 38* the expression "Date of Tender" means ...'. It seemed, therefore, that there was arguably no 'Date of Tender' applicable to clause 25. There were two possibilities. First (and according to the ordinary rules of construction), it could mean the actual date of tender. Secondly, the formula definition of date of tender could apply, i.e. 10 days before the date fixed for the receipt of tenders by the employer. In legal theory the first interpretation was the correct one, but in practice we found that both architects and contractors opted for the latter. In the first edition of this book, we urged the JCT to give urgent consideration to amending clause 1.3 so as to provide a definition for clause 25 purposes or, better still, provide a space in the Appendix for the date of tender to be stated for all purposes. This the Tribunal did in July 1987 by Amendment 4.

The clauses in IFC 84 are optional, as in JCT 63, but subject to an entry in the Appendix. The entry consists of the deletion of alternatives, and it is essential that the appropriate deletion is made; if it is not it is likely that the clause will be held to apply.

Local authority or statutory undertaker's work: JCT 63, clause 23(l);
JCT 80, clause 25.4.11;
IFC 84, clause 2.4.13.

These provisions cover delay caused by 'the carrying out by a local authority or statutory undertaker of work *in pursuance of its statutory obligations* in relation to the Works, or the failure to carry out such work' and the wording is to the same effect in both editions of the JCT Form.

In *Henry Boot Construction Ltd* v. *Central Lancashire Development Corporation* (1980), which arose from an award made in the form of a Special Case by an arbitrator, Judge Edgar Fay QC was concerned with the problem of whether 'statutory undertakers' were 'artists, tradesmen or others engaged by the Employer' for the purpose of JCT 63, clauses 23(h) and 24(l)(d). He was bound by the arbitrator's finding of fact that statutory undertakers carrying out particular work under particular circumstances were doing it by virtue of a contract with the employer. They were not doing the work because statute obliged them to do it but because they had contracted with the employer to do it and so, he found, were 'engaged by the employer in carrying out work not forming part of this contract'. It followed from this that extensions of time in respect of delays on their part should be granted under clause 23(h) rather than 23(1), and that the contractor could, therefore, claim direct loss and/or expense from the employer under clause 24(l)(d).

Despite some assertions to the contrary, this decision has made no difference whatever to the perfectly clear meaning to be attached to these words, which the arbitrator clearly had very firmly in mind. Extensions of time can *only* be granted under this head if the statutory undertakers are carrying out work that is a statutory obligation.

Statutory undertakers frequently do work that is not done under statutory obligation, even though only they can do it. In such a case, they will normally be considered to have been 'engaged by the employer' and any extension of time would be grantable under clause 25.4.8.1, with a possible claim for direct loss and/or expense under clause 26.2.4.1.

Statutory undertakers may, of course, affect the work in other ways. A Water Authority might, for example, be laying water mains in the public road which provides access to the site, not for the purposes of the particular contract works but perhaps for another site nearby. In that case, even though they might be under an obligation to lay the mains (and be carrying out the work as a matter of statutory obligation) they would not be doing so in relation to the works. In such a case, in our view there could be no extension of time under clause 25.4.11 because the statutory undertaker would be be carrying out 'work ... in relation to the Works' and, indeed, it seems to us that there is no provision in JCT 63 or 80 or in IFC 84 under which an extension of time could be granted. (Dubiously, it might be argued that such activities constituted *force majeure*.)

In practical terms, the question of under which sub-clause an extension of time should be granted for delays caused by local authorities and statutory undertakers depends entirely upon the sort of work they are doing and the circumstances under which they are doing it.

Failure to give ingress or egress: JCT 80, clause 25.4.12;
IFC 84, Clause 2.4.12

A new ground for extension of time is contained in JCT 80 clause 25.2.6:

'failure of the Employer to give in due time ingress to or egress from the site of the Works, or any part thereof through or over any land, buildings, way or passage adjoining or connected with the site and in the possession and control of the Employer, in accordance with the Contract Bills and/or the Contract Drawings, after receipt by the

> Architect of such notice, if any, as the Contractor is required to give, or failure of the Employer to give such ingress or egress as otherwise agreed between the Architect and the Contractor'.

Save for the words 'the Contract Documents' in place of 'the Contract Bills and/or the Contract Drawings' clause 2.4.12 of IFC 84 is identical.

The exact wording of this provision should be noted with great care because it is not as extensive as some architects and contractors appear to think. An extension of time can only be granted under this sub-clause where there is failure by the employer to provide access to or exit from the site of the works across any *adjoining or connected* 'land, buildings, way or passage' which is in his own *'possession and control'*. It does not, therefore, cover, for instance, failure to obtain a wayleave across an adjoining owner's property, or where, for example, access to the highway is obstructed. It would equally not extend to the situation where, as happened recently, 'peace protestors' impeded access to a military site where contractors were carrying out work.

It should be made clear that there is no right in the contractor to (or power in the architect to grant) an extension of time under this sub-clause for the employer's failure to give possession of the site itself on the date for possession. This is of particular importance where JCT 80 is being used in a form not incorporating Amendment 4, issued in July 1987, or where in such an amended contract the employer has not taken power to defer the giving of possession of the site to the contractor.

There is also a further limitation in the sub-clause itself. The wording refers to access, etc. 'in accordance with Contract Bills and/or Contract Drawings', which suggests that the undertaking to provide such access must be stated in the bills or drawings, and in that case any extension of time will be dependent upon the contractor giving whatever notice may be required by the provision in the bill before access is to be granted. But the clause goes further with its reference to 'or failure of the Employer to give such ingress or egress as *otherwise agreed between the Architect and the Contractor'*. This would seem to give the architect the authority to reach such an agreement on the employer's behalf so that the employer in effect becomes responsible for failing to honour such an agreement even though it may have been reached without his being consulted. This, if correct, seems to us an extraordinary and unwarranted extension of the architect's powers. In our view, the JCT should clarify the position. The architect's authority as the employer's agent is a limited one in law and the current (July 1982) *Architect's Appointment* make clear how limited his authority is.

Deferment of possession of site: JCT 80, clause 25.4.13;
IFC 84, clause 2.4.14

Following its first appearance in IFC 84, this ground was added to JCT 80 in July 1987 in response to widespread criticism since in practice, failure by the employer to give possession of the site is quite common. Clause 23.1 was accordingly amended in line with clause 2.4.14 of IFC 84 so as to enable the employer to defer giving the contractor possession of the site for a period of up to six weeks unless he has inserted a shorter period in the Appendix. He only has this power if it is expressly stated in the Appendix, the relevant entry being 'Clause 23.1.2 applies/does not apply' and one of the alternatives is to be deleted. Where the employer does defer the giving of possession, there will be entitlement to extension of time.

Chapter 3

Variations

INTRODUCTION

Variations are a fact of life in building contracts. There can only be a tiny minority of contracts of any size in which the subject-matter when completed is identical in every respect with what was contemplated at the outset.

Variations are inevitable in even the best-planned contracts simply because, in a matter as complicated as the construction of a building, it is virtually impossible for the building owner and his design team to foresee every eventuality. It must be said, however, that variations often arise quite unnecessarily, simply because the building owner had been unable to make up his mind at the design stage about precisely what he *does* want or because of lack of foresight on the part of the design team. This is not always their fault – on hospital projects, for instance, medical science advances so rapidly that it is often necessary to make major design changes during the course of construction to accommodate new techniques. Far too often, however, it is simply lack of proper planning, and too much haste to get the project under way, which lead to variations.

It has often been said – and we think there is a good deal of justice in it – that the bill of quantities system of contracting makes it too easy for a building owner or his team to change their minds. The effects of such changes can be easily seen and readily evaluated, and there is therefore a lack of incentive to make firm design decisions before work starts on the site. This leads building owners and their advisers into a false sense of security, often rudely shattered when the claim for 'direct loss and/or expense' arising from the resulting disruption and delay comes in.

VARIATION OF CONTRACT

It is important to distinguish between a variation expressly authorised under the terms of the contract and 'variation of contract'. The latter term is used to mean a change in the contract itself, not originally contemplated by its terms, agreed between the parties themselves – that is, between the employer and the contractor in the terminology used in the JCT Forms.

It is, of course, open to the parties to a contract to agree any changes to the terms of that contract which they please, provided that they are not illegal or do not render the contract invalid in some other way. The important point is that the parties must both agree to the change, and the change then becomes, in effect, another contract between them. It follows that, unless the change is made by deed, there must be 'consideration' for the change – that is there must be a return to one party for any benefit conferred upon the other party by the change.

One illustration of an attempted variation of contract of a kind fairly common in building contracts, but which was found to be invalid, is the case of *D & C Builders Ltd* v. *Rees* (1965). There the plaintiffs had carried out work to the value of £482, but the defendant failed to pay the account. The plaintiffs pressed for payment for several months. Finally, the defendant's wife, who knew that the plaintiffs were in financial difficulties, offered £300 in settlement, saying that if the offer were not accepted, nothing would be paid. The plaintiffs accepted a cheque for £300 and gave a receipt 'in completion of the account'. Later, they sued for the balance. The Court of Appeal held that the plaintiffs were not barred from recovering the balance. Quite apart from the fact that the plaintiff's consent had been obtained under pressure, there was lack of consideration, and there was no equitable ground disentitling the plaintiffs to recover.

On the other hand, if the contractor alleges that certain work is extra to the contract and refuses to carry it out unless the employer agrees to pay for it, and the employer does so agree, but it is subsequently found that the work was included in the original contract, the employer will not be bound to pay the extra price, as he will have received no value in return for the promise to pay. This, along with another important point of principle with which we shall be dealing later in this chapter, is illustrated by the case of *Sharpe* v. *San Paulo Railway* (1873). There, the contractor submitted a lump-sum price for the construction of a railway, based upon a quantified specification produced by the engineer, but there was no indication in the contract that the quantities were guaranteed to be correct. It turned out that the engineer had made an error of 2 million cubic yards in his calculation of earthworks. The engineer promised to make other changes in the works which would reduce the cost of the work as a whole so as to compensate the contractor for the effect of the error. However, he did not make the changes promised and, at the end of the contract, certified for payment the original contract sum with no allowance for the extra earthworks. The Court of Appeal held that, since the contractors had undertaken simply to build the railway from terminus to terminus for the lump sum stated, and the engineer's quantities did not form part of the contract, the contractors must be held to have contracted to carry out whatever work was necessary for the construction for the lump sum and could not recover any extra payment for the additional earthworks; nor was the engineer's undertaking to make compensating savings enforceable.

Unless variations are specifically authorised by the terms of the contract, any change in the work will become a 'variation of contract'. Also, if the power to order variations is in any way limited, any changes beyond the limits specified or implied will also be 'variations of contract'. For instance, the power of the architect to order variations under the JCT Forms, particularly the 1963 edition, is severely limited, and there will often be changes that will need to be made to the works, which must then become the subject of a separate agreement between the employer and contractor with which the architect will have no authority to deal unless both parties agree to give him that authority. The terms upon which the contractor may agree to carry out such changes will also become a matter of negotiation directly between the contractor and the employer unless both agree to authorise the quantity surveyor to negotiate for the employer.

VARIATION FROM WHAT?

Where variations are authorised by the terms of the contract, the question will arise: variation from what? In other words, what did the contractor agree to do in the first place? The question can even arise, as can be seen from the case of *Sharpe* v. *San Paulo Railway* quoted above: is this a variation at all, or is it something which the contractor agreed, or must be deemed to have agreed, to do as part of the contract?

In contracts incorporating bills of quantities the accuracy of which is guaranteed by the employer, these questions will be easy to answer, since anything that involves a change from what is set out in the bills will involve an adjustment of the contract sum based on the bills.

For instance, JCT 80, clause 14.1 says: 'The quality and quantity of the work included in the Contract Sum shall be deemed to be that which is set out in the Contract Bills'. Clause 2.2.2.2 says: 'If in the Contract Bills there is any departure from the method of preparation referred to in clause 2.2.2.1' (normally the Standard Method of Measurement of Building Works 6th, or now 7th, Edition) 'or any error in description or in quantity or omission of items, then such departure or error shall not vitiate this Contract but the departure or error shall be corrected and such correction shall be treated as if it were a Variation required by an instruction of the Architect under clause 13.2'.

Clause 2.2.2.2 means that the employer has, in effect, guaranteed the accuracy of the bills of quantities to the extent of agreeing that the contract sum shall be adjusted to take account of any errors of the kind listed. (This does not, of course, mean that the contract sum will be adjusted to take account of any errors in the *pricing* of the contract bills; the pricing is entirely a matter for the contractor, and clause 14.2 says: 'subject to clause 2.2.2.2 any error whether of arithmetic or not in the computation of the Contract Sum shall be deemed to have been accepted by the parties hereto'. In other words, it is only errors of the kind specified in clause 2.2.2.2 that will lead to an adjustment of the contract sum.) Clause 14.1 means that the contractor has contracted *for the contract sum* to carry out only what is shown in the contract bills and not necessarily, for instance, what is shown on the contract drawings if they differ from the bills. This is not to say that the contractor can refuse to carry out any work which is different from that shown in the bills if it is shown on the drawings, only that he is entitled to an adjustment of the contract sum if he is directed to follow the drawings rather than the bills.

Clause 2.3 states that if the contractor finds any discrepancy in or divergence between the contract drawings, the contract bills, any architect's instruction (other than those requiring variations, which will, of course, by definition involve a divergence from the contract drawings and/or bills) and any drawings or documents issued by the architect to supplement the contract drawings and bills, he must immediately notify the architect in writing and the architect must then issue instructions. Although not specifically stated, in our opinion any such instruction must be of a kind that is specifically authorised by other clauses of the contract conditions and, if it involves a departure from what is set out in the contract bills, it must be considered to be an instruction issued under the authority of clause 13, i.e. a variation.

CRITICISM OF THE BILLS OF QUANTITIES SYSTEM

The characteristic of the bills of quantities contract that has just been discussed, i.e. that the contractor has contracted, for the contract sum, to carry out only the work set out in the bills and no other, has been the subject of criticism by some commentators, notably by the learned editor of *Hudson's Building and Engineering Contracts*, 10th Edition, Mr I. N. Duncan Wallace QC, in chapters 5 and 8 of that influential work and elsewhere.

The criticism is on a basic point of principle. Generally, in the absence of specific contract provisions to the contrary, a contractor will be expected to do everything that may be necessary in order to carry the contract works to completion, irrespective of whether it is specifically referred to in the contract documents and even of whether it was possible to foresee the necessity for the work to be carried out beforehand. The case of *Sharpe* v. *San Paulo Railway*, already twice cited above, illustrates the point. There the contractors were expected to carry out the additional 2 million cubic yards of earthworks within the contract sum, even though they had been actively misled as to the quantity required in the documents provided to them for tendering purposes, because they had simply contracted to build the railway for the stated sum, and they must therefore do everything required to complete the railway. The position would, obviously, have been completely different had the contract stated that the contract sum covered only the work specifically referred to in the quantified specification; in that case the extra 2 million cubic yards of earthworks would have had to be measured and valued at the appropriate rates and the resulting amount added to the contract sum.

It is said, and it must be admitted with some justice, that the linking of the contract sum to the work set out in the bills transfers a substantial element of risk from the shoulders of the contractor to those of the employer. For example, if the contract works include a substantial element of reinforced concrete this will obviously imply the necessity for formwork; yet, if the quantity surveyor makes a mistake in preparing the bills and fails to measure the necessary formwork, the contractor will be entitled to claim extra payment for it even though, when tendering, he must himself have spotted the mistake. Without the bills, the contractor would be expected to provide the formwork within the contract sum even if not specifically referred to in the contract drawings or specification, and even though he may not himself have appreciated the extent of the formwork required at the time of tender.

With the very greatest respect, we consider that this disadvantage of the bills of quantities system can be very much overstated and is, in any case, greatly outweighed by the considerable advantage, to contractor and employer alike, of having a substantial area of possible, or even probable, dispute removed. Had a modern ICE contract been used, *Sharpe*'s case would never have reached the courts at all and, even though the employer would have had to pay for the extra 2 million cubic yards of earthworks, he would, in fact, have been paying the proper price for the job – and would always have had the option of proceeding against the engineer for negligence if real damage had been suffered. It seems to be far too often forgotten that there are two parties to a building contract, the employer and the contractor, and the contract should be so framed as to strike a fair balance between their interests. It is surely grossly unfair that a contractor should be required, within the contract sum, to carry out work far in excess of that which he could reasonably have anticipated or even, as in *Sharpe*'s case, which he was actively, if innocently, led to believe would not be required. It may, indeed, be extremely inconvenient, or even disastrous, for the employer to find during or at the end of the job that he has to pay for substantial additional works not taken into account in the original contract sum; the additional costs may, indeed, make the whole project no longer commercially viable. But it is he, after all who has instigated the project, and it is surely right, within reason, that he should pay for whatever has to be done to complete it.

A further consideration, far too often forgotten by commentators, is that a contractor who is required to take a risk will, unless he wishes to end up insolvent, include an allowance for that risk in his contract price. The employer will then have to pay that price even if the event allowed for never actually happens. If, say, the contractor is expected to allow in his pricing of excavations for the risk of having to excavate in rock if it is encountered, and then no rock is found, the employer will still have to pay whatever price the contractor allowed in his tender for that risk. If, on the other hand, bills of quantities include a provisional quantity for excavation in rock, to be remeasured according to the quantity actually found, the employer will end up paying only for the rock encountered – which may, of course, be more, but is just as likely to be substantially less than the provisional quantity allowed in the tender.

Of course it has to be recognised that, for some employers, it is more important that a stated cost for the works will not be exceeded than that they should pay only for what is done, because to exceed the stated cost would render the whole project economically unviable. If, say, a department store will only make a profit if the cost of construction does not exceed £2 million, the owner will be quite happy to pay that sum, even though with re-measurement of risk items the eventual cost might be £1¾ million, rather than run the risk of finding at the end of the contract that he has to pay £2¼ million because the risk items went the other way, and being landed with a store which will, at best, only break even or possibly make a thumping loss for every year of its life due to the extra financing costs. For such employers there is no doubt that the existing standard forms of building contract with quantities are less than satisfactory – though, even then, an efficient design team and careful cost monitoring during the course of construction will enable design adjustments to be made in order to bring the final cost within the budget.

There is one consideration, perhaps more speculative. The majority of cases cited in *Hudson* dealing with the contractor's obligation to carry out work not shown in documents provided at the time of tender date from the eighteenth and early years of the nineteenth centuries. The common law has moved rapidly since then, and we believe that a number of those cases, including *Sharpe*'s case, could well be decided differently were they to come before the courts now. The recent case of *Bacal Construction (Midlands) Ltd* v. *Northampton Development Corporation* (1975) shows that the courts will now require very strong wording indeed to be used in a contract or in the document itself in order to be persuaded that an employer should not be responsible for a document provided to a contractor at the time of tender in the knowledge that he is bound to rely on it in the preparation of that tender. Also, developments in the law of negligence over the past 20 years or so since *Hedley Byrne & Co Ltd* v. *Heller & Parners Ltd* (1964) mean that where, say, a contractor tenders on the basis of quantities provided to him on the principle that errors will not be adjusted, the contractor will undoubtedly now be able to sue the person who prepared the quantities direct, should they prove to be negligently inaccurate, if he suffers loss.

Indeed, bills of quantities enable the allocation of risk between the parties to be very precisely defined, and it is by no means the case that all the risk of unexpected eventualities is placed upon the employer in contracts on a bills of quantities basis. On bills prepared in accordance with the Standard Method of Measurement of Building Works (5th Edition), for instance, the contractor was expected to take the risk of excavating in, and upholding the sides of, any kind of soil encountered except rock and other similar hard material. (This has been substantially modified in the 6th and 7th Editions.) Bills prepared in accordance with the method of measurement applicable to civil engineering works require much greater degrees of risk to be taken by the contractor.

VARIATIONS UNDER JCT 80

Generally

Variations in general, and the execution of work against provisional sums, are dealt with in clause 13 of JCT 80 [as amended by Amendment 4 issued in July 1987] as follows:

13.1 'The term 'variation' as used in the Conditions mean:

13.1 .1 the alteration or modification of the design, quality or quantity of the Works as shown upon the Contract Drawings and described by or referred to in the Contract Bills; including

.1 .1 the addition, omission or substitution of any work,

.1 .2 the alteration of the kind or standard of any of the materials or goods to be used in the Works,

.1 .3 the removal from the site of any work executed or materials or goods brought thereon by the Contractor for the purposes of the Works other than work materials or goods which are not in accordance with this Contract;

13.1 .2 the imposition by the Employer of any obligations or restrictions in regard to the matters set out in clauses 13.1.2.1 to 13.1.2.4 or the addition to or alteration or omission of any such obligations or restrictions so imposed or imposed by the Employer in the Contract Bills in regard to:

.2 .1 access to the site or use of any specific parts of the site;

.2 .2 limitations of working space;

.2 .3 limitations of working hours;

.2 .4 the execution or completion of the work in any specific order;

but excludes

13.1 .3 nomination of a Sub-Contractor to supply and fix materials or goods or to execute work of which the measured quantities have been set out and priced by the Contractor in the Contract Bills for supply and fixing or execution by the Contractor.

13.2 The Architect may, subject to the Contractor's right of reasonable objection set out in clause 4.1.1, issue instructions requiring a Variation and he may sanction in writing any Variation made by the Contractor otherwise than pursuant to an instruction of the Architect. No Variation required by the Architect or subsequently sanctioned by him shall vitiate this Contract.

13.3 The Architect shall issue instructions in regard to:

13.3 .1 the expenditure of provisional sums included in the Contract Bills; and

13.3 .2 the expenditure of provisional sums included in a Sub-Contract.

13.4 .1.1 Subject to clause 13.4.1.2 all Variations required by the Architect or subsequently sanctioned by him in writing and all work executed by the Contractor in accordance with instructions by the Architect as to the expenditure of provisional sums which are included in the Contract Bills shall be valued by the Quantity Surveyor and such Valuation (in the Conditions called 'the Valuation') shall, unless otherwise agreed by the Employer and the Contractor, be made in accordance with the provisions of clause 13.5.

.1.2 The valuation of Variations to the Sub-Contract Works executed by a Nominated Sub-Contractor in accordance with instructions of the Architect/Supervising Officer and of all instructions issued under clause 13.3.2 shall (unless otherwise agreed by the Contractor and the Nominated Sub-Contractor concerned with the approval of the Architect) be made in accordance with the relevant provisions of Sub-Contract NSC/4 or NSC/4a as applicable.

13.4 .2 Where under the instruction of the Architect as to the expenditure of a provisional sum a prime cost sum arises and the Contractor under clause 35.2 tenders for the work covered by that prime cost sum and that tender is accepted by or on behalf of the Employer, that work shall be valued in accordance with the accepted tender of the Contractor and shall not be included in the Valuation of the instruction of the Architect in regard to the expenditure of the provisional sum.

13.5 .1 To the extent that the Valuation relates to the execution of additional or substituted work which can properly be valued by measurement such work shall be measured and shall be valued in accordance with the following rules:

.1 .1 where the work is of similar character to, is executed under similar conditions as, and does not significantly change the quantity of, work set out in the Contract Bills the rates and prices for the work so set out shall determine the Valuation;

.1 .2 where the work is of similar character to work set out in the Contract Bills but is not executed under similar conditions thereto and/or significantly changes the quantity thereof, the rates and prices for the work so set out shall be the basis for determining the valuation and the valuation shall include a fair allowance for such difference in conditions and/or quantity;

.1 .3 where the work is not of similar character to work set out in the Contract Bills the work shall be valued at fair rates and prices.

13.5 .2 To the extent that the Valuation relates to the omission of work set out in the Contract Bills the rates and prices for such work therein set out shall determine the valuation of the work omitted.

13.5 .3 In any valuation of work under clauses 13.5.1 and 13.5.2:

.3 .1 measurement shall be in accordance with the same principles as those governing the preparation of the Contract Bills as referred to in clause 2.2.2.1;

.3 .2 allowance shall be made for any percentage or lump sum adjustments in the Contract Bills; and

.3 .3 allowance, where appropriate, shall be made for any addition to or reduction of preliminary items of the type referred to in the Standard Method of Measurement, 6th Edition, Section B (Preliminaries).

13.5 .4 To the extent that the Valuation relates to the execution of additional or substituted work which cannot properly be valued by measurement the Valuation shall comprise:

.4 .1 the prime cost of such work (calculated in accordance with the 'Definition of Prime Cost of Daywork carried out under a Building Contract' issued by the Royal Institution of Chartered Surveyors and the National Federation of Building Trades Employers which was current at the Base Date) together with percentage additions to each section of the prime cost at the rates set out by the Contractor in the Contract Bills; or

.4 .2 where the work is within the province of any specialist trade and the said Institution and the appropriate body representing the employers in that trade have agreed and issued a definition of prime cost of daywork, the prime cost of such work calculated in accordance with that definition which was current at the Base Date together with percentage additions on the prime cost at the rates set out by the Contractor in the Contract Bills. Provided that in any case vouchers specifying the time daily spent upon the work, the workmen's names, the plant and the materials employed shall be delivered for verification to the Architect or his authorised representative not later than the end of the week following that in which the work has been executed.

13.5 .5 If compliance with any instruction requiring a Variation or any instruction as to the expenditure of a provisional sum substantially changes the conditions under which any other work is executed, then such other work shall be treated as if it had been the subject of an instruction of the Architect requiring a Variation under clause 13.2 which shall be valued in accordance with the provisions of clause 13.

13.5 .6 To the extent that the Valuation does not relate to the execution of additional or substituted work or the omission of work or to the extent that the valuation of any work or liabilities directly associated with a Variation cannot reasonably be effected in the Valuation by the application of clauses 13.5.1 to .5 a fair valuation thereof shall be made.

Provided that no allowance shall be made under clause 13.5 for any effect upon the regular progress of the Works or for any other direct loss and/or expense for which the Contractor would be reimbursed by payment under any other provision in the Conditions.

13.6 Where it is necessary to measure work for the purpose of the Valuation the Quantity Surveyor shall give to the Contractor an opportunity of being present at the time of such measurement and of taking such notes and measurements as the Contractor may require.

13.7 Effect shall be given to a Valuation under clause 13.5 by addition to or deduction from the Contract Sum.'

Clause 13.1 – Definition

Clause 13.1 defines two sorts of variation, that is variations in the work as set out in the contract documents, and variations in any obligations and restrictions imposed upon the contractor through the medium of the contract bills. It also imposes a prohibition (already present at common law) against the nomination of a sub-contractor to execute work included in the contract bills for execution by the contractor.

Variations in work

At first sight clause 13.1.1 appears to give the architect almost unlimited power to vary the works – see 13.1.1.1 'the addition, omission or substitution of *any* work'. However, we believe that this phrase must be read as subject to the overriding effect of the preceding reference to 'the alteration or modification of the design, quality or quantity of the Works as shown upon the Contract Drawings and described by or referred to in the Contract Bills' – i.e. that it is only the works as set out and described in the Contract Documents that may be altered or modified, and the architect's power does not extend to ordering any additions or substitutions that would require the contractor to execute work clearly not contemplated by the original contract. In other words, the architect cannot substantially alter the nature of the works – for instance by changing a steel-framed building into a reinforced concrete-framed building – since the contractor could fairly say that he would not have entered into a contract had he known that that would be the kind of work required, or at least would not have done so except on very different terms. Also, the architect cannot, by variation instruction, oblige the contractor to build something substantially in excess of what was envisaged under the contract; for instance, in a contract for the erection of twelve blocks of flats we would consider it doubtful if the contractor could be compelled to build a thirteenth block and to be paid for doing so on the terms set out in clause 13.5. There is little doubt, however, that the architect's powers of omission from the contract works are virtually unlimited; theoretically, for instance, the architect could omit, say, 75% of the works and yet the contractor would still be compelled under the contract to execute the remaining 25% since this would still be 'the contract works' and the financial consequences can be dealt with under the payment terms of the contract.

The wording of clause 13.1.1.3 is clearly related to that of clause 8.4, which authorises the architect to issue instructions 'in regard to the removal from the site of any work, materials or goods which are not in accordance with this Contract'; any such instruction would not, of course, entitle the contractor to any additional payment.

Variations in obligations or restrictions

Clause 13.1.2 authorises the architect to vary the obligations and restrictions which may be imposed upon the contractor through the medium of the contract bills in respect of five specific matters, that is (1) access to the site; (2) use to be made of specific parts of the site; (3) limitations of working space available to the contractor; (4) limitations of hours to be worked by the contractor; and (5) any requirements that the works be carried out or completed in any specific order. The architect's powers are limited to varying only those specific obligations and restrictions, and he has no power to vary obligations or restrictions of any other kind. Prior to the issue of Amendment 4 to JCT 80 it had been suggested (see Dr John Parris, *The Standard Form of Building Contract: JCT 80*, Section 3.10 New power to vary) that the wording of this clause further restricted the architect's power, in that he might only vary such restrictions which were already placed upon the contractor's methods of working in the contract bills. This certainly appeared to be so, but in that case we found the reference to 'the addition' of such restrictions puzzling. Was it intended to restrict the architect only to adding further restrictions of the kinds already specified in the contract bills or was it really intended, as we suspected, to give the architect the power to add *fresh* restrictions provided that they fell within the kinds of restriction listed? Say, for instance, that the bills contained a requirement restricting working hours on Monday to Friday to between 8 a.m. and 5 p.m. but there was no stated restriction at weekends. Could the architect, on finding that the contractor intended to work on Saturdays, impose a condition restricting Saturday working to between 8 a.m. and 12 noon? Was that a new restriction or simply an extension of an existing restriction? Or say that the bills contained no requirements for the work to be executed in a particular sequence, but during the course of the work the employer decided that he would like one section to be completed before another. Could the architect so instruct the contractor under this clause? Was it really intended that, if there were no obligations or restrictions of the kind listed in the contract bills in the first place, the architect would have no power to issue instructions imposing such restrictions during the course of the work? The wording was clearly unsatisfactory, and the clarification of the JCT's intention now provided by Amendment 4 is much to be welcomed. It is now clear that the architect's power is not confined to varying obligations and restrictions already imposed through the medium of the contract bills but extends to imposing fresh obligations or restrictions – but only of the kinds listed in clauses 13.1.2.1 to 13.1.2.4 and subject to the contractor's right of 'reasonable objection' discussed below.

The powers of the architect to order variations of this kind are, in any case, subject to a special restriction. Clause 4.1.1, JCT 80, reads as follows:

'The Contractor shall forthwith comply with all instructions issued to him by the Architect in regard to any matter in respect of which the Architect is expressly empowered by the Conditions to issue instructions; save that where such instruction is one requiring a Variation within the meaning of clause 13.1.2 the Contractor need not comply to the extent that he makes reasonable objection in writing to the Architect to such compliance.'

Shorn of its rather convoluted language, what this means quite simply is that, upon receipt of such an instruction from the architect, the contractor may object to it, and if that objection proves to be reasonable the contractor will not be obliged to comply with it. The question of whether or not the objection is 'reasonable' is, by clause 4.1.3.3, open to immediate arbitration – and rightly so, since this will obviously be a matter which needs to be cleared up very quickly. With respect to Dr Parris (op. cit.) we do not believe that the objection that the contractor 'will not make as much money as he would otherwise have made' can seriously be considered reasonable, since the financial effect of such a variation will, in any case, be dealt with under the contract terms. We would suggest that an objection would only be considered 'reasonable' to the extent that the contractor should be relieved of the obligation to comply with it if compliance would make the work impossible or, at least, unduly onerous. Say, for instance, that the architect ordered that noisy machinery should not be used except between certain specified hours, and that the reason for the instruction was that a neighbour had successfully obtained an injunction against the employer imposing such a restriction upon him; clearly no contractor could 'reasonably' object to compliance with such an instruction since he would be protected as to additional expense and a suitable extension of the time under the contract terms, and non-compliance could well result in severe penalties for the employer. But a contractor could 'reasonably' object to an instruction restricting access to the site if, unknown to the architect, the restriction would mean that essential goods could no longer be brought on to the site; in such a case the contractor's objection would bring the problem to the architect's attention and he could, no doubt, order further variations to the works which could overcome the problem – or withdraw the instruction.

In the original edition of this book we suggested that one factor in considering whether a contractor's objection was 'reasonable' would be that 'non-compliance would not bear unduly hardly on the employer'. In his excellent book, *Variations in Construction Contracts*, to which readers are referred for a more detailed study of the subject than space will allow in this chapter, Peter R. Hibberd states that that suggestion:

> 'is extremely debatable because surely the true intention of the clause is to protect the contractor against undue hardship ... where such hardship exists it is submitted that it is irrelevant whether it would bear unduly hardly upon the employer'.

Respectfully, we agree, and it was not our intention to suggest otherwise. We do suggest, however, that the question of whether hardship to the employer would result from non-compliance with an instruction under this clause is a factor to be taken into account if compliance would not make the work impossible or involve substantial hardship to the contractor but would simply be inconvenient or would involve a moderate degree of hardship to the contractor to be weighed against very real hardship to the employer. Just as compliance may make the work impossible for the contractor, so non-compliance may make continuance of the project impossible for the employer, for instance (as we have suggested above) by involving him in breach of an injunction obtained by adjoining owners; in such a case we suggest that the contractor's objection would effectively have to be real impossibility on his side rather than just hardship if it is to outweigh the hardship to the employer of abandonment of the project altogether. The contract does provide for the valuation of the effects of the instruction by the quantity surveyor as a variation and for an extension of time and reimbursement of 'direct loss and/or expense' which should protect the contractor against most forms of hardship likely to result from compliance with an instruction under this clause.

Omission of work to give it to others
It has always been a recognised principle of English contract law that (in the absence of express conditions to the contrary in the contract), once a

man has contracted to do a certain quantity of work, he has the right to do it if it is to be done at all; if the contract so provides, the work may be omitted, but only if it is not to be done at all, not in order to give it to someone else. Perhaps because it is so widely recognised a principle, there appear to be no English cases in support of it! The case most generally quoted, *Carr* v. *J.A. Berriman Pty Ltd* (1953) is, in fact, an Australian case. There, the contract provided that the employer would supply structural steel that would be fabricated and erected by the contractor; after a substantial delay in starting the work, due to the employer's failure to give possession of the site, the contractor was told that the employer had made other arrangements with another firm for the fabrication of the steel, which was to be omitted from the contract. This, taken together with the employer's failure to give possession of the site, was considered by the Australian court to be sufficient grounds for the contractor to treat the contract as having been repudiated, as they showed that the employer had no serious intention of considering himself bound by its terms.

A case even closer in comparison to the conditions of the JCT contracts is the American case of *Gallagher* v. *Hirsch* (1899). There, as in the JCT Forms, the contract provided for the omission of work without vitiating the contract and provided that such omissions should be valued and deducted from the contract sum. The American appeal court held that the word 'omission' meant only work not to be done at all, not work to be taken from the contractor under the contract and given to another to do.

Exactly the same applies with regard to the division of work within the contract. The original contract works will probably be divided up between work to be done and materials to be supplied by the main contractor on the one hand, and work to be done by nominated sub-contractors and materials to be supplied by nominated suppliers on the other. That division, once fixed by the contract, cannot be changed unilaterally by the employer acting through the architect. The main contractor has a right to do that work which is set out in the contract documents for him to do, and it cannot be taken away from him in order that it be done by a nominated sub-contractor. Conversely, if work is set out to be done by a nominated sub-contractor, the main contractor cannot be forced to do it instead; nor, for that matter, can he insist upon doing it himself (this was an important part of the *ratio decidendi* in the case *T. A. Bickerton & Son Ltd* v. *North West Metropolitan Regional Hospital Board* (1969) concerning the architect's obligation to nominate a new sub-contractor under the JCT Form 63 Edition where the original nominee could not complete).

Clause 13.1.3 of the 1980 Edition now spells out that restriction for the benefit of employers and architects who, not being lawyers, may not appreciate that it already exists, and therefore for the avoidance of the kinds of dispute over this very point that have so often arisen in the past – although, strangely enough, as has already been said, none of those disputes appear to have reached the courts of record, although no doubt they have often featured in arbitrations.

The restriction is somewhat modified by clause 35.1.4, which permits the nomination of a sub-contractor 'by agreement (which agreement shall not be unreasonably withheld) between the Contractor and the Architect on behalf of the Employer'. That clause would seem to empower the architect to agree with the contractor that work set out in the bills for the contractor to do will be done by a nominated sub-contractor; without that express provision any such agreement would have had to be between the contractor and the employer himself, since it would amount to a 'variation of contract' (see page 83). However, the contract is by no means clear as to exactly what financial adjustment would then be made to the contract sum; will the value of the work as set out in the bills be deducted from the contract sum and the amount of the sub-contractor's account plus the normal level of the contractor's profit on PC sums be added, or would the contractor be entitled, upon substantiation, to have added the higher level of profit he would have anticipated had he done the work himself? The contract is silent on the point.

Variation instructions

Clause 13.2 constitutes the architect's authority to issue instructions requiring a variation within the definition set out in clause 13.1, and also authorises him to 'sanction in writing any Variation made by the Contractor otherwise than pursuant to an instruction of the Architect'. It also states that 'No variation ... shall vitiate this Contract', an injunction the purpose of which we find slightly obscure, since the exercise of a power expressly conferred upon the architect by the terms of the contract can hardly be said to 'vitiate' it in any circumstances.

Clause 13.3 states that the architect *shall* issue instructions in regard to the expenditure of provisional sums, both in the contract bills and 'in a Sub-contract', a phrase which, by the definition of the term 'Sub-Contract' in clause 1.3, means a sub-contract with a nominated sub-contractor and *not* with a 'domestic' sub-contractor.

Clause 4.1.1 (set out earlier, page 94) requires the contractor 'forthwith' to comply with any instruction issued by the architect which the contract conditions expressly empower him to issue. Clauses 13.2 and 13.3 therefore set out this express power of the architect to issue instructions requiring variations and in regard to the expenditure of provisional sums, the latter being not only a power but an obligation as well. The contractor must therefore comply with any such instructions 'forthwith', subject to the proviso regarding reasonable objection to instructions about variations in obligations or restrictions imposed upon the contractor. 'Forthwith' in this context clearly does not necessarily mean 'immediately' since the instruction may vary work not yet to be done, but it does impose an obligation upon the contractor to carry out the work at the earliest possible opportunity.

By clause 4.3.1 all architect's instructions, including instructions under clause 13.2 and 13.3, *shall* be issued in writing; any instruction of the architect not issued in writing (and the phrase 'in writing' would include a drawing showing work to be varied even though not accompanied by an instruction expressed in words) is therefore not issued in accordance with the contract and is of no effect. By clause 1.3.2, however, any instruction of the architect issued otherwise than in writing is to be confirmed in writing by the contractor to the architect within 7 days, and if not dissented from in writing by the architect within a further 7 days from *receipt* (*not* despatch) is to take effect from the expiry of the second 7 days. If the architect himself confirms the instruction in writing within the first 7 days, the contractor need not confirm it himself but it will take effect from the date of the architect's confirmation. If neither the contractor nor the architect confirms the instruction within the time limit, but the contractor nevertheless complies with it, then the architect *may* confirm it himself at any time prior to the issue of the final certificate, and the instruction will then be deemed to have taken effect from the date it was originally given.

What all this means is that the contractor is under no obligation to comply with an architect's instruction issued otherwise than in writing, i.e. orally; indeed, not only is he under no obligation to comply, he is actually at risk if he does so since the architect may withdraw it or deny he ever gave it. The contractor's obligation to comply only arises when he has himself confirmed it within 7 days of issue and has allowed a further 7 days plus reasonable time for receipt of the confirmation by the architect, to elapse – say a total period of 15 or 16 days from the actual date upon which the instruction was issued orally. Of course, if the contractor does comply with the instruction during that time, and the architect does not dissent within the time limit, the architect must be deemed to have ratified the contractor's compliance. If the contractor inadvertently fails to confirm the instruction but nevertheless complies with it, he will again be at risk since the architect only *may* subsequently confirm it – he may refuse to do so, and the contractor may find himself unable to recover any cost involved in compliance (indeed, in the experience of one of the authors, this did happen with regard to a major variation on a contract in which he was involved and the contractor suffered a substantial loss as a result).

Provisional sums

Provisional sums are sums of money included in the contract bills to cover work which was uncertain in nature and/or scope at the time the bills were prepared. They must not be confused with prime cost (PC) sums which are included to cover work to be executed by nominated sub-contractors or materials to be supplied by nominated suppliers.

Clause 13.3 obliges the architect to issue instructions for the expenditure of such sums whether included in the main contract bills or in a contract with a nominated supplier. There is no express limitation on the instructions that the architect may issue in this regard, and his instruction may, indeed, be simply to omit the sum altogether and to do no work or spend no money against it.

By clause 35.1.2, an architect's instruction for the expenditure of a provisional sum in the main contract bills may include an instruction that the whole or any part of the work covered by the sum be executed by a nominated sub-contractor; by clause 36.1.1.2 it may also require goods to be supplied by a nominated supplier, either specifically, by naming the supplier concerned, or (clause 36.1.1.3) by implication, by requiring the contractor to obtain materials for the work against the sum for which there is only a single source of supply, in which case that source becomes a nominated supplier.

There is also no express limitation on the instructions that the architect is to issue in regard to the expenditure of provisional sums in nominated sub-contracts. However, as the standard sub-contract forms NSC/4 and 4a contain no provisions similar to those in the main contract for the nomination of sub-sub-contractors and suppliers, any instruction to place orders for work or supply of materials with specified firms will simply result in those firms becoming ordinary sub-sub-contractors or suppliers to the sub-contractor for which no special terms of contract are laid down. However, the sub-contract forms do contain a provision that, if the sub-sub-contractor or supplier concerned insists upon terms of contract which exclude liability in respect of their work or materials to a greater extent than the nominated sub-contractor's liability to the main contractor is limited, the nominated sub-contractor is to notify the main contractor, who will then notify the architect. If they both agree to the limitation in writing then the sub-contractor's liability to the contractor, and the main contractor's liability to the employer, will be limited in the same way. Without such express agreement the nominated sub-contractor is not obliged to enter into the sub-sub-contract or contract of sale containing the limitation.

Function of the quantity surveyor

By clause 13.4.1, all variations and all work executed by the contractor in accordance with the architect's instructions for the expenditure of provisional sums shall be valued by the quantity surveyor whose name appears in the Articles of Agreement.

Unless the employer and the contractor otherwise agree, therefore, it is solely the responsibility of the quantity surveyor to determine the price to be paid or allowed in respect of a variation. The architect has no authority to determine it or to influence in any way that determination. It follows that if the architect were to include, in an instruction requiring a variation, any purported instruction as to how it should be valued, such as 'the work executed against this instruction is to be valued as daywork', this would be of no effect and the quantity surveyor not only should, but must, ignore it and use his own judgment as to the manner in which the work should be valued under the terms of the contract. The architect also has no authority to accept a quotation from the contractor in respect of work which is ordered as a variation to the contract; neither has the quantity surveyor, since his function is to value the work in the manner laid down in the contract, which gives him no discretion in this respect. The clause provides that the quantity surveyor is to value the work in accordance with the provisions of clause 13.5 unless otherwise agreed by the employer and the contractor, who – as the parties to the contract – may, of course, agree any variation to its terms they wish (see under 'Variation of Contract', page 83).

Variations in nominated sub-contracts

Variations to work executed by nominated sub-contractors are also to be valued by the quantity surveyor appointed under the main contract. In actual practice, however, variations in specialist sub-contracts such as those for mechanical engineering services are frequently valued by the consulting engineer responsible for their design. Where this is the case it is strongly advised that the situation be clarified with all concerned so that it is absolutely clear with whom the responsibility for valuation actually does lie; if necessary the appropriate clause of the Sub-Contract Forms NSC/4 or 4a should be amended accordingly.

Variations in work done by the main contractor against PC sums

Clause 13.4.2 is to be read in conjunction with clause 35.2.2. If the main contractor tenders for and carries out work for which a PC sum is included in the contract bills, i.e. instead of a nominated sub-contractor, or tenders for and carries out work against a provisional sum for which the architect had otherwise intended to nominate a sub-contractor, any variations in that work are to be valued in accordance with the provisions of the contractor's tender for that work and not in accordance with clause 13. Clause 13.4.2 also provides, for the sake of clarity, that where the contractor tenders for and carries out work against a provisional sum for which the architect had intended to nominate a sub-contractor, that work, whether varied or not, is to be valued in accordance with the accepted tender and not as if it were 'work executed by the Contractor in accordance with instructions by the Architect as to the expenditure of provisional sums' as provided in clause 13.4.1.

Valuation by measurement

Where the valuation of the work executed against a provisional sum is capable of being valued by measurement, it is to be measured 'in accordance with the same principles as those governing the preparation of the Contract Bills', i.e. normally (unless clause 2.2.2.1 is amended to provide otherwise) in accordance with the Standard Method of Measurement of Building Works, 6th or 7th Edition, and is to be valued in accordance with the rules set out in clause 13.5.1. So far as variations are concerned, this obviously only applies to variations in the actual work to be carried out as defined in clause 13.1.1, to the extent that the work can reasonably be measured and is not of such a nature that it can only be valued on the basis of 'prime cost', i.e. as daywork. The rules of valuation are set out in clauses 13.5.1.1 to 13.5.1.3, supplemented by clauses 13.5.3.2, 13.5.3.3, 13.5.5 and 13.5.6.

In the basic rules set out in clause 13.5.1 there are three factors to be taken into account: the character of the work; the conditions under which the work is carried out; and the quantity of the work.

In respect of each individual item of measured work:

(1) If all three factors are unchanged from an item of work already set out in the contract bills – i.e. if the character and conditions are 'similar' and the quantity is not significantly changed by the variation – then the price set out in the contract bills against that item *must* be used for the valuation of the variation item.

(2) If the character is 'similar' to that of an item of work set out in the

contract bills, but the conditions are not 'similar' and/or the quantity is significantly changed from the variation, then the price set out in the contract bills against that item *must* still be used as the basis of the valuation of the variation item but must be modified so as to make a 'fair allowance', upwards or downwards, for the changed conditions and/or quantity.

(3) If all three factors are changed, then the items are to be valued by the quantity surveyor at 'fair rates and prices'.

It will be seen that, where the character of the variation item is 'similar' to that of an item in the contract bills these rules leave the quantity surveyor with little discretion; he *must* use the rates set out in the bills for their valuation, and the only modification he can make is in respect of changes in conditions or significant changes in quantity. It is only if the *character* is no longer 'similar' that the quantity surveyor is given complete discretion to make what, in his opinion, is a fair valuation of the work. It is therefore essential for the proper understanding of the quantity surveyor's function that the meaning of the phrase 'similar character' should be clearly understood; it is therefore unfortunate that it is this phrase which has given the most difficulty to commentators so far.

In our view, if these provisions are to make real practical sense, the word 'similar' in this context must mean 'identical to'. This interpretation has been authoritatively questioned and the contrary view is cogently put by Dr John Parris (*The Standard Form of Building Contract: JCT 80,* Section 6.20 Payments for variations) in this way:

'It has been suggested that the words "similar character" should be interpreted as meaning of identical character; but this is clearly wrong. Similar means similar in the sense of "of a like nature". While it may be, as has been suggested by Mr Donald Keating in his *Buildings Contracts*, 1978 edition, at page 316, that the words in JCT 63 clause 11 (4)(b) "similar conditions" may be construed as meaning similar site and weather conditions, a change in wording in JCT 80, clause 13.5.1.1 makes it clear that "similar conditions" applies to "the work set out in the Contract Bills" and not to conditions in which it may have been assumed that the work would be done. Only where the bills specify the conditions under which work is to be executed can it be said that the work was executed under dissimilar conditions. This, which is the plain meaning of the words, may make nonsense of this provision since the bills rarely specify the conditions under which work is to be executed. This part of the clause now clearly excludes work that can only be measured by time'.

With respect, we cannot agree with this analysis, and we persist in our view. Put as simply as possible, our opinion is that the words 'similar character' when applied to an individual measured item of work must mean that the verbal description of that item is identical in every respect to that of an item in the contract bills. Our reason for this statement, also put as simply as possible, is this. If the item is of 'similar character' the only grounds upon which the quantity surveyor can vary the price for the item from that which is set out in the bills is that the conditions are not similar or the quantity has significantly changed; otherwise he must use the price in the bills as it stands. Yet, if the verbal description of the item is *necessarily* changed by as much as a single word, it surely cannot be intended that the contractor should still be bound to carry out that item of work at a price attached to an item which is now different, even though the item may still be 'similar' in character if the word is interpreted in its broadest sense and in accordance with previous legal precedent. We suggest that, if the item description is necessarily different in any respect from that which is set out in the bills, the rules set out in clauses 13.5.1.1 and 13.5.1.2 cannot be applied and the quantity surveyor must be given the unfettered discretion under clause 13.5.1.3 to value the item at a 'fair' rate or price.

Peter R. Hibberd (*Variations in Construction Contracts*, page 104) suggests a slight variant of our proposition which he summarises as follows:

'Simply because an item of work is different in character does not in itself mean that the contract rates set out should not apply, for the work must be not only different in character but be required to be measured and/or described differently on account of this change; if such an item is required to be measured or described differently then it is not of similar character'.

This seems not far different from what we have suggested. However, Hibberd draws attention to an observation by Geoffrey Trickey in his book *The Presentation and Settlement of Contractors' Claims* (1983) which suggests that, for instance, brickwork in smaller areas or with more complicated setting-out might be said to be changed in character and requiring revised valuations while not involving any change in description or method of measurement. We would agree with Trickey's implication that changes in description or measurement are not the sole criteria by which a change in character requiring a revised valuation is to be judged, and that neither our original statement nor Hibberd's statement set out above go quite far enough. It may be necessary to investigate beyond simple matters of description or measurement in determining whether the rates and prices in the bills are to be set aside and a valuation at 'fair rates and prices' substituted.

In respect of 'conditions', of course, it is not necessary to apply the same strict interpretation to the word 'similar'. The 'character' of an item is precisely defined by its verbal description in the bills; the 'conditions' under which it is to be carried out cannot be so precisely defined, and the question of whether the conditions are 'similar' must be judged by vaguer criteria related to the conditions under which the contractor must be deemed to have anticipated the work in the original bills would be carried out and those under which the varied work actually was carried out. We would suggest also that the word 'conditions' cannot be read narrowly to mean only physical conditions; it must also extend to such things as the time the varied work is carried out in relation to other contract work and in particular to the work with which it is being compared for pricing purposes. In a contract on a firm price basis, that is, one without adjustment of the contract sum for fluctuations in the prices of labour and materials, the fact that an item of work included in a variation is being carried out at a later time than 'similar' items in the contract bills must clearly be taken into account – the adjustment being upwards or downwards depending upon whether prices are rising or falling at the time.

Perhaps fortunately, the word 'similar' is not used in connection with quantity, the criterion here being whether or not the quantity had been 'significantly changed' by the variation. This must be a matter for the objective judgment of the quantity surveyor, a small change in quantity may be significant for some items (particularly where the original quantity was small) but a very large change may not be significant for others. No firm rules can be laid down.

In relation to clause 13.5.1.2 we must again point out that the *only* factors in respect of which the rates and prices in the bills for items of 'similar character' can be adjusted are changed conditions or quantity. No matter how erroneous the rate or price can be demonstrated to be, whether in respect of its being too high or too low, the rate of price in the bills *must* be used as the basis and *only* be adjusted to take account of the changed conditions and/or quantity. The contractor has contracted to carry out variations in the work, and the employer has contracted to pay for them on this basis, and neither can avoid the consequences on the grounds that the price in the bills was too high or too low.

With respect to what may be considered 'fair rates and prices' for valuation under clause 13.5.1.3, we would suggest that the word 'fair' must be read in the context of the contract as a whole. A 'fair' price for varied work in a contract where the prices in the bills are 'keen' will be a similarly keen price. The quantity surveyor should determine his 'fair rates and prices' on the basis of a reasonable analsyis of the contractor's pricing of the items set out in the bills, including his allowances for head-office overheads and profit.

With some relief we point to the very simple rule for the valuation of omissions from the contract works; they are to be valued at the rates set out in the contract bills.

In valuing omissions, additional and substituted work, the quantity surveyor must take into account factors other than the prices set out in the contract bills against individual items or his 'fair valuation' of measured items. He must, by clause 13.5.3.2, make allowance for 'any percentage or lump sum adjustments in the Contract Bills', that is, any such percentages or lump sums (usually to be found in the general summary at the end of the bills) must be applied pro rata to all prices for measured work.

By clause 13.5.3.3 the quantity surveyor is also required to make 'allowance, where appropriate ... for any addition to or reduction of preliminary items of the type referred to in the Standard Method of Measurement, 6th Edition, Section B (Preliminaries)'. It is to be noted that the clause does not actually bind the quantity surveyor to use the rates and prices set out in the bills against such items, but simply to make allowance for any 'addition to or reduction of' such items. The wording is also curious in that it appears to confine the quantity surveyor's obligation and power in this respect to dealing with additions to or reductions of such items already set out in the bills and not to the introduction of new such items; we cannot believe that this is really intended. Peter R. Hibberd (*Variations in Constructions Contracts*, page 120) questions our interpretation of this clause; we hope he is right, but suggest that the wording is at least ambiguous and could with advantage be improved – see, for instance, the admirably terse equivalent clause 3.7.6 in IFC 84 (see below).

In relation to the adjustment of 'Preliminaries', it would be appropriate to draw attention here to the limitation on the duty and power of the quantity surveyor with regard to the valuation of variations set out in the proviso at the end of clause 13.5, that is that 'no allowance shall be made under clause 13.5 for any effect upon the regular progress of the Works or for any direct loss and/or expense for which the Contractor would be reimbursed by payment under any other provision in the Conditions' – the reference being, of course, to clause 26. In making any allowances in respect of preliminary items, therefore, the quantity surveyor must stop short of making allowance for the effect of the variation in question upon regular progress of the works. This is discussed further subsequently, when dealing with variations in obligations and restrictions imposed upon the contractor.

Buried in clause 13.5.6 is an obligation upon the quantity surveyor to make a 'fair valuation' of 'any ... liabilities directly associated with a Variation', the valuation of which 'cannot reasonably be effected in the Valuation by the application of clauses 13.5.1 to 5'. This, in our opinion, will include an obligation to make due allowance for factors such as the loss to the contractor involved where a variation to the work means that materials already properly ordered for the work as originally designed become redundant, which, under the 1963 Edition of the JCT Form, had to be the subject of an application by the contractor to the architect for reimbursement of 'direct loss and/or expense' under clause 11(6).

Finally, clause 13.5.5 requires the quantity surveyor, where the introduction of a variation results in other work not itself varied being executed under conditions other than those otherwise deemed to have been envisaged, to revalue that other work as if it had been varied. In practice this will mean that it must be revalued under clause 13.5.1.2 – that is, on the basis of the rates and prices in the contract bills against the appropriate items adjusted in respect of the changed conditions; but it may also be necessary for the quantity surveyor to make allowance for other factors such as consequential changes in preliminary items.

Dayworks

Where additional or substituted work cannot 'properly', i.e. reasonably, be valued by measurement, it is to be valued as 'daywork', that is on the basis of prime cost plus percentages as set out in clause 13.5.4. Clearly, while this may be a satisfactory method of valuation to the contractor, since it ensures that he will, at least, recover the cost to him of the work (subject to the limitations imposed by the relevant 'Definition of Prime Cost' defined in the clause) plus percentages to cover supervision, overheads and profit, it cannot be considered a satisfactory method for the employer since it imposes no incentive on the contractor to efficient working. It is therefore considered to be a 'last resort' to be used sparingly if at all by the quantity surveyor and only where measurement is literally impossible.

The machinery for submission of daywork vouchers, and particularly the timing is also highly unsatisfactory. The requirement that the vouchers should be 'delivered for verification to the architect or his authorised representative not later than the end of the week following that in which the work has been executed' is frankly unworkable. If the architect or his representative is to 'verify' what is set out on the voucher, i.e. to vouch for the truth of it, it is surely wholly unreasonable to expect him to be able to do so when a voucher for work executed on the Monday of one week does not have to be delivered to him for that purpose until Friday of the week following – an interval of 11 days.

There seems also to be a widespread impression that the clerk of works, if there is one, will be the architect's 'authorised representative' in this context – not surprisingly, since this is otherwise the only reference to the possible existence of such an individual as the architect's representative in the entire contract. Reference to clause 12, however, will show that the clerk of works, far from being a representative of the architect, is an 'inspector on behalf of the Employer', and that he therefore has no authority to 'verify' daywork vouchers unless the architect specifically gives him that authority – which will itself, of course, require the authority of the employer.

The only sensible way to deal with the problem of 'verification' of daywork vouchers, we suggest, is for the contractor to give advance notice to the architect of his intention to keep daywork records of a particular item of work; for the architect himself to attend the site or, if he is unable to do so, to nominate the clerk of works to act as his 'authorised representative' and to take his own records of the time spent and materials used; and for the vouchers to be submitted for 'verification' at the end of each day. In that way, at least, the quantity surveyor can be reasonably certain that the vouchers represent an accurate record of time and materials. Of course, he is still under no obligation to accept daywork as the method of valuation if, in his opinion, the work can properly be measured.

Valuation of 'obligations and restrictions'
Since the valuation of variations in the work to be executed under the contract or of work to be executed against provisional sums is comprehensively covered by clauses 13.5.1 to 13.5.5, clause 13.5.6 (apart from the reference to 'liabilities directly associated with a Variation' already dealt with above) must relate to the valuation of variations in 'obligations or restrictions imposed by the Employer in the Contract Bills' as defined in clause 13.1.2.

The clause requires the quantity surveyor to make a fair valuation of such variations; but this is subject to the proviso regarding the exclusion from the quantity surveyor's valuation of any effect of the variation upon the regular progress of the works or of any direct loss and/or expense reimbursed to the contractor under any other provision of the contract. It is difficult to envisage what would remain to be valued in respect of such a variation other than its effect upon the regular progress of the work; what other financial effect could it have? The quantity surveyor's function in respect of such variations would therefore seem to be very limited or even non-existent.

There would seem to be one very unfortunate and no doubt unintended effect of the proviso, and that is that, on a strict reading of its wording, it would seem to prevent the valuation of the effect of the removal of obligations or restrictions. The clause prevents allowance being made for *any* effect upon the regular progress of the works – including any possible improvement in progress resulting from the removal of an obligation or restriction; and this would seem to deprive the employer of the benefit of any such removal.

Rights of the contractor in respect of valuation
As has been said, subject to any agreement to the contrary between the employer and the contractor, the valuation of variations is solely the function of the quantity surveyor. The contractor has no contractual right to be consulted, no more than has the employer or the architect. The contractor has only one right, under clause 13.6, that of being given the opportunity of being present at the time of any measurement and of taking such notes and measurements as he may require. In theory, therefore, the situation is that the quantity surveyor may simply notify the contractor of his intention to take measurements, but if the contractor has a prior appointment the quantity surveyor, having given him the opportunity of being present, may safely proceed without him. When actually valuing the results of such measurement the quantity surveyor has no obligation to consult the contractor at all, but may proceed without him and at the end of the contract, as required by clause 30.6.1.2, may simply present the contractor with the 'statement of all the final Valuations under clause 13' – i.e. with a summary of the variation valuations, possibly without even measurements attached. The contractor would then either have to accept it or, if he violently disagreed with it, refer the matter to arbitration under clause 4.

This is the situation *in theory*. In practice, of course, quantity surveyors almost invariably measure and value variations in full consultation and, as far as possible, in agreement with the contractor, so that the 'statement of Valuations' will be an agreed document and a possible area of dispute will be removed. It is in everyone's interests, not least the employer's, that this practice be followed. Nevertheless, it is important to recognise that the quantity surveyor has the authority under the contract to proceed unilaterally in the manner laid down – an authority which he may well exercise if the contractor is unreasonable or obstructive in negotiations.

Payment in respect of variations

Clause 13.7 provides that 'effect shall be given to a Valuation under clause 13.5 by addition to or deduction from the Contract Sum'. By clause 3 this form of words should mean that the amount of the valuation should be 'taken into account in the computation of the next Interim Certificate'; but this clearly cannot be right since the amount should be taken into account in the next interim certificate after the work has been carried out, not after the valuation has been made. The position is correctly stated in clause 30.2.1.1, which states that there shall be included in interim certificates 'the total value of the work properly executed by the Contractor including any such work so executed to which clause 13.5 refers'. If the formal valuation has not been made by the time the work has been properly executed, a reasonably accurate allowance should be made for it in the next interim certificate.

VARIATIONS UNDER JCT 63

The equivalent clause in the 1963 Edition of the JCT Form is clause 11, which reads as follows:

11 (1) 'The Architect may issue instructions requiring a variation and he may sanction in writing any variation made by the Contractor otherwise than pursuant to an instruction of the Architect. No variation required by the Architect or subsequently sanctioned by him shall vitiate this Contract.

(2) The term 'variation' as used in these Conditions means the alteration or modification of the design, quality or quantity of the Works as shown upon the Contract Drawings and described by or referred to in the Contract Bills, and includes the addition, omission or substitution of any work, the alteration of the kind or standard of any of the materials or goods to be used in the Works, and the removal from the site of any work materials or goods executed or brought thereon by the Contractor for the purposes of the Works other than work materials or goods which are not in accordance with this Contract.

(3) The Architect shall issue instructions in regard to the expenditure of prime cost and provisional sums included in the Contract Bills and of prime cost sums which arise as a result of instructions issued in regard to the expenditure of provisional sums.

(4) All variations required by the Architect or subsequently sanctioned by him in writing and all work executed by the Contractor for which provisional sums are included in the Contract Bills (other than work for which a tender made under clause 27(g) of these Conditions has been accepted) shall be measured and valued

by the Quantity Surveyor who shall give to the Contractor an opportunity of being present at the time of such measurement and of taking such notes and measurements as the Contractor may require. The valuation of variations and of work executed by the Contractor for which a provisional sum is included in the Contract Bills (other than work for which a tender has been accepted as aforesaid) unless otherwise agreed shall be made in accordance with the following rules:

    (a) The prices in the Contract Bills shall determine the valuation of work of similar character executed under similar conditions as work priced therein;

    (b) The said prices, where work is not of a similar character or executed under similar conditions as aforesaid, shall be the basis of prices for the same so far as may be reasonable, failing which a fair valuation thereof shall be made;

    (c) Where work cannot properly be measured and valued the Contractor shall unless otherwise agreed be allowed:

       (i) The prime cost of such work calculated in accordance with the 'Definition of Prime Cost of Daywork carried out under a Building Contract' issued by the Royal Institution of Chartered Surveyors and the National Federation of Building Trades Employers and current at the date of tender as defined in clause 31(D)(6)(a) of these Conditions (or as defined in the Formula Rules where clause 31F of these Conditions applies) together with percentage additions to each section of the prime cost at the rates set out by the Contractor in the Contract Bills; or

      (ii) where the work is within the province of any specialist trade and the said Institution and the appropriate body representing the employers in that trade have agreed and issued a definition of prime cost of daywork, the prime cost of such work calculated in accordance with that definition current at the date of tender as defined in clause 31D(6)(a) of these Conditions (or as defined in the Formula Rules where clause 31F of these conditions applies) together with percentage additions on the prime cost at the rates set out by the Contractor in the Contract Bills.

Provided that in any case vouchers specifying the time daily spent upon the work (and if required by the Architect the workmen's names) and the materials employed shall be delivered for verification to the Architect or his authorised representative not later than the end of the week following that in which the work has been executed;

    (d) The prices in the Contract Bills shall determine the valuation of items omitted; provided that if omissions substantially vary the conditions under which any remaining items of work are carried out the prices for such remaining items shall be valued under rule (b) of this sub-clause.

(5) Effect shall be given to the measurement and valuation of variations under sub-clause (4) of this Condition in Interim Certificates and by adjustment of the Contract Sum; and effect shall be given to the measurement and valuation of work for which a provisional sum is included in the Contract Bills under the said sub-clause in Interim Certificates and by adjustment of the Contract Sum in accordance with clause 30 (5) (c) of these Conditions.

(6) If upon written application being made to him by the Contractor, the Architect

is of the opinion that a variation or the execution by the Contractor of work for which a provisional sum is included in the Contract Bills (other than work for which a tender made under clause 27 (g) of these Conditions has been accepted) has involved the Contractor in direct loss and/or expense for which he would not be reimbursed by payment in respect of a valuation made in accordance with the rules contained in sub-clause (4) of this Condition and if the said application is made within a reasonable time of the loss or expense having been incurred, then the Architect shall either himself ascertain or shall instruct the Quantity Surveyor to ascertain the amount of such loss or expense. Any amount from time to time so ascertained shall be added to the Contract sum, and if an Interim Certificate is issued after the date of ascertainment any such amount shall be added to the amount which would otherwise be stated as due in such Certificate.'

It will be seen that the differences from the provisions of clause 13 in JCT 80 are considerable.

To start with, the architect had no authority to require variations in obligations and restrictions imposed upon the contractor's methods of working in the contract bills. Indeed, since it was possible to interpret clause 12(1) of JCT 63 as limiting the function of the bills to the definition of the quantity and quality of work included in the contract sum only, it could be argued that the architect could not have been given authority to vary something which could not be set out in the bills but would have had to be effected by actual amendment of the contract conditions themselves. Whatever the true legal position, the lack of such authority was inconvenient.

Secondly, there was no set requirement as to the way in which varied work should be measured. We rather regret the imposition of this restriction in JCT 80, since it seems to us that the discretion of the quantity surveyor under JCT 63 to measure variations in whatever way best enabled him to value them was important.

Thirdly, the rules of valuation of measured variations were far less precise. Their effect was, we consider, much the same as the equivalent rules in JCT 80, clause 13.5.1, but there was no reference to the effect of significant changes in quantity.

Fourthly, there was no specific requirement for the quantity surveyor to take into account lump-sum or percentage adjustments set out in the contract bills or the effect of variations upon preliminary items. We still consider that the quantity surveyor was, in fact, under an obligation to take such matters into account, but the specific requirement for him to do so now incorporated into JCT 80 is useful clarification of the extent of that obligation.

Fifthly, the obligation to re-value work not itself varied where a variation changed the conditions under which it was to be carried out only related to the effect of omissions and not of additions or substituted work.

Sixthly, clause 11(6) dealt with all direct loss and/or expense arising from variations and not specifically covered by valuation of the varied work. The effects of this are fully discussed elsewhere (see p. 200).

VARIATIONS UNDER IFC 84

The clauses in the JCT Intermediate Form of Contract dealing with Variations and the expenditure if provisional sums are clauses 3.6, 3.7 and 3.8 which read as follows:

Variations

3.6   The Architect/The Contract Administrator may issue instructions requiring a Variation and sanction in writing any Variation made by the Contractor otherwise than pursuant to such an instruction. No such instruction or sanction shall vitiate the Contract.

The term Variation as used in the Conditions means:

3.6.1 the alteration or modification of the design or quality or quantity of the Works as shown upon the Contract Drawings and described by or referred to in the Specification/Schedules of Work/Contract Bills including
–   the addition, omission or substitution of any work,
–   the alteration of the kind or standard of any materials or goods to be used in the Works,
–   the removal from the site of any work executed or materials or goods brought thereon by the Contractor for the purposes of the Works other than work materials or goods which are not in accordance with this Contract;

3.6.2 the addition, alteration or omission of any obligations or restrictions imposed by the Employer in the Specification/Schedules of Work/Contract Bills in regard to:
–   access to the site or use of any specific parts of the site;
–   limitations of working space;
–   limitations of working hours;
–   the execution or completion of the work in any specific order.

Valuation of Variations and provisional sum work

3.7   The amount to be added to or deducted from the Contract Sum in respect of instructions requiring a Variation and of instructions on the expenditure of a provisional sum may be agreed between the Employer and the Contractor prior to the Contractor complying with any such instruction but if not so agreed there shall be added to or deducted from the Contract Sum an amount determined by a valuation made by the Quantity Surveyor in accordance with the following rules:

3.7.1 'priced document' as referred to in clauses 3.7.2 to 3.7.8 means, where the 2nd Recital, alternative A applies, the Specification or the Schedules of Work as priced by the Contractor or the Contract Bills; and, where the 2nd Recital, alternative B applies, the Contract Sum Analysis or the Schedule of Rates;

3.7.2 omissions shall be valued in accordance with the relevant prices in the priced document;

3.7.3 for work of a similar character to that set out in the priced document the valuation shall be consistent with the relevant values therein making due allowance for any change in the conditions under which the work is carried out and/or any significant change in quantity of the work so set out;

3.7.4 a fair valuation shall be made
   - where there is no work of a similar character set out in the priced document, or
   - to the extent that the valuation does not relate to the execution of additional, or substituted work or the omission of work, or
   - to the extent that the valuation of any work or liabilities directly associated with the instruction cannot reasonably be effected by a valuation by the application of clause 3.7.3;

3.7.5 where the appropriate basis of a fair valuation is Daywork, the valuation shall comprise
   - the prime cost of such work (calculated in accordance with the 'Definition of Prime Cost of Daywork carried out under a Building Contract' issued by the Royal Institution of Chartered Surveyors and the Building Employers Confederation, which was current at the Date of Tender) together with percentage additions to each section of the prime cost at the rates set out by the Contractor in the priced document, or
   [i] – where the work is within the province of any specialist trade and the said Institution and the appropriate body representing the employers in that trade have agreed and issued a definition of prime cost of daywork, the prime cost of such work calculated in accordance with that definition which was current at the Date of Tender together with percentage additions on the prime cost at the rates set out by the Contractor in the priced documents;

3.7.6 the valuation shall include, where appropriate, any addition to or reduction of any relevant items of a preliminary nature;

3.7.7 no allowance shall be made in the valuation for any effect upon the regular progress of the Works or for any other direct loss and/or expense for which the Contractor would be reimbursed by payment under any other provision in the Conditions;

3.7.8 if compliance with any such instructions substantially changes the conditions under which any other work is executed, then such other work shall be treated as if it had been the subject of an instruction of the Architect/the Contract

Administrator requiring a Variation under clause 3.6 to which clause 3.7 shall apply;

3.7.9 where the priced document is the Contract Sum Analysis or the Schedule of Rates and relevant rates and prices are not set out therein so that the whole or part of clauses 3.7.2 to 3.7.8 cannot apply, a fair valuation shall be made.

Instructions to expend provisional sums

3.8   The Architect/The Contract Administrator shall issue instructions as to the expenditure of any provisional sums.

It will be seen that these clauses bear a strong resemblance to the equivalent clause 13 in JCT 80, the differences mainly reflecting the very much more concise and business-like style of drafting adopted in IFC 84 generally. However a number of interesting points will require examination.

Instructions
Like clause 4.3.1 of JCT 80, clause 3.5.2 of IFC 84 states that all architect's instructions, including those requiring variations or relating to the expenditure of provisional sums, shall be in writing. However IFC 84 does not contain any provision similar to clause 4.3.2 of JCT 80 allowing instructions other than in writing to be confirmed by the contractor. It follows that no instruction can be binding on the contractor unless actually issued by the architect in writing. We agree with Peter R. Hibberd (*op. cit.*) that the slight difference in wording between clause 4.3.1 of JCT 80 ('all instructions ... shall be *issued* in writing') and clause 3.5.2 of IFC 84 ('all instructions ... shall be in writing') is of no real significance.

Definition of a variation
The definition of a variation in work in clause 3.6.1 of IFC 84 is identical to that in clause 13.1.1 of JCT 80. However it is curious that the JCT has not amended the definition of a variation in 'obligations and restrictions' in clause 3.6.2 in the same way as it has amended it in clause 13.1.2 of JCT 80. The clause therefore is still open to the same questions as we posed in the first edition of this book in examining clause 13.1.2 of JCT 80 in its original form – see page 93 above. There appears to be no logical reason for this failure to make such a sensible amendment and we can only assume it is due to some oversight by the JCT.

Valuation of variations
It will be seen that there is a change in emphasis in clause 3.7 of IFC 84

compared with clause 13.4.1 of JCT 80 so that agreement of a price between the employer and the contractor becomes the 'preferred option' rather than valuation by the quantity surveyor. We believe this reflects the rather less formalised approach envisaged by the JCT to a contract on IFC 84 compared to one on JCT 80. However it is still clearly advisable for an employer to seek advice from the quantity surveyor before accepting any price offered by the contractor so that he may be assured that it represents a 'good buy'.

The rules of valuation reflect the flexibility of contract documentation available under IFC 84.

A contract under IFC 84 may be entered into in two ways. It may be on the basis of drawings and a document which has been provided to the contractor by the employer at the time of tendering so that it may be priced by the contractor to form the basis of his tender and ultimately of the contract sum. Alternatively it may be on the basis of drawings and unpriced specification only.

A document to be priced by the contractor may be one of three kinds:

- a full bill of quantities prepared in accordance with a specified method of measurement
- a priceable specification of works, i.e. one set out in such a way that the contractor may attach a price to each item, the whole being totalled to form the basis of the tender and contract sum
- a 'schedule of work'; this is defined in clause 8.3 as 'an unpriced schedule referring to the Works which has been provided by the Employer and which if priced by the Contractor (as mentioned in the 2nd recital) for the computation of the Contract Sum is included in the Contract Documents' – i.e. any document which is neither a specification nor a bill of quantities but which in some way describes the works and is set out so that it may be priced by the contractor to form the basis of his tender and of the contract sum.

If the document is a full bill of quantities, clause 1.2 provides that 'the quality and quantity of the work included in the Contract Sum shall be deemed to be that which is set out in the Contract Bills' i.e. they have the same status in defining the work which the contractor has agreed to do for the contract sum as bills of quantities have under JCT 80 with Quantities – see the discussion on page 84–85 above. However, where the document is not a bill of quantities prepared in accordance with a specified method of measurement, clause 1.2 provides that 'where and to the extent that quantities are contained [in the document] the quality and quantity of the work included in the Contract Sum for the relevant items shall be deemed to be that which is set out in the [document]'. For all items to which quantities are not attached, if there is a conflict between such items and the contract drawings the quality and quantity of work included in the contract sum is deemed to be that which is set out in the drawings.

With all due respect to the JCT, this approach to the priority of documents where a full bill of quantities is not used but there is some other priced document which has formed the basis of the contractor's tender seems illogical. Surely, where the employer has provided a document which is intended by him to be used by the contractor as the basis for the tender, and that tender becomes the contract sum then, irrespective of the form the document takes, what is set out in that document, whether by way of words or quantities, should be deemed to be that for which the contractor has priced and should take priority over the contract drawings in that respect. There seems no logical reason to separate only those items to which quantities are attached as defining what the contractor has priced to do. It is to be hoped that the JCT will look again at this provision which is bad in principle and confusing in practice.

Where no document is provided to the contractor for pricing at tender stage the second recital to the form requires the contractor to supply 'to the Employer either a Contract Sum Analysis or a Schedule of Rates on which the Contract Sum is based'. A contract sum analysis is a type of document first introduced by the JCT as a cost control document in the Standard Form of Contract with Contractor's Design 1981. It is essentially a breakdown of the contract works into their component parts with a sum stated against each, the whole adding up to the contract sum. The definition in clause 8.3 says that it is to be 'provided by the Contractor in accordance with the stated requirements of the Employer', from which it appears that the employer must specify the form the analysis is to take when inviting tenders. The essential point is that, while the form it is to take is to be specified by the employer, the employer does not actually provide the document himself; if he were to do so it would become a 'priced Schedule of Work' and therefore a contract document.

In contrast to a contract sum analysis, a schedule of rates is simply a list of items with prices attached. It is not added up to show the total tender and contract sum, and there is therefore no means of checking that the prices shown in it actually are the prices used by the contractor in making up his tender. From the employer's point of view, therefore, it is a far less satisfactory document for use as the basis for valuing variations. Clause 3.7.3 requires that the valuation of work of 'similar character' to that set out in the priced document should be 'consistent with the relevant values' set out in that document. This may be contrasted with the equivalent provision in clause 13.5.1.1 of JCT 80 that the rates and prices for the work set out in the contract bills 'shall determine the valuation'. (It is interesting to note that, since the issue of Amendment 3 in March 1987, the 'without Quantities' version of JCT 80 also includes provision for a contract sum analysis as an alternative to a schedule of rates and now also requires that the valuation of work of similar character should be 'consistent with the relevant rates, prices or amounts for such work in the Priced Document'.)

There is room for some argument about the significance of this changed wording. It seems to us that the requirement that the valuation shall be *consistent with* the priced document rather than that the rates and prices in it shall *determine* the valuation gives some scope for greater exercise of discretion by the quantity surveyor. However we have no doubt that the intention is that, where there are actual rates and prices in the priced document as opposed to lump sums, those rates and prices should be applied to work of 'similar character' making due allowance only for changed conditions or significant changes in quantity. Where the priced document contains lump sums for parcels of work rather than rates and prices for items of measured work, the valuation should take account of the presumed level of pricing underlying the lump sum. Otherwise the general discussion on the valuation of variations by reference to rates and prices in the contract bills under JCT 80 earlier in this chapter can be read as applying equally to the similar exercise under IFC 84.

Daywork

There is an interesting contrast between the words of JCT 80 clause 13.5.4 and IFC 84 clause 3.7.5. The former states that daywork is to be used for the valuation of work 'which cannot properly be valued by measurement'; the latter states that it is to be used where it is 'the appropriate basis of a fair valuation'. We do not agree with Peter R. Hibberd (*op. cit.* page 138) that 'this means that it is possible in theory to resort to dayworks even though the varied work can properly be valued by measurement'; it seems to us quite clear that the intention is that daywork should only be used where it is the *only* means of arriving at a fair valuation, so that where a fair valuation can be achieved by measurement it should be.

Still less do we agree with him that 'under IFC 84 the argument that a fair valuation of work properly valued by measurement should be the same as the daywork is far more compelling than it is under JCT 80'. On the contrary, to us the opposite appears true, that is that if the application of daywork produces a valuation which is unfair compared with a valuation by measurement the latter should be used – and, of course, vice versa. Hibberd's proposition seems to suggest that the application of daywork is, by definition, productive of a fair valuation. To us the words of clause 3.7.5 suggest the opposite, that is that it is only if the application of daywork demonstrably produces a fair valuation judged by objective criteria that it is to be used.

It is interesting to note that the provision that vouchers showing the time spent and plant and materials employed on daywork are to be produced to the architect for verification within a stated time limit does not appear in IFC 84. Presumably the appropriate vouchers must, at the latest, be produced by the contractor 'either before or within a reasonably time after Practical Completion of the Works' as required by clause 4.5. Common sense would suggest that any contractor would be well advised to produce the vouchers well before then if he considers daywork to be the appropriate means of arriving at a fair valuation. Any quantity surveyor presented with daywork vouchers after practical completion for work carried out much earlier could well consider that they are unlikely to be productive of a 'fair valuation' and reject them in favour of some other objective test.

Indeed, it may be argued that any quantity surveyor would be entitled to view with some scepticism any daywork voucher produced as a basis for a 'fair valuation' unless the contractor has given prior notice of his intention to keep daywork records of the particular work so that a check may be placed on it by someone from the employer's team. How is he to judge whether the daywork will produce a 'fair valuation' unless he or some other member of the employer's team has had an opportunity of checking that the records do truly show the hours spent and plant and materials used? It will be obvious from our discussion of clause 13.5.4 of JCT 80 on pages 106 and 107 above that we welcome the omission of the unworkable requirement for 'verification' of the vouchers by the architect. We nevertheless agree with Hibberd that it is desirable to include some provision on the contract documents requiring the contractor to submit daywork vouchers within a specified time. We would also agree that, just as the contractor should be required to give prior notice of his intention to keep daywork records for particular variations, so also should the quantity surveyor give prior notice to the contractor requiring him to keep such records if, in the quantity surveyor's opinion, a particular variation instructed by the architect can only be fairly valued by daywork.

RELATIVE FUNCTIONS OF ARCHITECT AND QUANTITY SURVEYOR

The provisions for the valuation of variations now set out in clause 13 of JCT 80 and clause 3.7 of IFC 84, as compared with those in clause 11 of JCT 63, have, among other things, the advantage of clearly defining the relative responsibilities of architect and quantity surveyor in respect of variations. It is now clear that, once the architect has issued an instruction requiring a variation or requiring the contractor to carry out work against a provisional sum, responsibility for defining the financial effect of the work covered by the instruction now passes entirely to the quantity surveyor, whose valuation will be required to cover *all* the effects of the variation up to the point at which it becomes necessary for the contractor to make an application to the architect stating that the introduction of the work in question has affected or is likely to affect the regular progress of the works in some material respect. At that point responsibility passes back to the architect. It is he who bears the responsibility for determining questions concerning the progress of the works and, although the quantity surveyor may be brought into the matter again when ascertainment of the resulting direct loss and/or expense becomes necessary, this will only be at the discretion of the architect who still bears primary responsibility for that aspect.

In *County and District Properties Ltd* v. *John Laing Construction Ltd*, (1982), Mr Justice Webster said, of the quantity surveyor under JCT 63, that his 'function and his authority under the contract are confined to measuring and quantifying. The contract gives him authority, at least in certain instances, to decide quantum. *It does not in any instance* give him authority to determine any liability, or liability to make any payment or allowance.'

His lordship went on to deal with the words 'the valuation of variations ... unless otherwise agreed shall be made in accordance with the following rules' in clause 11 (4), JCT 63, which counsel had submitted meant 'agreed by or with the quantity surveyor'. He said:

'I reject that submission. In my view the word agreed can only mean 'agreed between the parties', although it may well be that on occasion a quantity surveyor may perhaps be given express authority by the employer to make such an agreement.

But the JCT contract does not give him the authority.

There are few express references to him in the contract. He is defined in Article 4 of the Articles of Agreement. By clause 11(4), he is given the express duty of measuring and valuing variations.

By 11(6), he is given the duty of ascertaining loss and expense involved in variation – but only if so instructed by the architect.

By 24(1), he is given a similar duty in respect of loss or expense caused by disturbance of the work etc – but again only if instructed by the architect.'

The position is, in our view, the same under JCT 80, and indeed in clause 13.4.1, (which is the equivalent of clause 11(4), JCT 63) the wording now is 'unless otherwise agreed by the Employer and the Contractor.' It is also the same under IFC 84.

Chapter 4

Direct loss and/or expense

INTRODUCTION

The money claims clauses of most standard form contracts use the phrase 'direct loss and/or expense' when dealing with the contractor's entitlement to payment for prolongation or disruption costs. This term is used in clauses 11(6), 24(1) and 34(3) of JCT 63 and in clauses 26.1 and 34.3 of JCT 80; it is also used in clause 13 of the related JCT Nominated Sub-Contract Form (NSC/4 and NSC/4a), in clause 13 of the BEC/FASS/CASEC Domestic Sub-Contract Form (DOM/1) and in clause 14.1 of the JCT Sub-Contract Conditions for Named Sub-Contractors (NAM/SC). The JCT Intermediate Form of Building Contract (IFC 84) uses the same expression in clause 4.11, as do the JCT Works Contract Conditions (Works Contract/2) in clauses 4.45, 4.49 and 4.50.

Similar phrases such as 'direct loss and/or damage' or 'direct loss and expense' are found in other standard forms, but their meaning is to all intents and purposes the same. Slightly different wording is used in Government Conditions GC/Works/1 (Edition 2), clause 53(1), which speaks of 'any expense in performing the contract' which the contractor 'properly and directly incurs' as a result of disruption or prolongation. In the BEC/CASEC/FASS Sub-Contract Conditions GW/S for use with GC/Works/1 the term used in clauses 66 and 67 is 'direct expense'. The common feature of all such phrases is that a distinction is drawn between those losses and/or expenses which the law regards as 'direct' and those regarded as being indirect or too remote. This is an important distinction.

We must confess with some surprise that some commentators appear to have found difficulty in interpreting the use of the word 'direct' in such clauses and even go so far as to suggest that it has no real significance. For example, Mr I.N. Duncan Wallace in *Building and Civil Engineering*

121

Forms, page 71, dealing with its use in clause 11(6) of JCT 63, says:

'It seems doubtful if the word "direct" can have any real significance in the context of this provision, unless the intention is to distinguish between loss or expense forming part of or occasioned by the varied work itself (e.g. interference with other work in the vicinity) as opposed to less direct expense (such as extended contract overheads). It would seem wrong as a matter of reasonable presumed intention so to cut down the words "loss or expense", and in any case almost impossible to lay down a precise dividing line between "direct" and "indirect" loss or expense.'

This statement is the more surprising as Mr Wallace then refers to the case of *Wraight Ltd* v. *P. H. & T. (Holdings) Ltd* (1968), which is one of the many cases that actually provide judicial interpretation of this or similar phrases. There, Mr Justice Megaw accepted that the phrase 'direct loss and/or damage' means

'what is its usual, ordinary and proper meaning in the law: one has to ask whether any particular matter or items of loss or damage claimed has been caused by the particular matter. ... If it has been caused by it, then one has to go on to see whether there has been some intervention or some other cause which prevents the loss or damage from being properly described as being the direct consequence of the [matter].'

'Direct loss and/or expense' or 'direct loss and/or damage' therefore means that the sums recoverable are equivalent to damages at common law: *F.G. Minter Ltd* v. *Welsh Health Technical Services Organisation* (1980).

The phrase 'direct loss and/or expense' is best considered separately as 'direct loss' and 'direct expense'. The word 'loss' is often used in the courts to include both loss of money which ought to have been received and expenditure of money which ought not to have been expended. The addition of the odd conjunction 'and/or' seems to have been made simply to remove any possible doubt as to the scope of the contractor's entitlement: see D. Keating, *Building Contracts* 4th Edition, page 317.

Effectively, the use of the dual phrase gives two separate heads of claim, first, actual losses incurred as a direct result of the circumstances giving rise to the entitlement, and secondly, actual expenditure occasioned as a direct result of the same circumstances. As Lord Justice Hodson remarked in *Chandris* v. *Union of India* (1956), 'the primary meaning of the word "expense" is actual disbursements'. The various usual heads of claim are discussed later in this chapter: see pages 126–158.

DIRECT v. INDIRECT

The law draws a distinction between direct and indirect (or consequential) loss or damage. In *Saintline Ltd* v. *Richardsons, Westgarth & Co. Ltd* (1940), Mr Justice Atkinson discussed the distinction. He had there to consider the meaning of a contract clause providing that a manufacturer's liability should not 'extend to any indirect or consequential damages whatsoever'. The contract was for the supply of engines to a ship, and the manufacturers broke the contract. The buyers claimed damages for loss of profit for the time they were deprived of the use of the ship, together with the expenses of wages, etc., and for fees paid to experts for superintendence. The judge held that all these items were recoverable as being a direct and natural consequence of the breach of contract.

In giving judgment he said:

'What does one mean by "direct damage"? Direct damage is that which flows naturally from the breach without other intervening cause and independently of special circumstances, while indirect damage does not so flow. The breach certainly has brought it about, but only because of some supervening event or some special circumstances. ... The words "indirect or consequential" do not exclude liability for damages which are the direct and natural result of the breaches complained of ... [The clause protects] the respondents from claims for special damages which would be recoverable only on proof of special circumstances and for damages contributed to by some supervening cause.'

A construction industry case where the same distinction was drawn is *Croudace Construction Ltd* v. *Cawoods Concrete Products Ltd* (1978). In that case the plaintiffs were main contractors for the erection of a school and they contracted with the defendants for the supply and delivery of masonry blocks. It was a term of the supply contract that the defendants were 'not under any circumstances ... liable for any consequential loss or damage caused or arising by reason of late supply or any fault, failure or defect in any materials or goods supplied by us ...'.

The plaintiffs claimed against the defendants in respect of alleged late delivery and defective materials. They sought to recover

(1) loss of productivity;
(2) inflation costs resulting from delay;
(3) the amount of a claim made by sub-contractors in respect of delay in their work.

The actual question in the case was whether such damages were to be regarded as 'consequential' loss. The Court of Appeal held that the items claimed were not excluded as 'consequential'. They were heads of direct loss. Their lordships quoted with approval the following statement of Lord Justice Maugham in *Millar's Machinery Co. Ltd* v. *David Way & Son* (1935), 'on the question of damages, the word "consequential" has come to mean "not direct"....'.

Croudace Construction Ltd was one of the cases considered by the Court of Appeal in *F. G. Minter Ltd* v. *Welsh Health Technical Services Organisation* (1980), which affirms the view that, in the JCT contracts, the term 'direct loss and/or expense' (and equivalent phrases in other contracts) in effect means that what is recoverable is substantially the same as the damages recoverable at common law according to the ordinary principles of remoteness of damage under the first limb of the rule in *Hadley* v. *Baxendale* (1854).

This rule was formulated by Baron Alderson in these words:

'Where two parties have made a contract which one of them has broken, the damages which the other party ought to receive in respect of such breach of contract should be, either such as may fairly and reasonably be considered arising naturally, i.e., according to the usual course of things, from such breach of contract itself, or such as may reasonably be supposed to have been in the contemplation of both parties at the time they made the contract, as the probable result of the breach of it'.

The first limb of this rule related to 'the damages which the other party ought to receive in respect of such breach ... [are] such as may fairly and reasonably be considered arising naturally, i.e. according to the usual course of things, from such breach of contract itself'. Such damages are called 'general'.

The second branch of the rule deals with abnormal damage arising because of special circumstances. *Hadley* v. *Baxendale* deals only with *remoteness of damage*, and not with the *measure of damages*, i.e., quantification in monetary terms. As a leading textbook puts it,

'The principle adopted by the courts in many cases dating back to at least 1848 is that of *restitutio in integrum*. If the plaintiff has suffered damage that is not too remote, he must, so far as money can do it, be restored to the position he would have been in had that particular damage not occurred'. (Cheshire, Fifoot & Furmston's *Law of Contract*, 11th edition, 1986, p. 580)

However, in practical terms the second part of the rule in *Hadley* v. *Baxendale* covers what are known as 'special damages'. It must be emphasised that the principle of *Hadley* v. *Baxendale* is merely one rule with two separate limbs or branches.

The principle of *Hadley* v. *Baxendale* was reformulated by Lord Justice Asquith in *Victoria Laundry (Windsor) Ltd* v. *Newman Industries Ltd* (1949), in terms of 'reasonable foreseeability':

'(1) It is well settled that the governing purpose of damages is to put the party whose rights have been violated in the same position, so far as money can do so, as if his rights had been observed. This purpose, if relentlessly pursued, would provide him with a complete indemnity for all loss *de facto* resulting from a particular breach, however improbable, however unpredictable. This, in contract at least, is recognised as too harsh a rule. Hence (2): In cases of breach of contract the aggrieved party is only entitled to recover such part of the loss actually resulting as was at the time of the contract reasonably foreseeable as liable to result from the breach. (3) What was at that time reasonably so foreseeable depends on the knowledge then possessed by the parties, or, at all events, by the party who later commits the breach. (4) For this purpose, knowledge "possessed" is of two kinds – one imputed, the other actual. Everyone, as a reasonable person, is taken to know the "ordinary course of things" and consequently what loss is liable to result from a breach of that ordinary course. This is the subject-matter of the "first rule" in *Hadley* v. *Baxendale*. But to this knowledge, which a contract-breaker is assumed to possess whether he actually possesses it or not, there may have to be added in a particular case knowledge which he actually possesses of special circumstances outside the "ordinary course of things", of such a kind that a breach in those special circumstances would be liable to cause more loss. Such a case attracts the operation of the "second rule" so as to make additional loss also recoverable. (5) In order to make the contract-breaker liable under either rule it is not necessary that he should actually have asked himself what loss is liable to result from a breach. As has often been pointed out, parties at the time of contracting contemplate, not the breach of the contract, but its performance. It suffices that, if he had considered the question, he would as a reasonable man have concluded that the loss in question was liable to result ... . (6) Nor, finally, to make a particular loss recoverable, need it be proved that on a given state of knowledge the defendant could, as a reasonable man, foresee that a breach must necessarily result in that loss. It is enough if he could foresee it was likely so to result.'

In *The Heron II* (1969), the House of Lords differed from Lord Justice Asquith, as to whether the damage should have been foreseen by the defendant (see item (6) in the foregoing quotation) and themselves adopted differing phrases. Lord Upjohn put the test in this way: 'In contract the parties have only to consider the consequences of a breach to the other; it is fair that the assessment of damages should depend upon their assumed common knowledge and contemplation and not on a foreseeable but most unlikely consequence.'

However, recovery will not be limited because the specific consequence could not have been foreseeable, provided the type of consequence was foreseeable. Thus, in *Parsons (Livestock) Ltd* v. *Utley Ingham & Co Ltd* (1978) the fact that a herd of pigs became ill with a *serious* disease as a result of a faulty pig-nut silo, whereas in the ordinary course of events only a relatively minor illness might have been expected to result, was held by the Court of Appeal not to limit the defendants' liability. It was reasonable to suppose that the parties would have contemplated at the time of the contract, in the event of the silo being defective, the serious possibility of illness and even death among the pigs.

The same principles apply to claims for 'direct loss and/or expense' arising under JCT contracts and other contracts where similar phraseology is used. It should be noted, however, that because the recovery of direct loss and/or expense is a specific term of the contract, this may permit the recovery of certain heads of claim which, for technical reasons, might not be recoverable at common law.

POTENTIAL HEADS OF CLAIM

Although the legal principles involved in formulating and ascertaining claims for 'direct loss and/or expense' are well settled, the application of those principles in practice is far from easy. The reimbursement is the means of putting the contractor back into the position in which he would have been, but for the delay or disruption. Merely because a particular head of claim has been allowed under one contract does not necessarily mean that it will be allowable under another. The contractor must, in every case, be able to prove on the balance of probability, the loss and/ or expense or, at the very least, reasonably to establish the probability that it has been incurred; e.g. where reduced efficiency of working is claimed, while it will probably be possible to prove the actual expenditure on labour or plant, it will be impossible to do more than establish a reasonable probability of what the cost would have been had the disruption not occurred.

The loss and/or expense must also be a 'direct' one in the sense discussed, and two simple examples may be contrasted. Assume a variation is ordered, which necessitates plant lying idle for some days. The plant was needed for the original work, but at a very late stage the work is varied and so the plant is not needed. Assume further that the plant is hired in. The contractor's hire charges, subject to any reletting or the plant owner accepting an early return, would, it is suggested, be a direct expense and thus reimbursable.

By way of contrast, suppose that a variation instruction substitutes slates for roof tiles. After the contractor has ordered the slates, problems are encountered at the slate quarry, which mean that the supply of slates is interrupted so that the supplier is in breach of the supply contract. The delay and disruption to the contract works consequent upon the interruption of supply is clearly a direct consequence of the supplier's breach of the supply contract and only an indirect consequence of the variation, i.e. it is not something within the contemplation of the parties to the building contract as a probable result of the variation, and in any case is the consequence of an intervening event. Accordingly, the loss is not recoverable under the claims provisions of the building contract. It is recoverable, if at all, under the supply contract from the defaulting supplier.

There is a further limitation in that the contractor must 'mitigate his loss' so far as it may be reasonable for him to do so. The legal position is admirably stated in Cheshire, Fifoot & Furmston's *Law of Contract*, 11th edition, p. 598 in the following terms:

> '[The] law does not allow a plaintiff to recover damages to compensate him for loss which would not have been suffered if he had taken reasonable steps to mitigate his loss. Whether the plaintiff has failed to take a reasonable opportunity of mitigation is a question of fact dependent upon the particular circumstances of each case and the burden of proving such failure rests upon the defendant.'

The application of this is illustrated by the example given above of plant standing idle as a result of a variation order. The contractor would not be entitled simply to accept the situation, but would be bound to make reasonable endeavours to use the plant productively elsewhere or to persuade the plant owner to accept an early return. In the first instance, the costs of, say, moving the plant to another site so that it might be so used would be recoverable as a part of a direct loss claim, provided of course that this sum did not exceed the costs which would have been otherwise incurred.

The position is, in fact, spelled out specifically in the JCT extension of time clause (see JCT 80, clause 25.3.4) in relation to delay, although the clause does not require the contractor specifically to mitigate the effects of a delay once encountered, but only to use his best endeavours to prevent delay occuring: see chapter 2. So far as the money claims provisions are concerned, the limitation is imposed by the general law.

There are two basic claims situations, and many potential heads of claim are common to both. The first situation is delay in completion of the contract works beyond the date when they otherwise would have been completed; this is often known as a *prolongation claim* and, sometimes – inaccurately – as a claim for extended preliminaries. The second is a claim for the effect of an event upon the contract works themselves, often referred to as a *disruption claim*, and does not necessarily involve a delay in completion of the contract works. A disruption claim may arise even where the works are completed within the contract period originally specified or even where they are completed within a shorter period programmed by the contractor.

The following are the more common heads of loss:

1. On-site establishment costs

These are often called site overheads and are perhaps the easiest head of claim to establish because the data should be readily available once the period of delay has been settled. They will consist of the supervisory and administrative staff engaged upon the site of the particular contract, site accommodation, plant and tools, telephone and electricity charges, costs of welfare and sanitary facilities, light and heat where not covered by electrical charges, and the like.

All these costs should be readily ascertainable from the contractor's cost records. A note of caution is necessary when extracting these costs from the contractor's records. In the normal course of events the contractor will be running down his site establishment as the contract work approaches its end. Simply to take these costs from the date when the work would have been completed to the date of actual completion may therefore be unfair to the contractor and some allowance should be made for the fact that the site establishment will have been running at full strength during the period when, had it not been for the delay, the establishment would have been running down.

On very large contracts it is desirable for the person actually responsible for the ascertainment to check that the staff on site are working exclusively in connection with the particular contract and are not 'helping out' with work on other contracts. Efficient contractors will require their staff to complete time-sheets and the architect or quantity surveyor should call for these and examine them.

2. Head-office overheads

On any contract, delay or disruption will lead inevitably to some increase in direct head-office administrative costs, relating not only to any period of delay but also to the involvement of staff in dealing with the problems caused by disruption, e.g. contract managers spending more time in organising additional labour, recasting programmes, etc., buying staff in, ordering additional materials, arranging plant hire and the like. As has been said, efficient contractors will require their staff to keep time records and where this is done the direct costs involved should be readily ascertainable.

Head-office overheads include not only costs of staff engaged upon individual contracts but also such general items as rent, rates, light, heating, cleaning, etc. and also clerical staff, telephonists, etc. and general costs such as stationery, office equipment, etc. Care must be taken to avoid double-recovery in respect of directly engaged administrative staff if some kind of formula is used to deal with the element of general overhead costs. It is important to distinguish between these two elements of overhead costs, even where, because no accurate time records are kept by the contractor, it is necessary to use some kind of formula approach to deal with this head of claim. Before a decision is made to use a formula, it is essential to ensure that it does not overstate the actual loss to the contractor, and the formula should be backed up by supporting evidence, e.g., the tender make-up, head office and project records and accounts, showing actual and anticipated before, during and after the period of delay. Any formula should be used with caution.

The formula approach

(a) The Hudson Formula

The best-known formula is called the Hudson formula, set out on page 599 of *Hudson's Building Contracts*, 10th Edition, which takes the allowance made by the contractor for head-office overheads and profit in his original tender, divides it by the original contract period and multiplies the result by the period of contract overrun.

The formula is as follows:

$$\frac{\text{HO/Profit percentage}}{100} \times \frac{\text{Contract sum}}{\substack{\text{Contract period} \\ \text{(e.g. in weeks)}}} \times \text{Period of delay (in weeks)}$$

We shall be dealing with loss of profit as a separate head of claim: see page 136.

The formula rather confusingly links head-office overheads and profit together on the assumption that contractors normally add a single percentage to their prices to cover both. It is true that the learned editor enters a caveat concerning the profit element in this calculation, pointing out that 'the formula assumes that the profit budgeted for by the contractor in his prices was in fact capable of being earned by him elsewhere had the contractor been free to leave the delayed contract at the proper time'. This appears to take a far too simplistic and, indeed, unrealistic, view of the problem. The formula is related entirely to an overrun of contract time, and its application would mean that a contractor would receive an increase in the actual amount paid to him under the contract in relation to head-office overheads and profit. This is to treat these two factors not as an element of loss, but as an element of expense, and we do not believe that this approach is justified.

It is unrealistic because it is based upon the contractor's allowances in his tender (which may never have been achievable), which is exactly the same point as the learned editor himself makes in relation to the profit element. The formula as set out above contains a mathematical inaccuracy because if used in that form it allows a claim for overheads and profit on the amount already included in the contract sum and if used at all the formula would be:

$$\frac{\text{HO/Profit \%}}{100} \times \frac{\text{Contract Sum (less overheads \& profit)}}{\text{Contract Period}} \times \text{Period of delay}$$

Furthermore, the formula itself cannot be used as it is printed unless adjustment is made to the various factors to allow for delays in completion for which recovery is not permitted (e.g. delays due to contractor's own inefficiency or to matters for which extensions of time may be granted without recovery of cost) and also for the effect of variations and fluctuations upon the contract sum. The formula assumes that there has been no change in the contract price. Where the value of the work carried out by the contractor has increased, e.g. because of variation, the pricing of those variations would normally include an allowance for overheads and profit by the application of the rates in the contract bills or under the 'fair valuation' rule, while fluctuations being recoverable net (except, of course, where formula price adjustment is used), must have the effect of reducing the percentage of overhead recovery on actual cost. The formula also ignores the fact that the contractor should make realistic efforts to deploy his resources elsewhere during a period of delay: *Peak Construction (Liverpool) Ltd* v. *McKinney Foundations Ltd* (1970).

In any event, considerable doubt is cast on the use of the 'Hudson formula' (or, indeed, of any 'formula' method) for calculating head-office overheads and profit by the decision of the High Court in *Tate & Lyle Food and Distribution Co. Ltd* v. *Greater London Council* (1982). This case casts doubt on the legitimacy of charging a percentage to represent head-office or any managerial time spent as a result of delay or disruption, at least in the absence of specific proof. In this case it was held that expenditure of managerial time in remedying an actionable wrong done to a trading company was claimable at common law as a head of 'special damage'. The actual claim failed because the company had kept no record of the amount of managerial time actually spent on remedying the wrong and, accordingly, there was no proof of claim. The High Court refused to speculate on quantum by awarding a percentage of the total of the other items of the claim, although it was expressly invited to do so by counsel, relying on an old line of cases in Admiralty matters. Although this was not a case involving building contracts, the principles enunciated are of general application. Although the case went to the House of Lords, the reasoning of the High Court discussed above was not at issue. Mr Justice Forbes said:

'I have no doubt that the expenditure of managerial time in remedying an actual wrong done to a trading concern can properly form the subject-matter of a head of claim. In a case such as this it would be wholly unrealistic to assume that no such additional managerial time was in fact expended. I would also accept that it must be extremely difficult to quantify. But modern office arrangements permit of the recording of the time spent by managerial staff on particular projects. I do not believe that it would have been impossible for the plaintiffs ... to have kept some record to show the extent to which their trading routine was disturbed ... In the absence of any evidence about the extent to which this has occurred the only suggestion ... is that I should award a percentage on the total damages ... While I am satisfied that this head of damage can properly be claimed I am not prepared to advance into an area of pure speculation when it comes to quantum. I feel bound to hold that the plaintiffs have failed to prove that any sum is due under this head'.

It seems to us that, in order to make a claim involving either overhead levels or profit levels (or both), one must deal with actual overheads and profits – and not merely with theoretical or assumed levels. 'Direct loss and/or expense' is, after all, the equivalent of what is claimable as damages for breach of contract at common law and accordingly the common law principles must apply.

For all these reasons we are of the view that the use of the Hudson formula cannot generally be justified as a method of ascertaining the contractor's entitlement under the contract terms unless backed up by supporting evidence and subject to the limitations we have indicated. In fairness to the learned editor of *Hudson* it should be said that the formula is quoted in the context of a discussion of damages recoverable at common law where such a broad-brush approach may well be adopted by the courts. It is unfortunate that some contractors tend to take the formula out of that context.

However, in *Ellis-Don Ltd* v. *Parking Authority of Toronto* (1978), the Supreme Court of Ontario applied the Hudson formula somewhat uncritically in respect of a contractor's claim for damages for off-site overheads and profit. It should be noted that Mr Justice O'Leary expressly found that (i) the overheads and profit would have been capable of being earned elsewhere had it not been for the delay caused by the employer and (ii) 'on this project without taking into account the results of this law suit Ellis-Don made 4 per cent of the contract price to be applied against overhead and as profit', the contractor having claimed that 3.87 per cent of the contract price had been included for these items.

(b) The Emden Formula
There is another formula published in a leading legal textbook, namely Emden's *Building Contracts and Practice*, 8th Edition, Volume 2, page N/

46, which runs as follows:

$$\frac{h}{100} \times \frac{c}{cp} \times pd$$

Where h equals the head-office percentage arrived at by dividing the total overhead cost and profit of the contractor's organisation as a whole by the total turnover; c equals the contract sum in question, cp is the contract period, and pd equals the period of delay, the last two being calculated in the same units, e.g. weeks.

This approach has the merit of having some relation to the reality of the contractor's overhead and profit recovery on his operations as a whole and on balance we prefer it to the Hudson approach, although it is open to some of the same criticisms. It can be very useful as an approach where actual costs of head-office staff directly engaged upon the individual contract are not obtainable. In that case, the proportion of the contractor's overall overhead costs that can be shown from his accounts to be spent upon staff directly engaged on contracts can be substituted for the element h to obtain a rough and ready approximation of the cost of staff engaged on the particular contract during the period of delay. However, clearly this approach does not make an allowance for the cost of greater staff involvement during the original contract period due to disruption. The essential difference between the 'Hudson' and 'Emden' formulae is that the former is based upon the percentage to cover profit and head-office costs as built into the tender, while the latter takes the percentage from the contractor's organisation as a whole, i.e. on costs and profit expressed as a percentage of annual turnover, as ascertained from his accounts.

(c) The Eichleay Formula
This is an American version of the Hudson formula, and is a three stage calculation which applies daily rates. It is usually expressed as follows:

1. $\dfrac{\text{Contract Billings}}{\substack{\text{Total contractor billings} \\ \text{for contract period}}} \times \substack{\text{Total HO overheads for} \\ \text{contract period}} = \text{Allocable overhead}$

2. $\dfrac{\text{Allocable overhead}}{\text{Days of performance}} = \text{Daily contract HO overhead}$

3. Daily contract HO overhead $\times$ Days of compensable delay $=$ Amount of recovery

Once again, the formula gives only a rough approximation; it does not require any proof from the contractor of his actual increased overhead costs from the delay and there is the possibility of double-recovery. In order to allow for this it is necessary at least to deduct any head-office overhead recovery allowed under the normal valuation rules. Furthermore, although it is widely used in American Federal Government Contracts and has been adopted in some other cases, it has equally been subject to judicial criticism and is not universally accepted. A very sensible view is expressed by the editors of *Building Law Reports*, volume 28, p. 103:

'Criticism of the formula is not of course criticism of the proposition that in a period of reduced activity on site a contractor will incur off-site overheads for which payment is not being recovered from revenue generated at site. However, unintelligent use of the formula will demonstrate its inherent weakness'.

Later (p. 105) they add, in relation to the Eichleay formula, that 'it will, for example, be necessary for the contractor still to establish, as a matter of fact, that the services provided at head office were under-funded in the period of delay because they were not designated as general services.'

Are general overheads recoverable?
It is arguable that the contractor's general head-office running costs will continue unaffected by any individual event on any individual contract. If this argument is accepted, it must follow that there can be no direct loss or expense involved in such costs resulting from either disruption or delay. Nevertheless, if 'direct loss and/or expense' is to be equated with the measure of damages at common law – as the case law now establishes – it must be said that the courts will normally assume some 'loss' under this head where a contract completion has been delayed, i.e. in a prolongation claim, on the basis that some such 'loss' would be reasonably foreseeable by the employer as a result of the delay.

There is one direct effect of disruption and delay which, beyond question, relates to general overhead costs. Where contract works are delayed and/or disrupted this will inevitably result in a reduction of 'cash-flow', i.e. the sums received by the contractor each month in respect of that contract will be less than they should have been. The contribution of that contract to the financing of general head-office overhead costs from month to month will therefore be reduced and it will be necessary for the contractor to find that money elsewhere, either by borrowing or by diverting money from other profit-earning uses.

In our view, if the principles enunciated in *F. G. Minter Ltd* v. *Welsh Health Technical Services Organisation* (1980) and *Rees & Kirby Ltd* v. *Swansea Corporation* (1985) are to be followed, the resulting additional financing charges (see section 8 below) must be considered to result directly from the delay and disruption concerned, and consequently are recoverable. It should be said that this principle and, indeed, the *Minter* decision itself, at first sight appears to conflict with a decision of the House of Lords in a case known as *The Edison* (1933), where Lord Wright said that

'the appellants' actual loss, in so far as it was due to their impecuniosity, arose from that impecuniosity as a separate and concurrent cause, extraneous to and distinct in character from the tort; the impecuniosity was not traceable to the respondents' acts, and, in my opinion, was outside the legal purview of the consequences of these acts'.

However, as Dr Parris observes when discussing this point (*The Standard Form of Building Contract: JCT 80*, Section 10.05 Interest as 'direct loss and expense'), 'this decision of the House of Lords has in fact long been ignored by the courts, if it has ever indeed been followed', and cites in support *Dodd Properties (Kent) Ltd* v. *The City of Canterbury* (1979). In our view *The Edison* has no application to the type of situation we envisage: see the comments of Lord Justices Megaw and Donaldson in *Dodd*, in (1980) 13 BLR at pages 54 and 61 ff.

Application of formulae

As it is hoped that we have made clear, we are not against the use of formulae in appropriate situations, but merely against their uncritical use without regard to the factual situation and without supporting evidence. In fact, it seems to us that two situations can be distinguished:

(i) A disruption situation, i.e. where the contract is not delayed or prolonged, in which case the *Tate & Lyle* principle applies and the 'management time' and overhead element are recoverable on proof as indicated by Mr Justice Forbes.
(ii) A prolongation situation, i.e. where there is a delay, in which case a modified formula approach may sometimes be used.

In either case – in our unrepentent view – the Hudson formula or any other formula has no general application. By far the best summary of the position is contained in Abrahamson's *Engineering Law*, at p. 369:

'It is claims for loss of overhead return and profit that are most likely to produce a dividend for the contractor beyond his actual losses. The theory is that the contractor's site and management resources are his revenue earning instrument, and that insofar as they are delayed on a contract by delay he will lose the earnings he would have made with them on some other contract out of which he would have paid his overheads and pocketed his profit. The reality is that in many cases, particularly where the delay affects a small part of a large contractor's total resources, the contractor's organisation has sufficient flexibility to cope with the extra time on site without sacrificing other contracts that may be available, so that the contractor's total overhead and profit is not in fact adversely affected on foot of the usual mathematical formula. On the other hand, where a large part of his resources are tied down on a site because of a delay, the ultimate length of which is not known, the contractor genuinely may be inhibited from tendering for other work at competitive rates: the edge may be taken off his tendering in a way not susceptible of very clear proof. The difficulty is to establish the real facts and some indication of the proof necessary has been given [in *Peak* v. *McKinney Foundations*]

This seems to us to be the position and, as Mr Abrahamson adds in a footnote, the Hudson formula 'is cited by claimants as scripture although the limitations on the application of the formula because of the questions it begs are immediately mentioned in *Hudson* itself'.

3. Profit

Loss of profit, which the contractor would otherwise have earned but for the delay or disruption, is an allowable head of claim. It is recoverable under the rule in *Hadley* v. *Baxendale* (1854). It should be noted that this applies only to the profit normally to be expected and if, for example, the contractor were prevented from earning an exceptionally high profit on another contract, this special profit would not be recoverable unless this fact were known to the employer at the time the delayed or disrupted contract has been entered into.

This is illustrated by the case of *Victoria Laundry (Windsor) Ltd* v. *Newman Industries Ltd* (1949), where the plaintiffs, who were launderers, contracted to buy a boiler from the defendants, who knew that the boiler was wanted for immediate use. Delivery of the boiler actually took place five months after the date specified in the contract. The Court of Appeal held that the plaintiffs were entitled to recover the profit which might reasonably have been expected to result from the normal use of the boiler during the five months in question, but that no account could be taken of the exceptionally profitable character of some of the contracts that they lost.

A construction industry case involving a successful claim for loss of profit is *Wraight Ltd* v. *P. H. & T. (Holdings) Ltd* (1968), where the plaintiff contractors properly determined their own employment under clause 26, JCT 63 and claimed as part of the 'direct loss and/or damage' the loss of the profit they would have earned had they been able to complete the contract work. Mr Justice Megaw, as he then was, allowed the claim. He said:

'In my judgment, the position is this: *prima facie*, the claimants are entitled to recover, as being direct loss and/or damage, those sums of money which they would have made if the contract had been performed, less the money which has been saved to them because of the disappearance of their contractual obligation.'

The judge's reference to '*those sums of money which they would have made*' is important, since it shows that what is recoverable is the actual profit on the particular contract, whether that is a greater or lesser profit than might normally be anticipated in the industry at large. This situation is distinct from that referred to above, where the contractor is prevented from obtaining an exceptional profit on another contract: see *Parsons (Livestock) Ltd* v. *Utley Ingham & Co Ltd* (1978). The *Wraight* case must also be distinguished from the usual run of claims for direct loss and/or expense arising from delay or disruption in that the profit lost was that which would have been earned on work that the contractor was not permitted to carry on.

A profit percentage is not invariably recoverable as a head of claim arising from disruption and delay. The better view is that such a claim is allowable only where the contractor is able to demonstrate that he has been prevented from earning profit elsewhere in the normal course of his business as a direct result of the disruption or prolongation, e.g. he has been prevented from taking up other work available to him. To some extent the success of such a claim may, therefore, depend on the economic climate at the time since it may be difficult for a contractor to show when there is a shortage of work that any actual loss of this kind has been suffered. In fairness, it should be pointed out that there is a possible line of argument to the effect that loss of overhead and profit-earning capacity of additional resources devoted to a contract because of delay or disruption is to be assumed without necessity of proof. In our view, this is probably a more sustainable argument in relation to *overhead* earning capacity and so far as profit-earning capacity is concerned it does not appear to be supported by the cases.

The proposition that loss of profit-earning capacity must be proved is supported by *dicta* in *Peak Construction (Liverpool) Ltd* v. *McKinney Foundations Ltd* (1970), which is also helpful in giving some indication of the sort of evidence needed to substantiate such a claim. In that case work was suspended on a contract for some 58 weeks, and although the case arose from a non-standard form of contract and involved some special facts, the principles are of general application.

We can do no better than to quote part of the judgment of Lord Justice Salmon at length:

'The way in which the claim for loss of profit was dealt with below has caused me some anxiety. The basis upon which the claim was put in the pleadings was that for 58 weeks no work had been done on this site. Accordingly, a large part of the plaintiffs' head office staff, and what was described as their site organisation, was either idle or employed on non-productive work during this period, and the plaintiffs accordingly suffered considerable loss of gross profit....

When the matter came before the court below the matter was put rather differently. The case was put on the basis that in the time during 1966 and 1967 when they were engaged in completing the construction of the East Lancashire Road project they were unable to take on any other work, which they would have been free to do had the East Lancashire Road project been completed on time, and they lost the profit which they would have made on this other work. When the case was argued in this court it seemed to me that the plaintiffs were a little uncertain about which basis they were opting for.

In the end however I think they came down in favour of the second basis: that is, the one that was argued before the court below ...'

'Possibly some evidence as to what the site organisation consisted of, what part of the head office staff is being referred to and what they were doing at the material times could be of help. Moreover, it is possible, I suppose, that a judge might think it useful to have an analysis of the yearly turnover from, say, 1962 right up to, say, 1969, so that if the case is put before him on the basis that work was lost during 1966 and 1967 by reason of the plaintiffs being engaged upon completing this block and, therefore, not being free to take on any other work, he would be helped in forming an assessment of any loss of profit sustained by the plaintiffs.'

Lord Justice Edmund Davies said, in the same case:

'Under this head (i.e., loss of profit) the plaintiffs were awarded the sum of £11,619. The defendants submit that this sum should be wholly disallowed, no loss of profit having been established. This outright denial is, in my judgment, probably untenable, it being a seemingly inescapable conclusion from such facts as are challenged that the plaintiffs suffered some loss of profit. The sum awarded was arrived at on the basis of a gross profit calculated at nine per cent of the main contract figure of £232,000. Whether this was a satisfactory method of approach need not be decided now, though I have substantial doubts on the matter.'

4. Inefficient or increased use of labour and plant

Delay and disruption can lead to increased expenditure on labour and plant in two ways. It may be necessary to employ additional labour and plant or the existing labour and plant may stand idle or be under-employed. The latter is sometimes referred to as 'loss of productivity'. While this is clearly an allowable head of claim, it can be difficult if not impossible to establish the amount of the actual additional expenditure involved. A reasonably efficient contractor should be able to establish actual costs incurred, but it will clearly be impossible to prove as a matter of fact what the costs would have been had the delay or disruption not occurred. However, it should be possible for the contractor to provide reasonable substantiation of his intended use of labour and plant by reference to the original programme of work, histograms, etc.

A further difficulty is that of relating particular items of additional expenditure under these or indeed other heads to particular events. Contractors seldom keep cost records in such a detailed form as to enable this to be done, particularly where there may be several concurrent causes of delay and disruption, some of which may be claimable and others not. All that can be said is that the architect or quantity surveyor must do his best to arrive at a reasonable conclusion from whatever evidence is available. In our view, it must be a reasonable assumption that some loss will have been suffered in these respects where delay or disruption has occurred and the architect or quantity surveyor cannot resist making some reasonable assessment simply on the grounds that the contractor cannot prove in every detail the loss he has suffered.

This is, in fact, one aspect of what is called 'the global approach', which is discussed in Chapter 11. In *London Borough of Merton* v. *Stanley Hugh Leach Ltd* (1985) one of the issues before the court was whether the terms of a JCT 63 contract allow the contractor to recover direct loss and/or expense 'when it is not possible for the contractor to state in respect of any such alleged event the amount of loss and/or expense attributable' to the specific event. Mr Justice Vinelott, following *J Crosby & Son Ltd* v. *Portland UDC* (1967), answered the question affirmatively. Where there is more than one head of claim, then provided that the contractor has not unreasonably delayed in making the claim and so created the difficulty himself, the architect or quantity surveyor must ascertain the global loss which is directly attributable to the various causes. However he must disregard any loss or expense which would have been recoverable had the claim been made under one head in isolation and which would not have been recoverable under the other head, also considered in isolation.

The learned judge, however, added an important reservation:

'It is implicit [in *Crosby*] that a rolled-up award can only be made in a case where the loss or expense attributable to each head of claim cannot in reality be separated and secondly that a rolled-up award can only be made where apart from that practical impossibility the conditions which have to be satisfied before an award can be made have been satisfied in relation to each head of claim'.

5. Winter working

One other factor that can lead to a claim which is effectively one for loss of productivity is the carrying out of work in less favourable circumstances, e.g. excavation work carried out in winter rather than in summer. In such circumstances, there is potentially a claim in respect of the additional costs caused by working in winter when, but for the delay, the work would have been completed during the summer period. The contractor must, of course, be able to prove a direct link between the cause of the delay and the working in worse conditions, with no compensating saving. A case which supports this view is *Bush* v. *Whitehaven Port & Town Trustees* (1888). One aspect of the case has been disapproved, though not overruled, by the House of Lords in a later case, but it has also been followed by a very strong Court of Appeal.

In *Bush* v. *Whitehaven Port Town Trustees*, Bush contracted with the Trustees to lay a 15 inch water main from Ennerdale Water to Whitehaven for £1335. The contract was made in June, and the Trustees contracted to be ready at all times to give Bush sufficient possession of the site to enable him to proceed with the works. In fact, through the fault of the Trustees, the whole of the site was not available until October. As a result of this delay, the contract was thrown into the winter months, and Bush was put to heavy extra expense for which he sued the defendants.

His claim was successful, despite the fact that there was an express term saying that 'non-delivery of the site ... shall not ... entitle the contractor to any increased allowance in respect of money ...'

In one sense the decision is unsatisfactory, since the Court advanced alternative bases for its decision, namely that a summer contract having, by implication, been in the contemplation of the parties when the contract was made, Bush was entitled to a *quantum meruit* ('as much as it is worth') or damages in respect of the increased expenditure.

As explained in the later case of *Sir Lindsay Parkinson, Ltd* v. *Commissioners of Works* (1950), the decision is based on an implied term about the circumstances in which the contract works were to be done. This certainly seems to have been the view of Lord Coleridge CJ in the *Bush* case itself. He dealt with the question whether a term could be implied for breach of which the plaintiff could recover damages, and was inclined to answer it in the affirmative, and referred again and again to the contract being made 'with reference to certain anticipated circumstances' and becoming inapplicable to the actual situation. What was to have been a summer contract had been turned into a winter contract. Lord Coleridge CJ said:

'It was turned into a winter contract when wages were different ... when days were short, instead of long; when weather was bad, instead of good; when rivers which had to be dealt with, and had to be crossed by the pipes, were full not empty; and when, in fact, ... a great many most important circumstances under which the contract was to be executed, had ... changed from those which ... were in the contemplation of the parties when the contract was entered into. The contract, nevertheless, was carried on and completed ... with the knowledge of the defendants ... the contractor [completed the works] under the altered conditions...'

Obviously, the prudent contractor will allow a contingency or float in his programme against delays which are his responsibility, but he is not bound to take the totally unforeseeable into account. Prolongation of a contract which means working through an additional winter period almost inevitably results in 'direct loss and/or expense' to the contractor, e.g. extra costs of extending protective measures to materials, or replacing them due to deterioration, labour disruption, 'extended preliminaries' and so on.

6. Plant

Plant is really part of site overheads, but raises particular problems and, as regards idle plant in a prolongation situation, more detailed consideration is desirable:

(1) Plant hired-in

Where plant is hired in – usually under Model Conditions of Plant Hire Terms – there is no difficulty. In that event, the amount claimable is the loss actually incurred, i.e. the sums payable to the plant owner under terms of the hire contract, subject to the normal legal principles of mitigation of loss.

Under the current Model Conditions (1979) there is in general a guaranteed minimum period of hire, and the whole of that guaranteed minimum period is chargeable as working time. The 'idle time' provisions of the Model Conditions (clause 25) only apply where the plant is idle as the result of something which is the plant owner's responsibility. However, in the case of prolonged disruption and delay, it is clear that the hirer (claimant contractor) must mitigate his loss by (a) trying to use the plant elsewhere (if this is possible); and/or (b) terminating the plant hire contract and returning the plant to its owner in accordance with the terms of the hire. The same principle applies to other items hired-in.

(2) Contractor's own plant

This is the problematical area. The first hurdle here (as, indeed, under (1) above), is to relate the loss and expense claim to the particular disruptive event relied on. Contractors seldom keep cost records in such a detailed form as to enable this to be done, particularly where there are several concurrent causes of delay or disruption, some of which may be claimable and others not: see, however, our discussion of the 'global approach' on p.316.

The case of *B. Sunley & Co. Ltd* v. *Cunard White Star Ltd* (1940) is illustrative of the principles involved. There, a machine had to be transported from Doncaster to Guernsey for use on a contract, but was delayed by 1 week in its arrival. While delayed in Doncaster it worked for 1 day and earned £16. The Court of Appeal held that in the absence of evidence as to actual loss of profit, the measure of damage was depreciation in the value of the machine during the period of delay, interest on the money invested in its purchase, costs of maintenance, and some wages thrown away. Assumptions were made as to the values involved and in the absence of firm evidence a figure of £30 was arrived at, less the £16, making a net award of £14. It is notable that, in arriving at the figure for depreciation, the Court of Appeal took into account that the machine would not depreciate as much while standing idle as it would when working, but the Court's apparently harsh attitude on this point was possibly influenced by the fact that the plaintiff's original claim had been for £577 on grounds which the Court considered wholly unsustainable and by the plaintiff's inability to produce any real evidence. A certain testiness is discernible in the judgment delivered by Lord Justice Clauson.

The ruling of the Court of Appeal is summarised in the headnote:

'*Held*: The machine was a chattel of commercial value and there were four possible heads of damage: (1) Depreciation; (ii) interest on money invested; (iii) cost of maintenance; and (iv) expenditure of wages thrown away. The plaintiffs could not complain that they were refused relief under heads (ii), (iii) and (iv) for they had not given any evidence on these legitimate topics. £20 would be allowed for depreciation, £10 for interest, maintenance and wages – in all £30 – against which receipts for £16 must be deducted leaving a net sum for damages of £14'.

At first instance ([1939] 3 All ER 641) Mr Justice Hallet held that the proper measure of damages was the amount the plaintiffs would have made by the use of the machine during the period it was idle, but the Court of Appeal took the view that, in the absence of proof of special damage, the plaintiffs could only recover nominal damages based largely upon a mathematical calculation of the rate of depreciation of the machine.

In our view, two consequences flow from this decision in the normal claims situation. *First*, if the contractor can prove his actual loss by detailed calculations based on actual cost records, he is entitled to recover that amount. *Secondly*, if the contractor cannot prove 'special damage', he is entitled to recover only a nominal amount, which is normally limited to depreciation. There is 'no authority for the proposition that, if the owner of a profit-earning chattel does not prove the loss he has sustained, the judge may made a fortuitous guess and award him some arbitary sum': *per* Lord Justice Clauson. The only real evidence in the *Sunley* case was that the capital cost of the machine had been £4500 and its life was three years. The Court of Appeal took the view that on a pure sinking-fund basis the depreciation for the claim period would be £29 for the week, but 'We cannot believe ... that a machine exposed to such working strains in use that it will last only three years depreciates as much when idle as it does when working and we, therefore, think that £20 for the week is as much as ought to be allowed for depreciation'. Despite Lord Justice Clauson's strictures, it seems that in assessing the loss (in the absence of actual proof) the architect must work on the same assumptions as did the Court of Appeal and must make a reasonable assumption that some loss will have been suffered where delay and disruption have occurred.

Hudson's *Building Contracts*, 10th Edition, page 600, uses the *Sunley* case as an illustration under the heading 'Site overheads' and points out that standing time of idle plant *may* overlap with a claim for loss of productivity. It is said there that:

> Standing time [of unproductive plant] is frequently claimed by contractors on the basis of hire-rates, which may result in the capital value of a new piece of plant being claimed over a relatively short period of time. *Hire-rates may sometimes be adopted by the Courts, where satisfied that loss of profit has occurred, and where evidence of that particular loss exists, but in the absence of evidence of profit opportunity, only depreciation and maintenance may be allowed.*' (Italics supplied.)

There are many permutations of the contractor's 'own plant' situation. If he can prove by means of satisfactory evidence that the plant could have been employed profitably elsewhere, that may well be a basis of claim in an appropriate case.

7. Increased costs

Additional expenditure on labour, materials or plant due to increases in cost during a period of delay is an allowable head of claim. Claims may also be sustainable where disruption has resulted in labour-intensive work being delayed into a period after an increased wage award. It should be noted that, where a claim of this kind is being made in respect of a delay in completion, it is not only the period of delay that should be considered. The correct measure would be the difference between what the contractor would have spent on labour, materials and plant and what he has actually had to spend over the whole period of the work as a result of the delay and disruption concerned.

In making this calculation, of course, due allowance must be made for any recovery of increased costs under the appropriate fluctuations clauses in the contract.

8. Financing charges and interest
A. FINANCING CHARGES

Whatever the position may be at common law about interest on outstanding debts and claims, it is now settled law that under the 'direct loss and/or expense' provisions of the JCT Forms – and, it is submitted, under similarly worded provisions in other forms – finance charges by way of interest expended are allowable as a head of claim. Indeed, the loss of interest that might have been earned on the money diverted from investment, i.e., compensation for the loss of use of money. The contractor is to be compensated for the financial burden arising from the fact that primary loss or expense would have been incurred some time before ascertainment and certification. 'Direct loss and/or expense' covers the financial burden to the contractor of being stood out of his money; it is *not* interest on a debt but a constituent part of the loss and/or expense.

This principle was first established by the decision of the Court of Appeal in *F G Minter Ltd* v. *Welsh Health Technical Services Organisation* (1980), which recognised the realities of the financing situation in the construction industry and gave a sensible and practical interpretation to the claims provisions. Lord Justice Stephenson summarised the position in this way:

'[In] the building and construction industry the "cash flow" is vital to the contractor and delay in paying him for the work he does naturally results in the ordinary course of things in his being short of working capital, having to borrow capital to pay wages and hire charges and locking up in plant, labour and materials capital which he would have invested elsewhere. The loss of the interest which he has to pay on the capital he is forced to borrow and on the capital which he is not free to invest would be recoverable for the employer's breach of contract within the first rule in *Hadley* v. *Baxendale* (1854) without resorting to the second, and would accordingly be a direct loss, if an authorised variation of the works, or the regular progress of the works having been materially affected by an event specified ... has involved the contractor in that loss.'

In that case, the plaintiff was engaged to construct a hospital in Wales. The contract was in JCT 63 form. As the work progressed substantial numbers of variations were ordered, and these affected regular progress of the works as a whole and a nominated sub-contractor's work was materially affected by a lack of necessary instructions. Claims were made and paid under clauses 11(6) and 24(1)(a) (now JCT 80, clause 26.1.). The plaintiff challenged the amounts paid because they had not been certified until long after the losses and expenses had been incurred. They claimed that finance charges which they had incurred as a result of being kept out of their money were 'direct loss and/or expense'. The Court of Appeal agreed, and rejected the employer's argument that they were not 'direct' but were 'a naked claim for interest'.

The decision of the Court of Appeal can be summarised in this way:

(1) The words 'direct loss and/or expense' must be interpreted as covering those losses and expenses which arose naturally and in the ordinary course of things, i.e. the same criteria applicable whenever common law damages are being considered. A particular item of loss or expense is regarded as 'direct' if it can fairly be said to fall within the first branch of the rule in *Hadley* v. *Baxendale* (1854).

(2) In the construction industry, in the ordinary course of things, contractors who are required to finance particular operations will require to utilize capital. This will either have to be borrowed (in which case they will have to pay borrowing charges) or else made available from their own resources. In that case, they will forgo the interest which might otherwise have been earned. Accordingly, whenever the carrying out of varied work or the fact that regular progress of the works had been materially affected by one of the specified events, has involved the contractor in laying out money which is not reimbursed by interim payments for the total value of the work properly executed as provided for by the contract, the amount paid for or lost by obtaining the use of the necessary capital is a part of the loss or expense which arises in the ordinary course of things.

(3) In the context of JCT 63, the financing charges are implicitly part of the recoverable direct loss and/or expense or, as Lord Justice Ackner put it, what was being claimed 'is not interest on a debt, but a debt which has as one of its constituent parts interest charges which have been incurred'.

(4) On the wording of the JCT 63 provisions, recovery was restricted to direct loss and/or expense incurred up to the date of the contractor's application, i.e. for the period between the loss and/or expense being incurred and making of the written application for reimbursement.

Consequently, under JCT 63, subsequently incurred charges are recoverable only under successive applications. This is because JCT 63 does not deal with *continuing or future* losses; it refers only to losses and expenses *which have already been incurred*. Under JCT 63 the cut-off point is the date of the contractor's notice: see Chapter 6, p. 196.

There is no such limitation under JCT 80, clause 26.1 or IFC 84, clause

4.11, where only one application or notice from the contractor is required to cover loss and/or expense *'that he has incurred or is likely to incur'*. In fact, proper application of the JCT 80 and IFC 84 provisions *should* ensure that little in the way of finance charges is incurred by the employer.

The matter has been taken a stage further by the decision of the Court of Appeal in *Rees & Kirby Ltd* v. *Swansea City Council* (1985) where the Court of Appeal applied the principles established in *F. G. Minter Ltd* v. *Welsh Health Technical Services Organisation*. Their lordships extended those principles by stating that finance charges should be calculated on a compound interest basis.

Lord Justice Robert Goff said:

'...[It] seems to me, we must adopt a realistic approach. We must bear in mind, moreover that what we are considering is a debt due under a contract ... [It is] a claim in respect of loss or expense in which a contractor has been involved by reason of certain specified events. The [contractors] ... operated over the relevant period on the basis of a substantial overdraft at their bank, and their claim in respect of financing charges consists of a claim in respect of interest paid by them to the bank on the relevant amount during that period. It is notorious that banks do themselves, when calculating interest on overdrafts, operate on the basis of periodic rests: on the basis of [the *Minter* principle], which we here have to apply, I for my part can see no reason why that fact should not be taken into account when calculating the [contractor's] claim for loss or expense ...'

In *Rees and Kirby Ltd* v. *Swansea City Council*, in 1972 the plaintiffs were engaged to construct a housing estate for the defendants, under a fixed-price contract in JCT 63 terms. The contract completion date was in July 1973. A large number of variations were ordered and there were delays in issuing instructions and information. The works were in fact practically completed in July 1974. By a letter of 4 July 1973 the contractors notified the Corporation of the causes of delay, giving further additional details and notified a claim for reimbursement of loss and/or expense by a letter in general terms dated 18 December 1973.

During 1972 there was a sharp escalation in construction industry wage rates and it soon appeared that this would convert the contract into a substantial loss-maker. In October 1973, the Minister for Housing and Construction issued a statement that local authorities could in appropriate cases consider making *ex gratia* payments to contractors working on fixed-price contracts. In light of this, the plaintiffs' contractual claims were put aside while the parties negotiated for an *ex gratia* settlement or alternatively for the contract to be converted into a fluctuating price one. By the end of 1976 the plaintiffs concluded that no settlement was possible. On 24 December 1976 they wrote to the plaintiffs indicating that their losses were being 'aggravated by interest charges on monies outstanding for our contractual claim'. On 11 February 1977 it became clear that negotiations had failed. The plaintiffs' detailed formal claim was finally submitted in June 1978, but, despite chasing letters, the architect did not respond until February 1979. He then granted the full extension of time claimed (52 weeks), but said that the interest claim was not a matter for his decision.

Between February and August 1979 the architect issued various interim certificates in respect of the direct loss and/or expense claimed. None of the sums certified included any element of interest. The contractors signed the draft final account on 10 August 1979, but expressly reserved the claim for interest. The final certificate was issued without prejudice to the contractor's right to press that outstanding claim.

The ruling of the Court of Appeal was as follows:

(1) The contractor's application under clauses 11(6) and 24(1)(a) of JCT 63 need not be in any particular form, but must contain a reference sufficient to make it clear that it includes some loss or expense suffered because the contractor has been kept out of his money. Lord Justice Robert Goff emphasised that, even under JCT 63, he did

'not consider that more than the most general reference is required, sufficient to give notice that the contractor's application does include loss or expense incurred by him by reason of his being out of pocket in respect of the relevant variation or delayed instruction, or whatever may be the relevant event giving rise to a claim under the clause'.

The position is, it seems, different under both JCT 80 and IFC 84, because of the revised wording.

'[The] clauses in question have since been revised to allow for applications in respect of loss or expense which the contractor has incurred or *is likely* to incur; and it may be (though I express no opinion upon it) that, under clauses so revised there need be no express reference to interest as financing charges'.

In our respectful opinion, this *dictum* of Lord Justice Robert Goff is the correct interpretation of the revised wording but, to avoid uncertainty, even under JCT 80 and IFC 84, the wise contractor's application will include reference to finance charges.

(2) Normally, the contractor's notice must be given within a reasonable time of the loss or expense having been incurred as the clause makes plain. However, on the facts the Council could not rely on the delay between practical completion and the formal application of June 1978 since they were estopped from enforcing their strict legal rights under the principle of promissory estoppel first stated by Lord Cairns LC in *Hughes* v. *Metropolitan Railway Co.* (1877). This is an important point, but if negotiations for a settlement are taking place, it is sensible practice for the contractor expressly to reserve his legal rights, both as to interest or otherwise: see below.

(3) There is no cut-off point at the date of practical completion as the Council had argued. In the words of Lord Justice Robert Goff:

'I can see no reason why the financing charges should not continue to constitute direct loss or expense in which the contractor is involved by reason of, for example, a variation, until the date of the last application made before the issue of the certificate issued in respect of the primary loss or expense incurred by reason of the relevant variation. At the date of the issue of the certificate, the right to receive payment in respect of the primary loss or expense merges in the right to receive payment under the certificate within the time specified in the contract, so that from the date of the certificate, the contractor is out of his money by reason either (1) that the contract permits time to elapse between the issue of the certificate and its payment, or (2) that the certificate has not been honoured on the due date, but I can for my part see no good reason for holding that the contractor should cease to be involved in loss or expense in the form of financing charges simply because the date of practical completion has passed'.

(4) The delay in payment which occurred because of negotiations for an *ex gratia* settlement, which was between the date of practical completion and 11 February 1977 when it became clear that the plaintiffs' claim must be advanced under the terms of the contract, was delay which was attributable to an independent cause, and not to the ordering of variations or the giving of late instructions. The financing charges incurred by the contractor during this period, were not direct loss and/or expense for the purposes of the contract.

If only for this reason, it is advisable for the contractor to reserve his rights to finance charges if negotiations are taking place or, alternatively, to give notice of arbitration. This part of the Court of Appeal's reasoning involves difficult problems of causation and has caused some comment. It raises potential legal and practical difficulties: see the commentary on the case in *Building Law Reports*, volume 30, pp. 5–6. The best that can be said is that the facts of *Rees & Kirby Ltd* were rather special.

(5) The contractors were entitled to recover finance charges for the period from 11 February 1977 (when the architect notified them that in effect the claim must be processed under the terms of the contract) until 10 August 1979 when they appended their signature to the draft final account. These finance charges were to be calculated on the basis of compound interest.

Rees & Kirby Ltd v. *Swansea City Council* has silenced the debate as to whether financing charges are a proper head of claim under contracts in JCT terms. The principles it establishes are applicable to other similarly worded forms of contract. Indeed, in 1984 the PSA formally accepted, in principle, that in appropriate circumstances financing charges are recoverable under Edition 2 of GC/Works/1.

However, some problems still remain, for example as regards deciding the rate of interest on money diverted from investment. Where a contractor is, in fact, operating on borrowed money the position is simple, since supporting evidence as to the additional financial charges incurred can readily be obtained from his bankers but this is subject to what is said below. However, where what the contractor is claiming is loss of investment potential, it may be necessary for him to show the manner in which he customarily invests his money and the interest that a contractor in his position could have expected to have earned; *Tate & Lyle Food & Distribution Co. Ltd* v. *Greater London Council* (1982).

Special difficulties will be encountered where a contractor in a small or medium way of business wavers from a credit to a debit situation and back again during the period of the contract. It may become very difficult to establish at any particular point in time whether what he is entitled to claim is interest on overdraft or loss of investment potential. In such cases it is suggested that some reasonable average be drawn, having regard to the realities of the investment market. Indeed, the actual percentages involved may differ very little. If the contractor customarily invests money in a building society, or other institution where tax is deducted at source, this must be taken into account, either by making an appropriate addition to the rate of interest or (if the Inland Revenue agrees) by providing the contractor with the appropriate evidence for the recovery of the tax deducted.

With the abolition of minimum lending rate, overdraft rates tend to fluctuate at short intervals and will also vary as between contractors as, indeed, has always been the case. Where a wholly exceptional and possibly penal rate of interest is being charged to the particular contractor, his recovery would be limited to a 'normal' rate, because that must be presumed to be what was in the contemplation of the employer as a foreseeable consequence.

This view is supported by the decision of Mr Justice Forbes in *Tate & Lyle Food and Distribution Co. Ltd* v. *Greater London Council* (1982). This case was admittedly concerned with statutory interest on damages, but seems to us (and others) to be authority for the view that any interest or finance charges allowed as part of direct loss and/or expense should be assessed at a rate equivalent to the cost of borrowing (or normal investment, as the case may be), disregarding any special position of the contractor. As Mr Justice Forbes said in that case, one looks

'... at the cost to the plaintiff of being deprived of the money which he should have had. I feel satisfied that in commercial cases the interest is intended to reflect the rate at which the plaintiff would have had to borrow money to supply the place of that which was withheld. I am also satisfied that one should not look at any special position in which the plaintiff may have been; one should disregard, for example, the fact that a particular plaintiff could only borrow money at a very high rate or, on the other hand, was able to borrow money at specially favourable rates. The correct thing to do is to take the rate at which plaintiffs in general could borrow money. This does not, however, ... mean that you exclude entirely all the attributes of the plaintiff other than that he is a plaintiff ... [It] would always be right to look at the rate at which plaintiffs with the general attributes of the actual plaintiff in the case (though not, of course, with any special or peculiar attribute) could borrow money as a guide to the appropriate interest rate. ..'

This seems to be a sensible approach under JCT terms. The alternative is to take the rate at which the contractor is borrowing money, or the rate of investment interest he is receiving if he has a deposit – and ask him to produce an auditor's or banker's certificate in support. Many architects and quantity surveyors prefer this approach because the calculation is based on actual costs, for the contract refers to 'the amount of such loss and/or expense which has been or is being incurred by the contractor'. But if the particular contractor was paying for his overdraft at above the normal rate, it is at least arguable that the excess should be disallowed.

Either method of arriving at the interest rate is reasonable in practice, although if the claimant is paying a specially high rate of interest (or is receiving above-average investment interest), the judicial approach is preferable. The rate at which an ordinary commercial borrower can borrow money is probably the safest guide.

The financial pages of the 'quality' daily newspapers will be a useful source of reference and it may well be that in practice it is acceptable to average-out rates of interest over a period rather than go through the tedious mathematical exercise of detailed calculation on the basis of rates from day to day.

The interest allowable on an overdraft is that actually payable by the contractor (subject to what has been said above) and would therefore be compounded at the normal intervals adopted by the contractor's bank, e.g. quarterly or half-yearly.

B. INTEREST

At common law it is well settled that debts do not carry interest so that, for example, an employer who pays late on a certificate discharges his obligation by paying the sum certified. This principle follows from the decision of the House of Lords in *London, Chatham and Dover Railway Co.* v. *South Eastern Railway Co.* (1893). The rule has recently been affirmed by the House of Lords in *President of India* v. *La Pintada Cia Navegacion SA* (1984). Their lordships thought that the rule was unsatisfactory, and expressed the view that the position should be altered by statute, as had been recommended by the Law Commission in its report on Interest in 1978 (Cmnd 7229).

A limited statutory right to interest was conferred by section 3 of the Law Reform (Miscellaneous Provisions) Act 1934 which gave a court – and in all probability an arbitrator – the right to make an award of simple interest on 'the sum for which *judgment* is given', but this applied only 'in any proceedings *tried*'. Although this applied to both debts and other damages, if the debtor paid the original sum in full, even part way through the trial or hearing, he avoided payment of interest.

This unjust anomaly has been corrected by section 15 of the Administration of Justice Act 1982 (amending the Supreme Court Act 1981, section 35A) by empowering the court to award interest provided the money was outstanding at the time proceedings were commenced.

By section 19A of the Arbitration Act 1950 (inserted by section 15 and Schedule 1 to the Administration of Justice Act 1982) arbitrators have a like power. Section 19A provides:

'(1) Unless a contrary intention is expressed therein, every arbitration agreement shall, where such a provision is applicable to the reference, be deemed to contain a provision that the arbitrator ... may, if he thinks fit, award simple interest at such rate as he thinks fit

  (a) on any sum which is the subject of the reference but which is paid before the award, for such period ending not later than the date of the payment as he thinks fit, and

  (b) on any sum which he awards, for such period ending not later than the date of the award as he thinks fit.

(2) The power to award interest conferred on an arbitrator ... by subsection (1) above is without prejudice to any other power of an arbitrator ... to award interest':

Although this provision did not come into force until 1 April 1983, it has been held to apply to arbitration agreements made before, as well as after, that date: *Food Corporation of India* v. *Marastro Co Naviera* (1986). Both judgment debts and sums directed to be paid by an arbitrator's award carry interest at the prescribed statutory rate as from the date of judgment or the award.

The parties to a contract may, of course, expressly agree that a debt or other sum due under the contract shall carry interest. Such a provision is made by section 60(6) of the ICE Conditions of Contract for Works of Civil Engineering Construction, under which the employer must pay interest on overdue payments. The Joint Contracts Tribunal would do well to consider making a similar provision in its standard forms as the current situation is manifestly unjust.

One other situation must be considered and that is the case of interest as *special damage*. Where a creditor is able to establish that he has suffered special damage, for example by himself having to pay interest on an overdraft, as a result of the debtor's late payment of a debt, the creditor is entitled to claim that special damage, provided that he can bring himself within the second part of the rule in *Hadley* v. *Baxendale* (1854). This follows from the decision of the Court of Appeal in *Wadsworth* v. *Lydall* (1981), which was approved by the House of Lords in *La Pintada* (1984).

In *Wadsworth* v. *Lydall*, the plaintiff contracted to sell a property to the defendant, and in anticipation of receiving the purchase price of £10,000 from his purchaser, contracted to buy another property. The defendant (the purchaser) defaulted, and in fact paid a lesser sum very late. As a result the plaintiff had to pay his vendor interest on the unpaid purchase price of the other property, and also incurred the cost of raising a mortgage to meet the balance. Subsequently he sued the defaulting purchaser, claiming, *inter alia*, £355 in respect of interest which he had to pay his vendor for late completion and £16.20 for mortgage costs.

The Court of Appeal allowed these two items as special damage, i.e., as an application of the second limb of the rule in *Hadley* v. *Baxendale* (1854), Lord Justice Brightman put the matter in this way:

'The defendant knew or ought to have known that if the £10,000 was not paid to him the plaintiff would need to borrow an equivalent amount or would have to pay interest to his vendor or would need to secure financial accommodation in some other way. The plaintiff's loss in my opinion is such that it may reasonably be supposed that it would have been in the contemplation of the parties as a serious possibility, had their intention been directed to the consequences of a breach of contract.'

The Court of Appeal distinguished the *London, Chatham and Dover Railway Co.* case (*supra*). Lord Justice Brightman said on this point:

'In my view the Court is not constrained (i.e. in relation to interest) by the decision of the House of Lords. In *London, Chatham and Dover Railway Co.* v. *South-Eastern Railway Co.* the House of Lords was not concerned with a claim for special damages. The action was an action for an account. The House was concerned only with a claim for interest by way of general damages. If a plaintiff pleads and can prove that he has suffered special damage as a result of the defendant's failure to perform his obligation under a contract, and such damage is not too remote, on the principle of *Hadley* v. *Baxendale* (1854), I can see no logical reason why such special damage should be irrecoverable merely because the obligation on which the defendant defaulted was an obligation to pay money and not some other type of obligation....'

This case seems to us, therefore, to open up the way to such claims for interest as 'special damage' in arbitration proceedings arising under building contracts generally. This is borne out by *Holbeach Plant Hire Ltd* v. *Anglian Water Authority* (1988) where it was held that a contractor may be entitled to interest or financing charges if he pleads and proves them as special damage, the court applying propositions laid down by Lord Justice Neill in *President of India* v. *Lips Maritime Corporation* 1987. The position under JCT Forms is clearly dealt with in *F. G. Minter Ltd* v. *Welsh Health Technical Services Organisation* (1980) and *Rees & Kirby Ltd* v. *Swansea City Council* (1985), as already explained.

An interesting application of the principle of *Wadsworth* v. *Lydall* is to be found in the decision of the High Court of Justice in Northern Ireland in *Department of the Environment for Northern Ireland* v. *Farrans (Construction) Ltd* (1981), which arose under the JCT Form (1963 Edition) and adds to the debate in the construction industry about the recovery of interest or financing charges in building contract cases. Under clause 22, JCT 63 (clause 24, JCT 80), once the architect has issued his certificate of delay, the employer is entitled to deduct liquidated and ascertained damages at the prescribed rate from moneys due or to become due to the contractor. If, subsequently, the architect grants an extension of time so that a refund is due to the contractor, is the contractor entitled in law to make any claim against the employer for interest upon or financing charges which are attributable to the moneys refunded?

This was the point at issue in the Ulster decision, but it should be noted that Mr Justice Murray was not asked to decide the question whether, under JCT 63, the architect can issue more than one certificate under clause 22. For the purposes of the case, the parties agreed that he could, but the point is not free from doubt. The wording of clause 22 presupposes action by the architect only after the contractor's failure to complete by the due date resulting in the employer recovering liquidated damages. Mr Donald Keating (*Building Contracts*, 4th Edition, page 345) suggests that more than one certificate can be issued under clause 22,

'... e.g. when the completion date is past and a certificate has been issued but subsequently a cause of delay arises entitling the contractor to an extension of time ... because if the architect cannot grant a further extension the original certificate would become bad and it follows that an architect would never be safe in issuing a certificate until after completion'.

Mr Justice Murray decided, on the facts before him, that where several certificates were issued, with the result that sums previously deducted as liquidated damages fell to be repaid, the contractor was entitled to interest thereon. He ruled that clause 22 was to be construed as meaning that when the employer received the first or any subsequent certificate it was open to him to start deducting liquidated damages. The employer did this at his own risk in the sense that if a later certificate was issued, which had the effect of vitiating the earlier certificate, the employer was without protection against a claim for breach of contract in failing to pay on the due dates the amounts shown in the relevant interim certificates. In those circumstances, the contractor was entitled to the remedy appropriate for a common law claim for breach of contract. His lordship applied *Wadsworth* v. *Lydall* and held that the arbitrator had power to award damages, which could include interest incurred or lost as a foreseeable consequence of the employer's breach of contract.

Of course the contractor had to prove that because of the interest charges he suffered loss or damage through the employer's breach of contract in failing to pay monies on the due date *and* that a reasonable person in the employer's position would have had such loss or damage in contemplation as a likely result of the breach.

We must confess that we find Mr Justice Murray's reasoning very difficult to follow. It appears to be summarised in the following passage from his judgment:

'It was the employer's own voluntary decision to make the deductions and no doubt it took the decision in what it thought to be its own financial interest. The only basis on which the employer can justify the deductions ... is that there was a succession of dates on which the Works ought reasonably to have been completed – each date so to speak being valid and effective while the relevant certificate stood – but I see nothing in the contract to justify such an extraordinary conception and I reject it.'

With great respect to Mr Justice Murray there is nothing extraordinary in that conception, which is, in our view, what the contract plainly contemplates. Indeed, the argument appears to be that if several clause 22 certificates are issued, the subsequent certificates act retrospectively so as to make the employer's previous deduction of liquidated damages (under the earlier clause 22 certificate) a breach of contract retrospectively, even though, at the time the deduction was made, the deduction was in accordance with the terms of the contract. In our view, this decision is unlikely to be followed in English courts.

In any event, we suggest that the position is quite different under JCT 80, clause 24.2.2, which provides that if the architect

'fixes a later completion date the employer shall pay or repay to the contractor any amounts recovered allowed or paid under clause 24.2.1 for the period up to such later completion date'.

There is nothing about interest or financing charges on such sums, and according to normal rules of contract interpretation a gloss cannot be added to these very plain words. The wording makes it plain, in our view, that the employer is not making good an earlier breach of contract. Clause 24.2.1 confers on him the right to deduct liquidated damages once the architect has issued a certificate under clause 24.1 and the employer has given written notice of intended deduction to the contractor. Once these two conditions are satisfied the employer has a contractual right to deduct liquidated damages – and clause 24.2.2 deals with what is to happen if the completion date is later altered in the contractor's favour; by refunding sums deducted under clause 24.1 the employer is not thereby making good a breach of contract.

9. Costs of Claim

It is generally accepted that the contractor is not entitled to reimbursement for any costs he has incurred in preparing the claim, since he is not required to prepare a claim as such, but merely to make a written application to the architect, backed up by supporting information, as explained in subsequent chapters. Most certainly fees paid to claims specialists or to outside quantity surveyors or other professional advisers are not in principle allowable as a head of claim at law. Where a claim proceeds to arbitration or litigation, of course, the contractor is entitled to claim his costs and the arbitrator's award or judgment of the court can condemn the employer in costs. In *James Longley & Co. Ltd* v. *South West Regional Health Authority* (1984), on a summons to review taxation of costs of an arbitration which was settled during the hearing, the fees of a claims consultant in respect of work done in preparing the contractor's case for arbitration (the preparation of three schedules annexed to the Points of Claim) were allowed as those of a potential expert witness in the arbitration. The practice of the High Court is that 'costs follow the event', i.e., in the ordinary way, the successful party will receive his costs, and an arbitrator must follow the same principle: see the very useful discussion in Mustill and Boyd, *The Law and Practice of Commercial Arbitration in England*, (1982), pages 347–355.

However, it has been held that the expenditure of managerial time spent in remedying an actionable wrong done to a trading company can properly form the subject-matter of a claim for 'special damage' in an action at common law: *Tate & Lyle Food and Distribution Co. Ltd* v. *Greater London Council* (1982), referred to in our discussion of head-office overheads on page 131. It seems to us that in light of this decision there can in principle be a claim for the cost of managerial time spent on preparing a claim, assuming that this is not covered by any claim for head-office overheads, in appropriate circumstances, and subject to proof that the time had been spent in a manner in which it would not have been spent otherwise. Under the same principle, the cost of employing an outside expert might be recoverable as damages for breach of contract.

10. General

The foregoing are not intended to be exhaustive heads of claim, but simply those that most generally apply. The basic principle to be borne in mind is that, subject to the restrictions of directness and foreseeability, the contractor should be put into the financial position which he would have been in had the delay or disruption not occurred. If this general principle is borne in mind, there should be no difficulty in judging or putting forward other heads of claim where the particular circumstances permit.

Chapter 5

Money claims under JCT 80 and the Intermediate Form (IFC 84)

INTRODUCTION

There are two provisions in JCT 80 that may give rise to money claims by the contractor. They are clause 26, which deals with loss and expense caused by matters materially affecting regular progress of the works, and clause 34.3, which deals with loss and expense arising from the finding of 'fossils, antiquities and other objects of interest or value' found on the site or when excavating the same (in IFC 84 the relevant provisions are the clauses 4.11 and 4.12). The bulk of this chapter is concerned with clause 26 claims, which are the most common and important in practice.

Both of these clauses impose obligations on the contractor and on the architect and/or quantity surveyor. Each of them confers on the contractor a legally enforceable right to financial reimbursement for 'direct loss and/or expense' suffered or incurred as a result of specified matters provided that he observes the procedures laid down by the provisions. Once the claims machinery has been put in motion by the contractor, the architect and/or quantity surveyor must carry out the duties imposed upon them.

However, the provisions for the giving of notice or the making of applications are not merely procedural. The true position has been well stated by the learned editors of *Building Law Reports* in the following terms:

'Contractors sometimes forget that provisions in the contract requiring them to give notice or to make an application if they wish to recover additional sums are not inserted solely as administrative procedure to be operated (like the handle on a fruit machine) when the right opportunity arrives. They are included in the contract not only to provide the engineer or architect with the opportunity of investigating

159

the claim reasonably close to the time when material events occurred (so that the facts can be established with reasonable certainty), but also to provide the client with the chance to reconsider his budget (so that if necessary additional finance may be made available or savings may be made where it is still possible to do so).' [*Building Law Reports*, Volume 5, page 123 in commenting on *J. Crosby & Sons Ltd* v. *Portland Urban District Council* (1967).]

JCT 80 CLAUSE 26

Clause 26 is long and complex but the contractor's entitlement to recovery under the clause depends on the correct operation of its machinery. It is therefore vitally important that all those concerned – contractors, architects and quantity surveyors – should fully understand its intention and the way in which it works.

The greater part of clause 26 (26.1 to 26.5) deals with the contractor's and nominated sub-contractor's rights to financial reimbursement for events which are breaches of contract by, or which are within the control of, the employer himself, others for whom he is responsible, or the architect acting on the employer's behalf.

It is extremely important to note that a number of the events to which the clause refers are *not* breaches of contract by the employer or those for whom he is responsible. For instance, an instruction to open up work for inspection or requiring a variation is one which the architect is specifically empowered to issue under the contract, and its issue therefore clearly cannot be a breach of contract which would otherwise entitle the contractor to recover damages. It follows that the clause contains the *sole* right of the contractor to compensation for such events, and if the contractor loses his right to compensation under the clause, for instance by failing to make an application at the proper time, the preservation of his common law rights under clause 26.6 will avail him nothing. This consideration applies to the events described in clauses 26.2.2, 26.2.5 and 26.2.7 and to deferment of possession of the site where clause 23.1.2 applies.

The clause is divided into six sub-clauses:

26.1 sets out the machinery. It sets out the rights and obligations of the contractor if he wishes to obtain payment and the rights and obligations of the architect and/or quantity surveyor in response thereto.

26.2 sets out the grounds that may entitle a contractor to payment.

26.3 sets out the architect's obligation, in certain circumstances, to notify the contractor of the grounds upon which he has granted extensions of time. This is a sub-clause of which the authors strongly disapprove, and the matter is discussed later (see page 182).

26.4 provides the machinery whereby the similar provisions in the Standard Nominated Sub-Contract Forms NSC/4 and NSC/4a are operated under the main contract.

26.5 in conjunction with clause 30, provides for certification and payment of amounts found due to the contractor.

26.6 preserves the contractor's common law and other rights if for any reason he cannot or does not wish to claim under clauses 26.1 to 26.5.

The full text of clause 26 (as amended by Amendment 4 issued in July 1987) is as follows:

26   Loss and expense caused by matters materially affecting regular progress of the Works

26.1 If the Contractor makes written application to the Architect stating that he has incurred or is likely to incur direct loss and/or expense in the execution of this Contract for which he would not be reimbursed by a payment under any other provision in this Contract due to deferment of giving possession of the site under clause 23.1.2 where clause 23.1.2 is stated in the Appendix to be applicable or because the regular progress of the Works or of any part thereof has been or is likely to be materially affected by any one or more of the matters referred to in clause 26.2; and if and as soon as the Architect is of the opinion that the direct loss and/or expense has been incurred or is likely to be incurred due to any such deferment of giving possession or that the regular progress of the Works or of any part thereof has been or is likely to be so materially affected as set out in the application of the Contractor then the Architect from time to time thereafter shall ascertain, or shall instruct the Quantity Surveyor to ascertain, the amount of such loss and/or expense which has been or is being incurred by the Contractor; provided always that;

26.1 .1 the Contractor's application shall be made as soon as it has become, or should reasonably have become, apparent to him that the regular progress of the Works or of any part thereof has been or was likely to be affected as aforesaid, and

26.1 .2 the Contractor shall in support of his application submit to the Architect upon request such information should reasonably enable the Architect to form an opinion as aforesaid, and

26.1 .3 the Contractor shall submit to the Architect or to the Quantity Surveyor upon request such details of such loss and/or expense as are reasonably necessary for such ascertainment as aforesaid.

26.2 The following are the matters referred to in clause 26.1:

26.2 .1 the Contractor not having received in due time necessary instructions, drawings, details or levels from the Architect for which he specifically applied in writing provided that such application was made on a date which having regard to the Completion Date was neither unreasonably distant from nor unreasonably close to the date on which it was necessary for him to receive the same;

26.2 .2 the opening up for inspection of any work covered up or the testing of any of the work, materials or goods in accordance with clause 8.3 (including making good in consequence of such opening up or testing), unless the inspection or test showed that the work, materials or goods were not in accordance with this Contract;

26.2 .3 any discrepancy in or divergence between the Contract Drawings and/or the Contract Bills and/or the Numbered Documents;

26.2 .4 .1 the execution of work not forming part of this Contract by the Employer himself or by persons employed or otherwise engaged by the Employer as referred to in clause 29 or the failure to execute such work;

.4 .2 the supply by the Employer of materials and goods which the Employer has agreed to provide for the Works or the failure so to supply;

26.2 .5 Architect's instructions under clause 23.2 issued in regard to the postponement of any work to be executed under the provisions of this Contract;

26.2 .6 failure of the Employer to give in due time ingress to or egress from the site of the Works, or any part thereof through or over any land, buildings, way or passage adjoining or connected with the site and in the possession and control of the Employer, in accordance with the Contract Bills and/or the Contract Drawings, after receipt by the Architect of such notice, if any, as the Contractor is required to give, or failure of the Employer to give such ingress or egress as otherwise agreed between the Architect and the Contractor;

26.2 .7 Architect's instructions issued under clause 13.2 requiring a Variation or under clause 13.3. in regard to the expenditure of provisional sums (other than work to which clause 13.4.2 refers).

26.3 If and to the extent that it is necessary for ascertainment under clause 26.1 of loss and/or expense the Architect shall state in writing to the Contractor what extension of time, if any, has been made under clause 25 in respect of the Relevant Event or Events referred to in clause 25.4.5.1 (so far as that clause refers to clauses 2.3, 13.2, 13.3 and 23.2) and in clauses 25.4.5.2, 25.4.6, 25.4.8 and 25.4.12.

26.4 .1 The Contractor upon receipt of a written application properly made by a Nominated Sub-Contractor under clause 13.1 of Sub-Contract NSC/4 or NSC/4a as applicable shall pass to the Architect a copy of that written application. If and as soon as the Architect is of the opinion that the loss and/or expense to which the said clause 13.1 refers has been incurred or is likely to be incurred due to any deferment of the giving of possession where clause 23.1.2 is stated in the Appendix to apply or that the regular progress of the Sub-Contract Works or of any part thereof has been or is likely to be materially affected as referred to in clause 13.1 of Sub-Contract NSC/4 or NSC/4a and as set out in the application of the Nominated Sub-Contractor then the Architect shall himself ascertain, or shall instruct the Quantity Surveyor to ascertain the amount of such loss and/or expense.

26.4 .2 If and to the extent that it is necessary for the ascertainment of such loss and/or expense the Architect shall state in writing to the Contractor with a copy to the Nominated Sub-Contractor concerned what was the length of the revision of the period or periods for completion of the Sub-Contract Works or of any part thereof to which he gave consent in respect of the Relevant Event or Events set out in clause 11.2.5.5.1 (so far as that clause refers to clauses 2.3, 13.2, 13.3 and 23.2 of the Main Contract Conditions), 11.2.5.5.2, 11.2.5.6, 11.2.5.8 and 11.2.5.12 of Sub-Contract NSC/4 or NSC/4a as applicable.

26.5 Any amount from time to time ascertained under clause 26 shall be added to the Contract Sum.

26.6 The provisions of clause 26 are without prejudice to any other rights and remedies which the Contractor may possess.'

Clause 26.1 – The Claims Machinery: Paraphrase

When the contractor considers that '*regular progress of the Works or of any part thereof has been or is likely to be materially affected by any one or more of the matters referred to in Clause 26.2*' and if he also considers that this or any deferment of giving possession of the site is likely to result or has resulted in his incurring '*direct loss and/or expense*' on the specific contract '*for which he would not be reimbursed by payment under any other provision*' in the contract he must, '*as soon as it has become, or should reasonably have become, apparent to him*' make a written application to the architect.

The architect is then required to form an opinion as to whether or not the contractor is correct and may, to assist him in forming his opinion, request the contractor to submit such information as will enable him to do so. If the architect agrees with the contractor, he is required either himself to ascertain, or to instruct the quantity surveyor to ascertain, the amount of the direct loss and/or expense which the contractor is incurring or has incurred. The architect or the quantity surveyor may, in order to enable them to carry out the ascertainment, require such details of loss and/or expense as are reasonably necessary for that purpose.

There follows a commentary on the text of the clause.

1. Written application essential
The making of a written application by the contractor at the proper time is clearly a condition precedent. In other words, failure by the contractor to apply in writing in the time specified in the contract is fatal to his claim for payment under the contractual machinery.

2. Nature of application
The contractor's application should be in writing, but no particular form is specified. Clearly it should state that the contractor has incurred or is likely to incur loss and/or expense arising directly from the deferment of giving possession of the site or the material effect upon the regular progress of the works or any part of the works of one or more of the seven matters listed in clause 26.2. Although it is not specifically stated in the sub-clause, we are of the opinion that the application should clearly specify whether it is deferment of possession or which of the matters listed in clause 26.2 is relied upon. It is also advisable, even at this stage, for the contractor to go into a certain amount of detail about the circumstances that have given rise to his application. For example, suppose the architect has failed to supply a necessary piece of information in due time. The contractor's written application should refer to clause 26.2.1, and should state the date on which he specifically applied in writing for the information in question, the date on which it should have been supplied to him, and the effect which the lack of information has had, is having and will have upon contract progress, going into as much relevant detail as possible.

From the wording of clause 26.1 it is plain that the contractor need make only one written application in respect of loss and/or expense arising out of the occurrence of any one event. This will entitle him to recover past, present and future loss and/or expense arising from that event, and there is no need to make a series of applications as was the case under the equivalent provisions of JCT 63: see chapter 6. As Lord Justice Stephenson pointed out in *F. G. Minter Ltd* v. *Welsh Health Technical Services Organisation* (1980), it was to meet the difficulties created by the need for successive applications under JCT 63 that clause 26.1 has been re-drafted,

'to require applications to be made "as soon as it has become, or should reasonably have become apparent to him [the contractor] that the regular progress of the works or any part thereof has been or *is likely to be affected*" by specified events ... and to state "that he has incurred or *is likely to incur* direct loss and/or expense" ...' (Italics in judgment.)

It is equally plain that a so-called 'general' or 'protective' notice is not sufficient under clause 26.1. Specific written applications must be made in respect of each event. Further, the issue of an 'automatic' application every time one of the events listed occurs does not satisfy the requirements of clause 26.1 and the practice of so doing cannot be too strongly condemned. If the architect receives such an 'automatic' application every time he issues an instruction, for instance, he will ultimately come to disregard every such application since he cannot possibly be expected to distinguish between those that are genuine and those that are not.

The contractor's written application under clause 26.1 is related to the degree to which one or more of the matters listed in clause 26.2 has affected or is likely to affect regular progress, and the contractor must have genuine and sustainable grounds for believing this to be the case.

3. *Timing of application*

Clause 26.1.1 requires that the contractor's written application should 'be made as soon as it has become, or should reasonably have become, apparent to him that regular progress of the Works or any part thereof has been or was likely to be' materially affected. Although not specifically referred to, in the case of deferred possession, we suggest that an application should be made as soon as notification is received from the employer that possession of the site is to be deferred. The application must, therefore, be made at the earliest possible time and certainly before regular progress of the works is actually affected, unless there are good reasons why the contractor could not foresee that this would be the case. Although clause 26.1 allows for an application to be made at the time of or after the event, the intention is clearly that the architect should be kept informed at the earliest possible time of all matters likely to affect the progress of the work and likely to result in a money claim.

Failure to notify the architect in advance, where it is practicable to do so, will deprive him of the opportunity to take any remedial action open to him and the contractor may therefore be under some difficulty in establishing why it was not possible for him to give earlier notice. An early, rather than a late, application is therefore essential to enable the contractor to demonstrate that he has taken all reasonable steps to mitigate the effect upon progress and the financial consequences. If the architect fails to take advantage of this, then clearly it is his responsibility and not the contractor's when answering to the employer for the extra cost involved.

The objective of the whole machinery of application is to bring the architect's attention to the possibility that disruption is likely to occur and be costly to the employer unless he takes action to avoid it. There should be no question of the contractor's written application being made after the event if it is reasonable for him to anticipate trouble in the future. Even if it is not reasonable for the contractor to anticipate disruption, the application must be made as soon as the trouble occurs, and not just within a 'reasonable time' of it occurring.

This said, there are occasions when the question of whether a written application under clause 26.1 should be made is itself difficult to resolve. Clearly, the making of the application should be the result of a deliberate decision made by the contractor and not an automatic response to, for instance, the issue of every architect's instruction. There are, therefore, cases in which it will be difficult for the contractor to determine whether progress is likely to be affected. Circumstances may already have affected progress so that the occurrence of the new event may at the time not seem likely to have any further effect.

In this connection, some views expressed by Lord Justice Willmer in *Tersons Ltd* v. *Stevenage Development Corporation* (1963) are of some interest, although the court was there concerned with the ICE Conditions (2nd Edition) and the question of whether certain notices were given 'as soon as practicable'. Lord Justice Willmer said:

'Notice of intention to claim, however, could not well be given until the intention had been formed ... [and] it seems to me that the contractors must at least be allowed a reasonable time in which to make up their minds. Here the contractors are a limited company, and that involves that, in a matter of such importance as that raised by the present case, the relevant intention must be that of the board of management [i.e. directors].'

His lordship emphasised later in his judgment that,

'in determining whether a notice has been given as soon as practicable, all the relevant circumstances must be taken into consideration .... One of the circumstances to be considered in the present case is the fact that it was not easy to determine whether the engineer's orders ... did or did not involve additional work ...'.

Similar circumstances can be envisaged in relation to architect's instructions.

However, such circumstances are likely to be wholly exceptional, and we must re-emphasise the need for contractors to make their applications under clause 26.1 at the earliest practicable time.

4. Architect's assumed state of knowledge

Clause 26 now clearly assumes, correctly in our view, that the architect cannot be expected to have more than a general knowledge of what is happening on site. As Lord Upjohn said in *East Ham Corporation* v. *Bernard Sunley & Sons Ltd* (1965), when speaking of the architect's duty to supervise work, 'the architect is not permanently on the site but appears at intervals, it may be of a week or a fortnight ...'. It is the contractor who is responsible for progressing the work in accordance with the requirements of the contract and the architect's instructions. The architect is entitled to assume, unless notified to the contrary, that work is progressing smoothly and efficiently and that there are no current or anticipated problems. For instance, if he issues an instruction – even one requiring extra work – and the contractor accepts it without comment, the architect is fully entitled to assume that the effects of that instruction can be absorbed by the contractor into his working programme without any consequential delay or disruption.

However, it is important to note a passage in the judgment of Mr Justice Vinelott in *London Borough of Merton* v. *Stanley Hugh Leach* (1985), quoting the interim award of the arbitrator as follows:

> 'Although I accept that the architect's contact with the site is not on a day to day basis there are many occasions when an event occurs which is sufficiently within the knowledge of the architect for him to form an opinion that the contractor has been involved in loss or expense.'

This is particularly so where there has been some default by the architect himself. It would be unsafe for an architect to rely too heavily on the strict letter of the contractor's obligation as to timing of the notice when he himself has been late in the issue of information which has been requested at the proper time and he must well know that this is bound to have a material effect on progress leading to the contractor incurring loss and expense.

5. 'Direct loss and/or expense'

The loss and/or expense which is the subject of the contractor's claim must be *direct* and not consequential. The listed event or events relied upon must be the cause of the loss and/or expense and the phrase may be equated with the common law right to damages. This matter is fully discussed in chapter 4.

6. *Payment under other contract provisions*

The reference to 'payment under any other provision of this Contract' is to prevent double payment, for instance where increased costs of labour and materials during a period of delay to completion are already being recovered under the fluctuations provisions of the contract. In relation to claims arising from clause 26.2.7 (below), obviously some care must be taken to distinguish between those costs which are covered by the quantity surveyor's valuation under clause 13 and those for which reimbursement may be obtained under this clause: see the proviso to clause 13.5 and the full discussion of variations in chapter 3.

7. *Material effect on regular progress*

The basis of the contractor's entitlement to claim under clause 26 is that 'the *regular progress of the Works* or of any part thereof *has been or is likely to be materially affected* by any one or more of' the seven matters listed in clause 26.2. In other words, it is the effect of the stated event upon the regular progress of the works, i.e. any delay to or disruption of the contract progress.

The various commentators express differing views about the meaning to be attributed to these important words and some suggest that the effect is to confine the contractor's entitlement to the financial results of *delay* to progress only. For example, I.N. Duncan Wallace, *Building and Civil Engineering Standards Forms*, page 113 (commenting on clause 24 of JCT 63) says:

'Bearing in mind that the most important of the matters listed in this clause (late instructions) is a breach of contract, it seems remarkable that a claim under the clause is limited to heads of damage caused by *delay to progress* and not to other possible consequences of the late instructions. The restriction or qualification seems unnecessary and unfair to the contractor, though no doubt the phrase "regular progress having been materially affected" may be interpreted liberally in the contractor's interest, *but it is clear that it does not cover loss of productivity.*' [Our italics.]

More recently, similar views have been expressed by Dr John Parris in *The Standard Form of Building Contract: JCT 80*, Section 10.04 What does 'direct loss and/or expense' mean?:

'The contractor is not entitled to compensation under JCT 80 clause 26 because any of the matters there set out cause him extra work, or greater expense in doing his work or more difficulty than he contemplated. *He will not be entitled to compensation for loss of productivity.* [Our italics.]

It is, perhaps, significant that in the second edition of Dr Parris' book the words: 'It is only the delay in progress for which he can be compensated' which ended the passage quoted in the first edition have been removed.

With respect, we cannot accept the views quoted above. Despite the change in the second edition of Dr Parris's book, both learned commentators appear to equate *effect upon progress* with 'delay' (since even following the deletion of the reference to 'delay' it is difficult to see the logical basis of Dr Parris's contention that the contractor 'will not be entitled to compensation for loss of productivity' can be other than that he is only entitled to compensation for delay) and this is manifestly not the case. In our view there can be a disturbance to regular progress, resulting in loss of productivity in working, without there being any delay as such either in the progress or in the completion of the work. The clause cannot be interpreted so as to confine the contractor's right to reimbursement to circumstances that delay progress. It covers circumstances that may give rise to, for instance, reduced efficiency of working without progress as a whole being delayed. This is not the same as saying that merely because the work has proved to cost more or to take longer to complete than was anticipated entitles the contractor to additional payment. It must be possible for him to demonstrate that the cause is directly attributable to one or more of the matters set out in clause 26.2 and the effect upon regular progress of the works.

No one with practical experience of building should have the slightest difficulty in interpreting the phrase to mean any disruption of normal working, whether it leads to delay or can be absorbed by 're-jigging' the programme, provided that the cost to the contractor of carrying out the work is increased thereby. This is not to say that the contractor is entitled to reimbursement under this clause for any acceleration measures that he may take, unless he can demonstrate that by taking such measures he has actually incurred less additional cost than would have been the case by continuing at the same pace and delaying completion of the contract works.

In our view, to interpret clause 26.1 on the basis that there must be 'delay' is to link the operation of the clause to the question of extensions of time under clause 25. Admittedly, both commentators cited refer or referred to 'delay to progress' and not to delay to completion, but the implication still seems to us to be that there is some connection between the two clauses, although elsewhere (page 260) Dr Parris correctly emphasises the lack of any such connection. It cannot be too strongly emphasised that questions of reimbursement under clause 26 have nothing to do with the granting of extensions of time under clause 25. The two clauses are entirely separate. Any extension of time granted may be a factor in the ascertainment of the amount recoverable by the contractor under clause 26 but has no other bearing on the matter. (See further our commentary on clause 26.3 on page 182.)

The words 'regular progress' often cause difficulty. In our view they are related to the contractor's obligation under clause 23.1 'regularly and diligently [to] proceed with' the works, which phrase was the subject of comment by Mr Justice Megarry, as he then was, in *London Borough of Hounslow* v. *Twickenham Garden Developments Ltd* (1970), where he said:

> 'These are elusive words on which the dictionaries help little. The words convey a sense of activity, of orderly progress, of industry and perseverance; but such language provides little help on the question of how much activity, progress and so on is to be expected. They are words used in a standard form of building contract and in those circumstances it may be that there is evidence of usage among architects, builders and building owners or otherwise, that would be helpful in construing the words. At present, all I can say is that I remain somewhat uncertain as to the concept enshrined in those words'.

Whether or not there is 'regular progress' and whether or not it has been, or is likely to be, 'materially affected' must be, it is submitted, a matter of objective judgment in each case. This judgment may be assisted by any programme of works prepared by the contractor and in our view the requirement for a master programme in clause 5.3.1.2 should be of great assistance in this respect. It is difficult to understand why the requirement for a master programme should be optional: in our view no sensible employer or professional adviser would contemplate deleting this clause.

However, a programme of works, whether master programme or otherwise, is not conclusive as to what 'regular progress' is, under the particular contract. We adopt the view expressed by D. Keating, *Building Contracts*, 4th Edition, page 352: 'An agreed programme of work is, it is submitted, some, but not conclusive, evidence of what regular progress should be.'

It is important to note that the contractor's *actual progress* at the time of the event or matter relied upon is critical. If the contractor's progress is already not regular, due to factors within his control or which do not give him entitlement to claim, it will be very difficult if not impossible for him to establish that regular progress has been or is likely to be materially affected by the particular event relied on.

The words 'or any part thereof' again clearly emphasise the distinction between clauses 26 and 25. Extensions of time under the latter clause must relate to delay in completion of the contract as a whole or, where the sectional completion supplement is used, to any defined section thereof. Reimbursement for disruption under clause 26 may relate to circumstances affecting any part of the work, even down to individual operations.

Regular progress must have been, or be likely to be *materially* affected. *Chambers Twentieth Century Dictionary* defines 'materially' as, among other things, 'in a considerable or important degree', and we suggest that this definition is applicable here. Trivial disruptions such as are bound to occur on even the best-run contract are clearly excluded. The circumstances must be such as to affect regular progress of the works 'in a considerable or important degree'. 'Materially' does not, however, in our view equate with 'substantially'. The precise point at which disruption becomes considerable or important is impossible to define in general terms. It must depend upon the circumstances of the particular case.

8. Architect's opinion

The initiative for taking action under clause 26 comes from the contractor who makes a written application. The initiative then passes to the architect: 'and if and as soon as the Architect is of the opinion that the direct loss and/or expense has been incurred or is likely to be incurred due to any ... deferment of giving possession or that the regular progress of the Works or any part thereof has been or is likely to be materially affected' as set out in the contractor's application, he must institute the next stage, which is the ascertainment of the resulting direct loss and/or expense.

It should be noted that it is the architect's opinion that is important. Contrary to the apparent belief of many contractors, the mere making of an application does not entitle the contractor to money if, in the architect's opinion, no money is due – though, of course, ultimately it may be the opinion of an arbitrator that will finally determine the matter. The process of ascertainment does not begin unless and until the architect has formed the opinion that deferment of possession has given rise to direct loss and/or expense or that regular progress has been or is likely to be materially affected *as set out in the application of the contractor*.

In *F.G. Minter Ltd* v. *Welsh Health Technical Services Organisation*

(1980), both the High Court and the Court of Appeal analysed the contractual machinery of the claims provisions of JCT 63 as a temporal sequence in chronological order. The following analysis is based on those judicial analyses.

In a clause 26 situation first comes (1) the deferment of possession or an event under clause 26.2; (2) a written application by the contractor under clause 26.1; (3) the forming of an opinion by the architect as to whether the deferment of possession has given or is likely to give rise to direct loss and/or expense or whether there has been or is likely to be a material effect on regular progress (to assist him in which he may require further information from the contractor – see later); (4) the incurring of direct loss and/or expense; (5) the ascertainment; (6) certification; (7) payment. Where the contractor could not reasonably have anticipated that regular progress would be affected, and therefore his application is made at the time of the effect, stages (3) and (4) may overlap or be contemporaneous.

If the contractor's application is not made at the proper time (see section 3, above) then the architect may properly reject it (subject to our *caveat* in section 4 above), whatever its merits may be, and he is under no obligation to form an opinion about it. Further, the architect can deal only with matters that are set out in the contractor's written application; he has no authority to deal with any matters affecting regular progress that are not the subject of a written application from the contractor.

9. Further information

Clause 26.1.2 entitles the architect to request the contractor to supply such further information as is reasonably necessary to enable him to form an opinion as to the effect on regular progress or whether the deferment of possession has given or is likely to give rise to direct loss and/or expense. We re-emphasise that it is in the contractor's own interest to provide as much relevant information as possible at the time of his written application and not to wait until the architect asks for it under this sub-clause. The information which the architect is entitled to request is that which should *reasonably* enable him to form an opinion; an architect is not entitled to delay matters by asking for more information than is reasonably necessary. For example, where the contractor's application relates to a 'late instruction', the architect could reasonably ask the contractor to show how progress already compared with programme, and the result might well be to show that progress was already behind schedule and that therefore the 'lateness' of the instruction in fact would have no effect on regular progress. (*Note*: This would not necessarily mean that the contractor would not be entitled, independently, to an extension of time under clause 25 – see chapter 2 – although it could nevertheless mean that no money could be recovered since there would be no consequential effect on progress or delay in completion giving rise to direct loss and/or expense beyond that already being incurred by the contractor due to his own delay.)

10. The ascertainment

The word 'ascertainment' is defined in the *Concise Oxford Dictionary* as meaning 'find out (for certain), get to know'. It is not therefore simply a matter for the judgment of the architect or quantity surveyor; the duty upon them is to *find out* the amount of the direct loss and/or expense for certain, not to estimate it. It also follows that the loss and/or expense that has to be found out must be that which is being or has been actually incurred. References to estimated figures included in the contract bills have no relevance unless, due to the contractor's failure to keep proper records, there are no better data, and therefore an assessment rather than an ascertainment is the best that can be done. The architect cannot refuse to certify payment to the contractor of a reasonable assessment of direct loss and/or expense that he has incurred because no better information is available, though clearly in such circumstances the contractor may have to accept an assessment figure that is less than his actual loss. It is therefore up to contractors to keep adequate records.

The architect may instruct the quantity surveyor to ascertain the direct loss and/or expense, and while ultimate responsibility for certification of the amount still lies with the architect, it will clearly be difficult for him in these circumstances to certify anything other than the amount ascertained by the quantity surveyor, and effectively the architect is bound by the quantity surveyor's ascertainment where he has so instructed him. The views expressed by Lord Radcliffe in *R.B. Burden Ltd* v. *Swansea Corporation* (1957) to the effect that there is nothing 'in the contract which suggests that the architect is bound to accept the quantity surveyor's opinion or valuation when he exercises his own function of certifying sums for payment' are, it is suggested, not applicable to this situation, where it is an ascertainment and not a valuation that is in question. That case was, in any event, about the 1939 Edition of what is now the JCT Form and the wording was entirely different.

It is always possible for the architect to ask the quantity surveyor for assistance in ascertaining the amount to be paid without formally instructing him to ascertain. This has the advantage of keeping the final decision in the architect's own hands and avoids the difficult situation that can arise if the architect, having formally delegated the task to the quantity surveyor, disagrees with the result produced.

It is essential, however, that the contractor should be informed of the position so that he knows that the amount negotiated with the quantity surveyor is subject to the final approval of the architect. It is also essential that the architect's request for assistance and the quantity surveyor's agreement to assist are in writing so as to establish the quantity surveyor's responsibility to the architect should his advice be given negligently.

In any case, whether the architect formally instructs the quantity surveyor or simply asks for his assistance in ascertaining the amount due to the contractor, the employer must be informed of this arrangement, since fees will be involved.

There is in our view a positive advantage to the architect in delegating responsibility for the ascertainment to the quantity surveyor, particularly where the reason for the claim is some default of the architect, such as his failure to supply information in due time. The involvement of the independent quantity surveyor will to some extent counter possible accusations that the architect is unduly influenced by his own involvement in responsibility for the situation.

11. Details of loss and/or expense

As the duty of the architect or the quantity surveyor is to ascertain the amount of the direct loss and/or expense as a matter of fact (so far as this may be attainable) it is necessary for them to look to the contractor as the person in possession of the facts to provide them. Clause 26.1.3 provides that the contractor must submit on request such details of the loss and/or expense as are reasonably necessary for the ascertainment. This does not necessarily mean the submission of a moneyed-out claim, although it may well be in the contractor's interest to provide it. It is suggested that such details might include comparative programme/progress charts pinpointing the effect upon progress, together with the relevant extracts from wage sheets, invoices for plant hire, etc. The documentation side of claims is considered in chapter 11. It must be said, however, in regard to the provision of information by the contractor that, to quote Emden's *Building Contracts and Practice*, 8th Edition, Volume 2, page N/48, 'the mere fact that something is stated as so in a document, does not mean that that statement is true'.

Unless the architect or quantity surveyor is provided by the contractor with the necessary details of the direct loss and/or expense the ascertainment thereof cannot be carried out, and an assessment will have to be made, which may not be satisfactory to the contractor.

Clause 26.2 – 'Matters' giving rise to entitlement
In *Henry Boot Construction Ltd* v. *Central Lancashire New Town Development Corporation* (1980) Judge Edgar Fay QC said this of JCT 63 provisions equivalent to those now found in JCT 80, clauses 25 and 26:

> 'The broad scheme of these provisions is plain. There are cases where the loss should be shared, and there are cases where it should be wholly borne by the employer. There are also those cases which do not fall within either of these conditions and which are the fault of the contractor, where the loss of both parties is wholly borne by the contractor. But in the cases where the fault is not that of the contractor the scheme clearly is that in certain cases the loss is to be shared; the loss lies where it falls. But in other cases the employer has to compensate the contractor in respect of the delay, and that category, where the employer has to compensate the contractor, should, one would think, clearly be composed of cases where there is fault upon the employer or fault for which the employer can be said to bear some responsibility.'

Clause 26.2 deals with those cases where the employer must compensate the contractor and it is only if the contractor can establish that he has incurred direct loss and/or expense not otherwise reimbursable as a direct result of one or more of the seven matters listed in the clause (or, of course, as a direct result of deferment of possession of the site) that he is entitled to reimbursement. Each of these seven matters will now be discussed.

1. Late instructions, drawings, details or levels
This ground covers failure by the architect to provide necessary information to the contractor at the proper time to enable the contractor to use it for the purpose of the works. It ties in with the scheme of the contract, which is essentially that the contractor builds only what he is told to build. Consequently, until the contractor has received the appropriate information, he has no obligation and indeed cannot proceed with the contract works. This point is emphasised by the wording of clause 5.4, which says:

> 'As and when from time to time may be necessary the Architect without charge to the Contractor shall provide him with two copies of such further drawings or details as are reasonably necessary either to explain and amplify the contract drawings or to enable the Contractor to carry out and complete the Works in accordance with the Conditions.'

In clause 26.2 the reference to 'instructions' is to any written instructions which the architect may validly issue under the contract: see clause 4.1.1. The 'drawings and details' include those that the architect is bound to furnish under clause 5.4, and the 'levels' are those that the architect is obliged to determine under clause 7.

Although the architect is bound to provide the contractor with the necessary instructions, drawings, details and levels, the contractor has no claim for financial reimbursement for the consequences of the architect's failure to provide them, unless he has himself specifically asked for them in writing at the right time. This point is emphasised by Mr I.N. Duncan Wallace (*Building and Civil Engineering Standard Forms*, page 115) when he says that 'a specific application in writing which is too early or too late will invalidate a claim under the clause'.

Unfortunately, the wording of the clause as to the timing of the contractor's application for information is rather obscure and imprecise. The contractor must have 'specifically applied in writing ... on a date which having regard to the Completion Date was neither unreasonably distant from nor unreasonably close to the date on which it was necessary for him to receive [it]'.

The 'date on which it was necessary for [the contractor] to receive' the information must have regard to the contract completion date, and the application itself must be made on a date which is 'neither unreasonably distant from nor unreasonably close to' the date for the receipt of the information.

Some help and guidance may be found in the civil engineering case of *Neodox Ltd* v. *Borough of Swinton & Pendlebury* (1958), which is also authority for the view that it is an implied term of the contract that the architect will issue all necessary instructions, etc. in reasonable time for the contractor to do the work. Mr Justice Diplock considered fully the question of terms to be implied as to the time within which further drawings, details or instructions must be given. In giving these instructions the architect is acting as agent for the employer, and if the architect fails to give such instructions within a reasonable time, the employer is liable in damages for breach of contract.

Mr Justice Diplock said:

'What is a reasonable time does not depend solely upon the convenience and financial interests of the claimants. No doubt it is to their interest to have every detail cut and dried on the day the contract is signed, but the contract does not contemplate that. It contemplates further details and instructions being provided, and the engineer is to have a time to provide them which is reasonable having regard to the point of view of him and his staff and the point of view of the Corporation, as well as the point of view of the Contractors .... What is a reasonable time is a question of fact having regard to all the circumstances of the case ....'

Those words apply equally to the JCT contracts and the position of the architect under them and are really business common sense. The application of these common-sense principles seems to cause considerable difficulties in practice.

First, to consider the date upon which it is necessary for the contractor to receive the information: this must have regard to the date for completion fixed under the contract. The contractor has a date to work to; initially it is the date stated in the Appendix and, later, if the architect grants an extension of contract time, it is the new date so fixed. The contractor has an obligation to work towards that date and he is also entitled not to be hindered in his efforts to achieve that date by any act or default on the part of the architect or the employer.

If the contractor asks for a specific piece of information on a date upon which, in his opinion, it is necessary for him to receive it in order to achieve completion by the due date, the architect cannot refuse to provide the information at that time on the grounds, for instance, that the contractor is so far behind programme due to his own inefficiency that he could not use the information if he had it. To do so may be to deprive the contractor of the opportunity to make up lost ground. The contractor must ensure, however, that his written application for the information is made at a time that is not unreasonable, having regard to the contract completion date.

The contractor's request must also be specific. 'Specific' means 'definite or distinctly formulated' according to the dictionary, and thus merely presenting the architect with a blanket request or 'information supply programme' at the outset of the contract is not sufficient to satisfy the requirements of this clause. He must state precisely what information is required; and he must do this at the correct time as the works proceed.

The reference to 'neither unreasonably distant from nor unreasonably close to' the date on which it is required clearly means that the architect must be given sufficient time to prepare the necessary information, and his work-load must be taken into account. For example, suppose that during the construction of a building's foundations, the contractor makes a request in writing for complete door, window and ironmongery schedules the day after tomorrow. The date for the receipt of the information may be reasonable from the contractor's point of view, having regard to possible delays in manufacture and delivery, but the date of the application would most certainly not be reasonable. The architect would be justified in refusing to provide the information and in taking a reasonable time – say a fortnight – to provide it. If, as a result, the contractor's orders were placed late and delays occurred, it would be entirely the contractor's fault; and in our view he would have no claim under clause 26.2.1.

On the other hand, for the contractor to allow too long an interval between his application and the necessary date for the information to be received, the architect could justifiably set the matter aside, and the request might be overlooked by inadvertence. Again, the contractor might well have difficulty in establishing that the blame should lie at the architect's door in view of the requirements of the clause.

(See also the discussion of the similar words in clause 25.4.6 in Chapter 2, pages 72–75 and the cases there referred to.)

2. Opening up for inspection and testing

Clause 8.3 entitles the architect to require work to be opened up for inspection and to instruct the contractor to arrange for or carry out the testing of materials and executed work in order to ensure that they comply with the contract. It is a curious feature of the wording of clause 8.3 that the cost of such opening up and testing is to be reimbursed to the contractor unless the inspection or tests show that the materials or work are not in accordance with the contract. In other words it is for the architect to show that they are not in accordance with the contract and not for the contractor to show that they are. The same considerations apply to the question of whether the contractor is entitled to an extension of time under clause 25.4.5.2 and to the question of entitlement to reimbursement under this clause. Each of these provisions assumes that the contractor will be so entitled unless the inspection or tests demonstrate that the materials or work are not in accordance with the contract.

3. Any discrepancy in or divergence between the contract drawings and/or the contract bills

The contractor's entitlement to direct loss and/or expense is limited to that resulting from the clearing up of discrepancies or divergences in and between the contract drawings and/or the contract bills under clause 2.3. The simplicity of the wording of clause 26.2.3 contrasts sharply with the elaborate provisions of clause 2.3 itself, which refers to discrepancies in or divergences between any two or more of (1) the contract drawings; (2) the contract bills; (3) any architect's instructions other than variations; and (4) any necessary drawings or documents issued by the architect for the general purposes of the contract. No doubt it is considered that these other discrepancies are adequately covered by other entitlements. In order to found a claim under clause 26.2.3, the contractor must, of course, have advised the architect *immediately*, as required by clause 2.3.

4. Work not forming part of the contract

Clause 26.2.4 covers the situation where the employer himself carries out work not forming part of the contract or arranges for such work to be done by others while the contract works are being executed by the contractor; it also covers the situation where the employer has undertaken to provide materials or goods for the purposes of the works and defaults on that obligation.

The second situation is self-explanatory, but so far as the first is concerned it is important to refer to clause 29. This provides that, where the work in question is adequately described in the contract bills, so that the contractor has been able to make adequate allowance for the effect upon him in the contract sum and in his programme for the works, the contractor must permit such work to be done. In that situation, it will only be if the work concerned causes an unforeseeable delay or disruption to the contractor's own work that any claim will lie under this sub-clause. However, clause 29 also provides that if the work in question is not adequately described in the contract bills but the employer wishes to have such work executed, the employer may arrange for it to be done with the consent of the contractor, which is not to be unreasonably withheld. In that event, a claim will almost inevitably arise under clause 26.2.4.1 since the contractor is unlikely to have been able to make adequate allowance in his programme and price.

A claim under clause 26.2.4.1 may, in certain circumstances, relate to work carried out by statutory undertakers, where that work is carried out by them as a matter of contractual obligation, rather than as one of statutory obligation. This follows from the decision of Judge Edgar Fay QC in *Henry Boot Construction Ltd* v. *Central Lancashire New Town Development Corporation* (1980), which is of relevance to JCT 80 as to the meaning of the words in this sub-clause 'work not forming part of this contract'. The general legal position of statutory undertakers is that they are under a statutory obligation to carry out certain work and, when so doing, their obligation if any 'depends on statute and not upon contract':

Clegg Parkinson & Co. v. *Earby Gas Co.* (1896). When acting in that capacity, any interference on their part with the contractor's work does not give rise to any monetary claim against the employer under this or any other provision in the contract, but may give rise to a claim for extension of time under clause 25.4.11. In the *Henry Boot* case the arbitrator found as a fact that the statutory undertakers 'were engaged under contract by the respondents to construct the said mains', and it would appear that he also found that most, if not all, of the work being carried out by the statutory undertakers was not covered by their statutory obligation, but was being executed by them voluntarily at the employer's request and expense. Judge Edgar Fay said:

> 'These statutory undertakers carried out their work in pursuance of a contract with the employers; that is a fact found by the arbitrator and binding on me .... In carrying out [their] statutory obligations they no doubt have statutory rights of entry and the like. But here they were not doing the work because statute obliged them to; they were doing it because they had contracted with the [employers] to do it.'

5. Postponement of work

The scope of clause 26.2.5 is often misunderstood. It refers to the power of the architect, under clause 23.2, to 'issue instructions in regard to the postponement of *any work* to be executed under the provisions of (the) Contract' (italics supplied). In our view, clause 23.2 does *not* empower the architect to issue an instruction postponing the date upon which *possession of the site* is to be given to the contractor as stated in the Appendix, nor does he have power to do so under any other express or implied term of the contract, and this is emphasised by the newly introduced clause 23.1.2 which gives the *employer*, and not the architect, the right to defer possession of the site for a period not exceeding six weeks or any shorter period stated in the Appendix.

The contractor's right to possession of the site on the date given in the Appendix was, before the introduction of clause 23.1.2, an absolute one. His right to possession is an express term of the contract (see clause 23.1) and in any event there is at common law an implied term in any construction contract that the employer will give possession of the site to the contractor in time to enable him to carry out and complete the work by the contractual date: *Freeman* v. *Hensler* (1900). In *London Borough of Hounslow* v. *Twickenham Garden Developments Ltd* (1970), Mr Justice Megarry said 'The contract necessarily requires the building owner to give the contractor such possession, occupation or use as is necessary to enable him to perform the contract'.

Accordingly, subject to the right to defer possession for a limited time under clause 23.1.2 if that clause is stated in the contract Appendix to apply, any failure by the employer to give possession on the due date is a breach of contract, entitling the contractor to bring a claim for damages at common law in respect of any loss that he suffers as a consequence: *London Borough of Hounslow* v. *Twickenham Garden Developments Ltd* (1970). (See chapter 10 as to claims at common law.) In the Australian case of *Carr* v. *A.J. Berriman Pty Ltd* (1953) it was clearly held that, where there was failure to give possession of the building site to a contractor, this constituted a breach of contract, and on the facts the contractor was there to be entitled to treat the contract as repudiated.

Moreover, if clause 23.1.2 does not apply and the employer fails to give possession of the site to the contractor on the due date, or if the clause does apply and possession is deferred for more than the stated maximum period, since the architect has no power to grant an extension of time for completion on that ground it follows that the employer will forfeit any right to liquidated damages and the contractor's obligation will be to complete within a reasonable time: *Amalgamated Building Contractors Ltd* v. *Waltham Holy Cross UDC* (1952); *Peak Construction (Liverpool) Ltd* v. *McKinney Foundations Ltd* (1970). The case of *Percy Bilton Ltd* v. *Greater London Council* (1982) establishes that the architect has no power to extend time on grounds other than those set out in clause 25.

Although the clause refers to instructions issued under clause 23.2, such instructions may arise *de facto*: see *M. Harrison & Co. (Leeds) Ltd* v. *Leeds City Council* (1980), where an instruction expressed as a variation order was held to be in fact an order for postponement.

6. Failure to give ingress to or egress from the site

Clause 26.2.6 covers the situation where either there is a provision in the contract bills and/or drawings, or an agreement has been reached between the contractor and the architect, permitting the contractor means of access to the site 'through or over any land, buildings, way or passage adjoining or connected with the site and *in the possession and control of the Employer*'. The contractor must, of course, comply with any requirement as to notice.

The words emphasised above should be noted; the clause does not apply where the employer may have undertaken to obtain a wayleave across land which is not in his possession *and* control. In such a case failure by the employer to obtain the wayleave would give rise to a claim at common law. It should be further noted that the land, etc. must be in both the possession *and* the control of the employer, and the land, etc. must also be 'adjoining *or* connected with the site', which would suggest that there must be contiguity but not necessarily physical contact.

7. *Variations and work against provisional sums*

Valuations of the work involved in and general consequences of variations and instructions issued by the architect for the expenditure of provisional sums are dealt with in clause 13, which is discussed in chapter 3. Clause 26.2.7 covers disturbance costs where the introduction of the variation or provisional sum work materially affects the regular progress of the works in general.

Clause 26.3 – Money claims and extensions of time

Clause 26.3 provides that if, and to the extent that it is necessary for the purpose of ascertainment of direct loss and/or expense, the architect shall state in writing to the contractor what extension of time, if any, he has granted under clause 25 in respect of those events which are also grounds for reimbursement under clause 26.

In our view there is no logical justification for the inclusion of this provision, which, in effect, appears to give contractual sanction to the mistaken belief that there is some automatic connection between the granting of an extension of time and the contractor's entitlement to reimbursement. We reiterate that there is or ought to be no such connection: see *H. Fairweather & Co. Ltd* v. *London Borough of Wandsworth* (1988). An extension of time under clause 25 has only one effect. It defers the date from which the contractor becomes liable to pay to the employer liquidated damages. An extension of contract time does not in itself entitle the contractor to any extra money. The correct position is well stated by Dr John Parris, *The Standard Form of Building Contract: JCT 80*, Section 10.03 The relationship of JCT 80 clause 25 to clause 26:

> 'JCT 80 clause 25 entitles the contractor to relief from paying liquidated damages at the date named in the contract. It does not in any way entitle him to one penny of monetary compensation for the fact that the architect has extended the contractor's time completion. He is not entitled to claim even items set out in "Preliminaries" for the extended period.'

Moreover, this information is of no interest or relevance to the contractor and cannot and should not have any relevance to any ascertainment of direct loss/or expense under clause 26. An extension of time is, furthermore, essentially an estimate of what is likely to happen *before* the event. The ascertainment of direct loss and/or expense under clause 26 is essentially a finding-out of facts *after* the event.

It is for the architect or quantity surveyor (not the contractor) to ascertain the amount of loss and/or expense. It seems to us nonsensical, then, to require the architect to provide the contractor with information that is only of interest (if it is of interest at all) to the person responsible for the ascertainment.

It is also impracticable, Clause 25 does not require the architect to give a breakdown of extensions of time between causes of delay, since this is of no relevance to the effect of an extension, as stated previously. If, as so often happens, there are a number of overlapping causes of delay, to separate out the overall extension between those various causes will often be impossible: see *H. Fairweather & Co. Ltd* v. *London Borough of Wandsworth* (1988).

The possible difficulties of the inclusion of this sub-clause may be illustrated by reference to a late supply of instructions by the architect. As has been said earlier, this may entitle the contractor to be relieved from the obligation to pay liquidated damages to the employer since the late delivery of an instruction may have prevented him from taking steps to make good delays which have already occurred, and which are his own responsibility. Nevertheless, the late delivery of the instruction will not actually have caused him to incur any loss or expense beyond that which he has already incurred due to his own inefficiency. Clause 26.3 would, however, seem to imply that the contractor would be entitled to recover from the employer, which in our view is wholly wrong. Further, an extension of time of (say) 10 weeks might well have been granted for a particular event as an estimate of the expected delay in completion, yet in the event it could transpire that the actual result was a delay of only 8 weeks. Even in the case of an actual delay through a cause that is also reimbursable under clause 26, the length of the delay does not necessarily or even usually bear any relationship to the actual amount of direct loss and/or expense.

Relevance of contract completion date

Clause 23.1 places an obligation upon the contractor to complete the works '*on or before*' the completion date, i.e. the date for completion stated in the Appendix or any later date fixed by an extension of time under clause 25 or clause 33.1.3. It is therefore clear that the contractor may, if he wishes to do so, and can reasonably do so, while complying with all the other terms of the contract, complete the works before the date fixed under the contract. If follows that the only significance of the completion date is to fix the date from which the employer may be entitled to recover liquidated damages. The contractor is not obliged to remain on site until that date. Indeed, by clause 17 he is entitled to a certificate of practical completion whenever he in fact has finished the works, whether it is before or after the contract date for completion.

Therefore, when the cost of remaining on site for a longer period than would otherwise have been necessary is a factor to be included in the ascertainment of direct loss and/or expense, the period of time which will form the basis of the ascertainment will not necessarily be measurable from the contract completion date, but may be measureable from an earlier or later date, i.e. the date when the contractor would otherwise have been able to complete.

However, there is one event listed in clause 26.2 when the use of an earlier date than the contractual date for completion would not be appropriate, and that is clause 26.2.1, dealing with late instructions. While the employer or architect must not prevent the contractor from meeting an earlier date, which he would otherwise have been able to meet, they are not obliged positively to assist him to do so. The architect's obligation is to provide necessary information, instructions, etc. in due time, which clearly must mean at a time that will enable the contractor to meet his obligations as to completion. Accordingly, if the architect has provided necessary information at dates that have permitted the contractor (without undue effort or additional cost) to meet the contract completion date, then the architect has by definition fulfilled his obligations and the contractor will have no claim. This position is, in our view, unaffected by the architect 'accepting' a programme from the contractor showing an earlier date for completion than that set out in the Appendix.

This view, expressed in the first edition of this book, has now received judicial support from Judge James Fox-Andrews QC, sitting as an Official Referee, in the case of *Glenlion Construction Ltd* v. *The Guiness Trust* (1988) in considering the similar provisions in JCT 63. One of the questions the judge had to consider was

'whether there was an implied term of the contract ... that, if and in so far as the programme showed a completion date before the date for completion [stated in the contract] the employer by himself, his servants or his agents should so perform the said agreement as to enable the contractor to carry out the works in accordance with the programme and to complete the works on the said completion date.'

i.e. information etc. should have been supplied at times which would have enabled the contractor to meet the earlier completion date. The judge's answer to the question was 'no'. As he said,

'it is not suggested by Glenlion that they were both entitled *and* obliged to finish by the earlier completion date. If there is such an implied term it imposed an obligation on the Trust but none on Glenlion.'

This was manifestly wrong and there was therefore no obligation on the Trust or its architect to provide information at any times earlier than those necessary to enable the contractor to complete by the contract date.

Clause 26.4 – Nominated Sub-Contract claims

Clause 13 of JCT Nominated Sub-Contract Form (NSC/4 or NSC/4a) is a provision corresponding to clause 26 of the main contract form enabling the nominated sub-contractor to claim against the employer *through* the main contractor in respect of direct loss and/or expense and on similar grounds to those given to the main contractor by clause 26. Clause 26.4 provides the necessary machinery by which the contractor is to pass such claims on to the architect, and the architect's decision is to be passed back to the nominated sub-contractor.

Clause 26.4.2 corresponds to clause 26.3 in a nominated sub-contractor situation and the same objections are equally sustainable in respect of it.

For a discussion of sub-contract claims see chapter 9.

Clause 26.5 – Certification of direct loss and/or expense

Clause 26.5 provides for amounts ascertained to be added to the contract sum. By clause 3, this also means that as soon as an amount of entitlement is ascertained in whole *or in part*, that amount is to be taken into account in the next interim certificate. By clause 30.2.2.2, such amounts are *not* subject to retention. The reference to ascertainment 'in part' in clause 3 means, in our view, that it is not necessary for the full process of ascertainment to have been completed before an amount can be certified for payment. This is important from the point of view of both the contractor and the employer: in particular, where the direct loss and/or expense is being incurred over a period of time, in our view the proper operation of the contractual machinery should ensure that the matter is dealt with in interim payments from month to month so far as is practicable. This provision for payment of sums ascertained 'in part' permits the inclusion in interim certificates of allowances for direct loss and/or expense where full ascertainment has not been possible in the time available, thereby ensuring proper cash-flow to the contractor and reducing the employer's possible liability for financing charges; see *F. G. Minter Ltd* v. *Welsh Health Technical Services Organisation* (1980) and the discussion in chapter 4.

CLAUSE 26 CLAIMS: A SUMMARY

For a claim under clause 26.1 (other than a claim in respect of deferred possession of the site) to be sustainable it must meet the following requirements:

(1) The written application must be made at the proper time. If it is made out of time the architect may reject it, irrespective of merits.
(2) It must show that possession of the site has been deferred or that regular progress of the works has been or is likely to be affected by one or more of the seven matters set out in clause 26.2.
(3) As much relevant detail as possible should be given in the initial application, and the contractor must be prepared on request to give sufficient further information and details as are necessary.
(4) The claim must relate only to direct loss and/or expense not recoverable under any other provision of the contract.

26.6 Contractor's other rights and remedies
Clause 26.6 preserves the contractor's common law and other rights. The rights set out in clauses 26.1 to 26.5 confer a specific contractual remedy on the contractor in the circumstances there defined, and subject to the conditions there imposed. But the contractor's other rights are unaffected, in particular his right to claim damages for breach of contract.

In other words, the specific contractual right to claim reimbursement for direct loss and/or expense is additional to any rights or remedies which the contractor possesses at law, and notably to damages for breach of contract. In the vast majority of cases, such other rights are more apparent than real, but in rare cases it may be that because of the limitations imposed by the contract machinery the contractor will be advised to pursue these independent remedies: see chapter 10. However, see the discussion regarding those events which are not breaches of contract on page 160 above.

CLAUSE 34.3

Clause 34 generally provides for what is to happen if 'fossils, antiquities and other objects of interest or value' are found on site or during excavation. The contractor is required to use his best endeavours not to disturb the object and to cease work as far as is necessary and to take all steps necessary to preserve the object in its position and condition. He is to inform the architect or the clerk of works. The architect is then required to issue instructions and the contractor may be required to allow a third party, such as an expert archaeologist, to examine, excavate and remove the object. All this will almost undoubtedly involve the contractor in direct loss and/or expense and clause 34.3.1 provides that this is to be ascertained by the architect or quantity surveyor without necessity for further application by the contractor.

The text of clause 34.3 is as follows:

34.3 .1 'If in the opinion of the Architect compliance with the provisions of clause 34.1 or with an instruction issued under clause 34.2 has involved the Contractor in direct loss and/or expense for which he would not be reimbursed by a payment made under any other provision of this Contract then the Architect shall himself ascertain or shall instruct the Quantity Surveyor to ascertain the amount of such loss and/or expense.

34.3 .2 If and to the extent that it is necessary for the ascertainment of such loss and/or expense the Architect shall state in writing to the Contractor what extension of time, if any, has been made under clause 25 in respect of the Relevant Event referred to in clause 25.4.5.1 so far as that clause refers to clause 34.

34.3 .3 Any amount from time to time so ascertained shall be added to the Contract Sum.'

Rather curiously, it is to be noted that there are no provisions similar to those in clauses 26.1.2 and 26.1.3 requiring the contractor to give further information and details. In practice, of course, an ascertainment can only be made if the relevant information and details are provided by the contractor to the architect or quantity surveyor.

Claims under 34.3 are not uncommon and are likely to increase. Modern technology, and especially aerial survey, indicates that there are approaching half-a-million archaeological sites in England and Wales, which is far more than has hitherto been supposed. The provisions of the Ancient Monuments and Archaeological Sites Act 1979, which came into force in 1982, affect contractors working in 'areas of archaeological importance', which are a new concept introduced by Part II of the Act. Moreover, if an 'ancient monument' were suddenly discovered in the course of contract works, where one was unexpected, the possibility of its being scheduled under the Act (and thus protected) could not be completely discounted. In fact, this has happened only twice in the past 30 years. Instead, the Department of the Environment might make financial help available for the relocation of piling or the rafting-over of the remains, and in such a case the contractor would have a claim under clause 34.3.

Clause 34.3.2 is open to similar objections to those already made in respect of clause 26.3.

THE JCT INTERMEDIATE FORM OF BUILDING CONTRACT (IFC 84)
Clauses 4.11 and 4.12 of IFC 84 run as follows:

Disturbance of regular progress

4.11 If, upon written application being made to him by the Contractor within a reasonable time of it becoming apparent, the Architect/the Contract Administrator is of the opinion that the Contractor has incurred or is likely to incur direct loss and/or expense, for which he would not be reimbursed by a payment under any other provision of this Contract, due to

(a) the deferment of the Employer giving possession of the site under clause 2.2 where that clause is stated in the Appendix to be applicable; or

(b) the regular progress of the Works or part of the Works being materially affected by any one or more of the matters referred to in clause 4.12,

then the Architect/the Contract Administrator shall ascertain, or shall instruct the Quantity Surveyor to ascertain, such loss and expense incurred and the amount thereof shall be added to the Contract Sum provided that the Contractor shall in support of his application submit such information required by the Architect/the Contract Administrator or the Quantity Surveyor as is reasonably necessary for the purposes of this clause.

The provisions of this clause 4.11 are without prejudice to any other rights or remedies which the Contractor may possess.

Matters referred to in clause 4.11

4.12 The following are the matters referred to in clause 4.11:

4.12.1 the Contractor not having received in due time necessary instructions, drawings, details or levels from the Architect/the Contract Administrator for which he specifically applied in writing provided that such application was made on a date which having regard to the Date for Completion stated in the Appendix or any extended time then fixed was neither unreasonably distant from nor unreasonably close to the date on which it was necessary for him to receive the same;

4.12.2 the opening up for inspection of any work covered up or the testing of any of the work, materials or goods in accordance with clause 3.12 (including making good in consequence of such opening up or testing), unless the inspection or test showed that the work, materials or goods were not in accordance with this Contract;

4.12.3 the execution of work not forming part of this Contract by the Employer himself or by persons employed or otherwise engaged by the Employer as referred to in clause 3.11 or the failure to execute such work;

4.12.4 the supply by the Employer of materials and goods which the Employer has agreed to supply for the Works or the failure to supply;

4.12.5 the Architect's/the Contract Administrator's instructions under clause 3.15 issued in regard to the postponement of any work to be executed under the provisions of this Contract;

4.12.6 failure of the Employer to give in due time ingress to or egress from the site of the Works, or any part thereof through or over any land, buildings, way or passage adjoining or connected with the site and in the possession and control of the Employer, in accordance with the Contract Documents after receipt by the Architect/the Contract Administrator of such notice, if any, as the Contractor is required to give, or failure of the Employer to give such ingress or egress as otherwise agreed between the Architect/the Contract Administrator and the Contractor;

4.12.7 the Architect's/the Contract Administrator's instructions issued under clauses
1.4 *(Inconsistencies)* or
3.6 *(Variations)* or
3.8 *(Provisional sums)*
or, to the extent provided therein, under clause
3.3 *(Named sub-contractors)*.

There is no equivalent of clause 34.3 of JCT 80 dealing with the discovery of antiquities.

It will be seen that these clauses are essentially a condensed version of clause 26 of JCT 80 (as now revised). The basic features remain:

- the requirement for a written application from the contractor as a starting point
- the architect to form an opinion as to whether the contractor has incurred or is likely to incur direct loss and/or expense
- the architect, or the quantity surveyor if so instructed, to ascertain the amount of the loss and/or expense
- the contractor to provide such information 'as is reasonably necessary' to enable the clauses to be operated
- the right of the contractor to reimbursement under the contract is limited to deferment of possession of the site or specified causes materially affecting the regular progress of the works.

However, there are a few significant differences to note.

(1) The obligation of the contractor to provide information in support of his application is not subject to any request from the architect or quantity surveyor. It is therefore an absolute obligation. If the contractor is to recover under the clause he must provide whatever information is 'reasonably necessary' to enable the architect and/ or the quantity surveyor to carry out their own obligations.

(2) Instead of a reference to 'any discrepancy in or divergence between the Contract Drawings and/or the Contract Bills' as in JCT 80 clause 26.2.3, the reference is to 'the Architect's/Contract Administrator's instructions issued under [clause] 1.4 (*Inconsistencies*)'. That clause requires the architect to issue instructions in regard to the correction of

- any inconsistency in or between the contract documents or drawings or details reasonably necessary to enable the contractor to carry out and complete the works (clause 1.7) or the determination of levels and the dimensioned drawings required for setting-out (clause 3.9)
- any error in description or in quantity or any omission of items in the contract documents
- any error or omission in the particulars provided of the tender of any named sub-contractor (clause 3.3.1)
- any departure from the standard method of measurement upon which bills of quantities (if provided as one of the contract documents) have been prepared.

It will be seen that this extends considerably beyond the very limited reference in JCT 80 to discrepancies only between or within the contract drawings and the contract bills to cover discrepancies between the contract documents and any other details provided by the architect including levels and setting-out drawings, errors in or omissions from the contract documents (which, in addition to drawings, may be bills of quantities, priceable schedules of work or specifications, priceable or otherwise) and errors in the tender documents of named sub-contractors. It is also clear that it is the effect on progress of the architect's instructions for the correction of the error or discrepancy which gives rise to the contractor's entitlement. All this seems so eminently sensible and reasonable that it is difficult to understand why JCT 80 has not been amended similarly.

(3) The effect of certain architect's instructions regarding named sub-contractors upon regular progress is made a ground for claim. The

special position of named sub-contractors in IFC 84 is not a subject for this book, and readers are referred to '*A Commentary on the JCT Intermediate Form of Building Contract*' by Neil F. Jones and David Bergman (BSP Professional Books 1985) for an excellent exposition of the subject. Briefly the contractor is obliged to employ as sub-contractors persons or firms who are named, either in the contract documents or in an instruction from the architect for the expenditure of a provisional sum, to carry out specified parcels of work. The naming process involves the use of a standard form of invitation to tender, tender and articles of agreement (Form NAM/T) and standard conditions of sub-contract incorporated into the sub-contract by reference (Form NAM/SC), together with an optional form of Employer/Sub-Contractor Agreement (ESA/1) similar in effect to Form NSC/2 under JCT 80.

In contrast to the position regarding nominated sub-contractors under JCT 80, named sub-contractors under IFC/84 become effectively 'domestic' sub-contractors to the main contractor. Once the naming procedure has been completed the architect generally speaking has no further involvement with the administration of the sub-contract. He does not direct the main contractor as to the payments to be made to the named sub-contractors and he is not required to certify practical completion of their work. Matters such as extensions of time for the sub-contractor and settlement of his account are matters between the sub-contractor and the main contractor and neither the architect nor the quantity surveyor under the main contract will be involved.

However, the architect may become involved and may be required to issue instructions if things go badly wrong. In certain such circumstances the main contractor may be entitled to reimbursement of any direct loss and/or expense arising from the effect of such instructions on the regular progress of the works. Those circumstances are:

(1) If a sub-contractor is named in the contract documents but the main contractor finds that he is unable in the event to enter into a sub-contract with the named firm (perhaps because the firm withdraws or no longer exists or because of some inconsistency between the sub-contract particulars and the main contract) the main contractor is to notify the architect specifying the reason. If the architect is satisfied that the reason is valid he may issue an instruction to

- change the particulars of the proposed sub-contract so as to remove the problem, or
- omit the work from the contract altogether, in which case the employer may have the work carried out under a separate contract, or
- omit the work from the contract documents and substitute a provisional sum, which would then entitle him to instruct the main contractor to do the work or name another sub-contractor.

Instructions issued under the first two options are to be regarded as variation instructions, therefore entitling the contractor to an extension of time if the works are delayed and to direct loss and/or expense arising from any effect of the instruction (including the effect of the employment of others to carry out the work if the second option is followed) on the regular progress of the works. If the third option is followed the 'naming' of a replacement sub-contractor becomes a 'naming' against a provisional sum; see below.

(2) If a sub-contractor is named in an instruction for the expenditure of a provisional sum, any direct loss and/or expense caused to the contractor by the effect of the instruction on regular progress of the works is recoverable under the reference to clause 3.8 in clause 4.12.7. For instance, if the named sub-contractor's programme is inconsistent with the main contract programme so that his employment will cause disruption and/or delay, the main contractor may make a 'reasonable objection' to entering into the sub-contract. If he is nevertheless instructed to proceed, he will be entitled to recover the direct loss and/or expense arising from the resulting disruption and/or delay.

(3) If the employment of a named sub-contractor is determined by the main contractor because of the sub-contractor's default or insolvency, the contractor is to notify the architect who may then issue an instruction to

- name another sub-contractor to do the remaining work, or
- instruct the contractor to make his own arrangements for completion of the work, in which case the contractor may sub-let the remaining work to a sub-contractor of his own choice, or
- omit the remainder of the work from the contract, in which case the employer may employ someone else to do it.

If the original sub-contractor was named in the contract documents the exercise of the first option by the architect will entitle the
contractor to an extension of time for any resulting delay, but will
not entitle him to recover direct loss and/or expense from the
employer. Both the other options, and if the original sub-
contractor was named against a provisional sum all three options,
will entitle the contractor both to an extension of time and to
recovery of direct loss and/or expense arising from the resulting
effect on progress. If either of the first two options is adopted the
contract sum is to be adjusted to take account of the difference in
price between what would have been payable to the original sub-
contractor and what is now payable to the replacement sub-
contractor if one is appointed or to the main contractor if he is
instructed to make his own arrangements for completion. However, the contractor is under an obligation to pursue the original
sub-contractor to seek to recover the additional expense which the
employer is required to meet subject to certain indemnities from
the employer (see clause 3.3.6(b)).

All this seems impossibly complex, and is certainly very difficult to follow
in the form due to the multiplicity of cross-referencing adopted, but the
principle is quite simple. Once a sub-contract has been entered into, if the
sub-contractor was named in the main contract documents the contractor
is deemed to have accepted that sub-contractor and to have accepted
basic responsibility for his performance. If something goes badly wrong
and the sub-contractor's employment has to be determined, this is to
some extent to be regarded as *force majeure* entitling the contractor to an
extension of time for the resulting delay, but he is not entitled to recover
any loss or expense in which the determination involves him, unless he
himself is required to take on full responsibility for the completion of the
work or the employer employs someone else to complete it. If, however,
the sub-contractor was named in an instruction for the expenditure of a
provisional sum and therefore after the main contract was entered into,
the employer accepts that greater degree of responsibility and will
reimburse to the contractor any direct loss and/or expense resulting from
the effect of the determination on progress in any event.

One interesting little point arises if the original sub-contractor was
named in the main contract documents, the architect instructs the
contractor to employ another sub-contractor and that sub-contractor
then delays progress so that the contractor suffers direct loss and/or
expense as a result of his default. The instruction naming the replacement

sub-contractor is not expressed as being an instruction for the expenditure of a provisional sum, and it would therefore seem that the contractor would not be entitled to recover the direct loss and/or expense arising from the replacement sub-contractor's delay.

Chapter 6

Money claims under JCT 63

INTRODUCTION

JCT 63 has been superseded by JCT 80 but claims will continue to arise under it for many years to come. Although we find it difficult to understand the reasons, it would seem that a number of contracts continue to be let on JCT 63 terms, despite the vastly improved provisions of JCT 80 and IFC 84.

In the light of the foregoing it is necessary to consider the money claims provisions of JCT 63, dealing in particular with the differences between the two sets of provisions.

There are three provisions in JCT 63 that may give rise to money claims by the contractor. They are clause 11(6), which deals with loss and expense arising from variations; clause 24(1), which deals with loss and expense 'caused by disturbance of regular progress of the Works' (to quote the wording of the side-note to the clause); and clause 34(3), which deals with loss and expense arising from the finding of fossils, etc. To a large extent clause 11(6) of JCT 63 has been combined with clause 24(1) to form JCT 80, clause 26, but there are important differences between the two versions. JCT 63, clause 34(3) is virtually identical with clause 34.3 of JCT 80 and is not separately considered in this chapter.

CLAUSE 11(6)

The full text of clause 11(6) is as follows:

'If upon written application being made to him by the Contractor, the Architect is of the opinion that a variation or the execution by the Contractor of work for which a provisional sum is included in the Contract Bills (other than work for which a tender made under clause 27(g) of these Conditions has been accepted) has involved the

Contractor in direct loss and/or expense for which he would not be reimbursed by payment in respect of a valuation made in accordance with the rules contained in sub-clause (4) of this Condition and if the said application is made within a reasonable time of the loss or expense having been incurred, then the Architect shall either himself ascertain or shall instruct the Quantity Surveyor to ascertain the amount of such loss or expense. Any amount from time to time so ascertained shall be added to the Contract Sum, and if an Interim Certificate is issued after the date of ascertainment any such amount shall be added to the amount which would otherwise be stated as due in such Certificate.'

Commentary

As with clause 26.1 of JCT 80, the process of claim is initiated by the contractor making a written application to the architect. This application must be made within a reasonable time of the loss or expense *having been* incurred. The application is therefore retrospective and there is no obligation upon the contractor to give prior notice of the likelihood of loss and/or expense being incurred, no matter how foreseeable it may have been. To our minds this has always constituted a very serious defect in this provision, and this has now been corrected in JCT 80. What is a reasonable time is a question of fact depending on the circumstances, but it is suggested that the courts would take a fairly generous view: see, for example *Tersons Ltd* v. *Stevenage Development Corporation* (1963).

In *F.G. Minter Ltd* v. *Welsh Health Technical Services Organisation* (1980), the Court of Appeal drew attention to some of the difficulties involved in the effective administration of clause 11(6). For example, Lord Justice Stephenson pointed out that 'the loss or expense must come before the application, not just *some* loss but *the* loss or expense to be included in the certificate'. This is because clause 11(6) requires the contractor's application to be made within a reasonable time of the loss or expense *having been incurred*, which, as the learned Lord Justice observed, 'must mean the loss in which the variation "has involved the contractor" and it is "the amount of such loss" which the architect has to ascertain and certify'.

The *Minter* case was, of course, concerned with the recovery of finance charges as part of 'direct loss and/or expense' and this aspect of the case is discussed on page 145. The Court of Appeal agreed with the High Court judge's interpretation of clause 11(6) and with his conclusion that the architect could only ascertain and certify the amount of loss and expense incurred *up to the date of the application*.

Lord Justice Stephenson said:

'It is these charges which are the subject of the application; it is these

charges which he has power to investigate, ascertain and certify ....
[The] architect would be exceeding his powers were he to take into
account further financial charges or other losses accruing [during the
process of ascertainment and certification], however long, and such
further charges and losses would be recoverable only, if at all, under a
subsequent application or subsequent applications ...'

Accordingly, under clause 11(6), the contractor must either make a
series of applications in respect of continuing loss and expense or wait
until all loss and expense have been incurred and then make a single
application, unless the architect obtains the employer's express approval
to waive the required successive applications.

A series of applications in respect of recurring losses obviously places
a considerable administrative burden upon the architect and/or the
quantity surveyor and also upon the contractor. Although clause 11(6)
does not contain any express requirement that the contractor should
supply the architect or quantity surveyor with information, there is no
doubt in our minds that it is the contractor's obligation so to do. The
matter was dealt with *obiter* in the *Minter* case where Lord Justice
Stephenson referred to the administrative burden being

'further increased by delay on the part of contractors ... in providing
information which [the architect] reasonably requires either for
forming his opinion or for ascertaining amounts under [clause 11(6)].
But contractors have a duty under clause 30(5)(b) of the main contract
... to send him "all documents necessary for the purposes of the
computations required" by the conditions of the contract ...'.

There are other difficulties involved in the clause. The contractor must
not only have been involved in direct loss and/or expense as the result of
'a variation' or the execution by him of provisional sum work, but it must
be loss and/or expense 'for which he would not be reimbursed by
payment in respect of a valuation made' under clause 11(4). The direct
cause of the loss and/or expense must be the variation, etc., and there
must be no intervening cause that would make the connection between
the variation and the loss and/or expense indirect. See the interesting
example quoted and analysed by Dr John Parris in *The Standard Form of
Building Contract: JCT 80*, Section 10.02 Valid claims?

The word 'reimbursed' also causes considerable difficulty and controversy. The *Concise Oxford Dictionary* equates the word with 'repaid'. If
taken literally, this would mean that the contractor could recover under

clause 11(6) any direct cost arising from a variation where a valuation under clause 11(4) would result in a lesser sum being payable since the valuation would not 'repay' the cost. In other words, the contractor would be entitled either to a valuation under clause 11(4) or to the prime cost of carrying out the work, whichever is the greater. It is submitted that this cannot possibly be the intention of the clause. It is suggested, therefore, that the word 'reimbursed' should be read as 'paid for', rather than 'repaid'. If so read the intention is clearly that under clause 11(6) the contractor will be entitled to loss and/or expense of a nature not covered by valuation under clause 11(4).

In fact, the interpretation of clause 11(6) has caused difficulty for the most eminent legal commentators even where they attempt to deal with it. In *Building and Civil Engineering Standard Forms*, page 70, Mr I. N. Duncan Wallace remarks:

> 'The situations at which this clause is aimed are not easy to visualise. It may be intended to cover cases where variation orders are given at a late date and cause dislocation, though it seems arguable that a "fair valuation" under rule (b) of sub-clause (4) would apply over much the same ground as this clause, and would necessarily take account of all direct loss or expense to the contractor.'

With the greatest respect, we must take issue with Mr Duncan Wallace. To start with, a 'fair valuation' would only be made where rates in the contract bills cannot be applied. If there are bill rates there must clearly be substantial scope for loss and/or expense to arise, which they would not cover. We also question whether the clause can be read to cover loss and/or expense arising as a direct result of the variation instruction being given at a late date rather than as a direct result of the variation itself.

It seems to us clear that the intention of the clause is to permit the contractor to recover loss and/or expense directly resulting from the variation, but not forming part of the cost of the varied work itself, i.e. the consequential effect of the introduction of the variation upon other unvaried work. It would also cover, we suggest, items of cost which, while directly related to the variation, cannot be covered by rates applied to measurement, e.g. the loss to the contractor involved where materials have already been ordered for the work as originally designed and made redundant by the variation.

Finally, there is one thing which in our view clause 11(6) is certainly not intended to permit, and that is recovery by the contractor of the effect of his own underpricing of items in the contract bills when those rates are applied to additional work in variations. The contractor has contracted to carry out variations as part of the works contemplated by the contract: see Article 1 of the Articles of Agreement, where the contractor undertakes to 'carry out and complete the works shown upon the Contract Drawings and described by or referred to in the Contract Bills and in the said Conditions' and has agreed to be paid for them in accordance with clause 11(4), subject only to clause 11(6).

This view appears to be supported by *Dudley Corporation* v. *Parsons & Morrin Ltd* (1969), where the contract appears to have been in JCT with quantities form. An item for excavating 750 cubic yards in rock was wrongly priced by the contractor at 2*s* per cubic yard when a reasonable price would have been £2. In the event, 2230 cubic yards of rock were excavated. It was held that the contractor was only entitled to be paid at the rate of 2*s* per cubic yard for the whole quantity excavated. (Noted in Abrahamson, *Engineering Law*, 4th edition, page 12 footnote (i), where it does not appear to support the proposition in the text.)

The above view is not universally held and some commentators appear to suggest that an erroneous rate can only be applied to the quantity originally envisaged in the contract.

CLAUSE 24(1)

The full text of clause 24 is as follows:

24 (1) 'If upon written application being made to him by the Contractor the Architect is of the opinion that the Contractor has been involved in direct loss and/or expense for which he would not be reimbursed by a payment made under any other provision in this Contract by reason of the regular progress of the Works or of any part thereof having been materially affected by:

    (a) The Contractor not having received in due time necessary instructions, drawings, details or levels from the Architect for which he specifically applied in writing on a date which having regard to the Date for Completion stated in the Appendix to these Conditions or to any extension of time then fixed under clause 23 or clause 33(1)(c) of these Conditions was neither unreasonably distant from nor unreasonably close to the date on which it was necessary for him to receive the same; or

    (b) The opening up for inspection of any work covered up or the testing of any of the work materials or goods in accordance with clause 6(3) of these Conditions (including making good in consequence of such opening up or testing), unless the inspection or test showed that the work, materials or goods were not in accordance with this Contract; or

    (c) Any discrepancy in or divergence between the Contract Drawings and/or the Contract Bills; or

(d) Delay on the part of artists tradesmen or others engaged by the Employer in executing work not forming part of this contract; or

(e) Architect's instructions issued in regard to the postponement of any work to be executed under the provisions of this Contract;

and if the written application is made within a reasonable time of it becoming apparent that the progress of the Works or of any part thereof has been affected as aforesaid, then the Architect shall either himself ascertain or shall instruct the Quantity Surveyor to ascertain the amount of such loss and/or expense. Any amount from time to time so ascertained shall be added to the Contract Sum, and if an Interim Certificate is issued after the date of ascertainment any such amount shall be added to the amount which would otherwise be stated as due in such Certificate.

(2) The provisions of this Condition are without prejudice to any other rights and remedies which the Contractor may possess.'

As will be seen, clause 24(2) is virtually identical with clause 26.6 of JCT 80, and its effect is exactly the same. Thus, no special comment is necessary, and readers are referred to our discussion of the latter sub-clause in chapter 10, page 301.

Commentary
There is an important distinction between claims under clause 24(1) and those under clause 11(6). Under clause 24(1) claims can arise only where 'regular progress of the Works or of any part thereof' has been materially affected; as has been seen, there is no such requirement in clause 11(6).

Another apparent difference between the two sub-clauses relates to the timing of the contractor's application. Clause 24(1) requires application to have been made 'within a reasonable time of it becoming apparent that the progress of the Works or of any part thereof has been affected', whereas clause 11(6), as we have seen, requires the application to be made 'within a reasonable time of the loss or expense having been incurred'. However, the Court of Appeal has pointed out that this apparent difference does not in fact exist since in both cases the application must relate to direct loss and/or expense which has already been incurred and the architect's authority in both cases is limited to ascertainment of the loss and/or expense incurred up to the date of the application: see *F. G. Minter Ltd* v. *Welsh Health Technical Services Organisation* (1980).

There is a third apparent difference between the two sub-clauses. In clause 24(1) the loss and/or expense claimed must be that for which the contractor 'would not be reimbursed by a payment made under *any other provision in this Contract*', whereas in clause 11(6) it must be that for which the contractor 'would not be reimbursed *by payment in respect of a valuation made in accordance with the rules contained in' clause 11(4)*. In our opinion this is a distinction without a difference. Clearly, it would not be proper for the contractor to recover under clause 11(6) any loss or expense that he would also be entitled to recover under some other provision of the contract, and indeed in law he cannot do so.

COMPARISON OF CLAUSES 11(6) and 24(1) WITH JCT 80, CLAUSE 26

The JCT Guide to the 1980 Edition of the Standard Form, Part III, page 23, contains very little by way of comparison of these provisions. For instance, its only reference to the changes in the procedure for application is to the specific provision 'for the supply of necessary information and details'; it then says 'otherwise Clause 26.1 substantially follows Clause 24(1)(1963)'. This seems to us to be misleading. The differences are in fact substantial, particularly with respect to the timing of the contractor's application:

'It is clear that under Clause 26.1 only one written application is required to be made by the Contractor in respect of loss and/or expense caused by an identifiable happening falling within one of the prescribed list of matters. Once the necessary application has been made to trigger the operation of Clause 26 then the loss and expense from time to time thereafter to be ascertained and certified will include loss and expense incurred *after* the written application as well as any such (if any) as was incurred prior thereto.' (Editorial comment in *Building Law Reports*, Volume 13, page 6.)

This is in contrast with the position under clauses 11(6) and 24(1) where the contractor's application is *terminus ad quem* rather than *terminus a quo:* the finishing point rather than the starting point. Further, the recovery of direct loss and/or expense in respect of variations under clause 26.2, JCT 80 is now confined to loss and/or expense resulting from the material effect of a variation upon the regular progress of the works. All other effects of variations are now to be dealt with by the quantity surveyor in his valuations under JCT 80, clause 13, including, for instance, the example already referred to of the loss in respect of materials rendered redundant by the variation: see clause 13.5.6, JCT 80 and the reference therein to 'liabilities directly associated with a Variation'.

Perhaps the most important of all the changes that have been made in these provisions of JCT 80 is the requirement for the contractor to give prior notice of problems that it is reasonable for him, as the person responsible for the carrying out of the work, to foresee. In our view this change is of immense benefit to the employer. The lack of any such obligation under the 1963 provisions is a serious lacuna. In our experience, this lacuna has frequently resulted in quite unnecessary further expenditure by the employer, which could have been avoided had the contractor been required by the contract terms to warn the architect of impending problems. This change alone justified in our view the comment that has been made that any professional consultant who advises an employer to use the 1963 Edition in preference to JCT 80 may well be liable to an action for professional negligence: see, for example, the views trenchantly expressed by Dr John Parris in *The Standard Form of Building Contract: JCT 80* Section 1.07 Why JCT 63 should not continue to be used.

Under the claims provisions of both JCT 63 and JCT 80 it seems to us that there must be implied a duty on the architect or quantity surveyor to carry out the ascertainment of direct loss and/or expense within a reasonable time of receiving reasonably sufficient information from the contractor: see *Crondace Ltd* v. *London Borough of Lambeth* (1984). What is a reasonable time will vary with the circumstances of each case. Indeed, if an architect or quantity surveyor delayed unreasonably in the ascertainment he might be liable personally, either directly or through the employer, to the contractor in damages. This proposition receives some support from an *obiter* observation of Mr Justice Parker in *F. G. Minter Ltd* v. *Welsh Health Technical Services Organisation* (1979) at first instance, where he said: '[If] the period was unreasonable the chain of causation would be completely broken. This might give rise to a claim against the architect ...'

Although the first instance judgment of Mr Justice Parker was reversed in part by the Court of Appeal, it appears to us that the learned judge's intimation of a possible personal liability of the architect or quanity surveyor is a correct statement of the law. That passage of the judgment of Lord Justice Stephenson touching upon this point in the Court of Appeal is far from clear. His lordship disagreed with Mr Justice Parker as to the breaking of the chain of causation but did not, in our view, express disagreement with Mr Justice Parker as to the possible personal liability of architect and quantity surveyor, indeed, *Calil* v. *Sallis* (1988) now establishes the architect's personal liability in appropriate circumstances. Given reasonable information from the contractor on which to base his ascertainment, it seems to us that it could not possibly be right to suggest that the architect or quantity surveyor could simply sit on that information indefinitely, and that the employer would still be liable for the resulting financial charges under the contract terms.

Even if the architect were under no duty towards the contractor – which is not the case – and given that the resulting financial charges were recoverable from the employer by the contractor under the terms of the contract, if the employer could establish that the architect or quantity surveyor had delayed unreasonably so as to increase his contractual liability, undoubtedly he would have a cause of action against the architect or quantity surveyor as appropriate, subject of course to the usual rules about proof of both liability and loss.

The whole matter of the respective rights and duties of contractor and architect/quantity surveyor under these clauses was examined in *London Borough of Merton* v. *Stanley Hugh Leach Ltd* (1985). One of the preliminary issues originally put forward for decision by the arbitrator ran as follows:

'Where a contractor notifies the architect in writing of the alleged existence of an event which the contractor maintains qualifies under clauses 11(6) or 24(1) so as to entitle the contractor to recover such loss or expense (if any) as he may have suffered:

(i)   Is the contractor under a duty to particularise that entitlement?
(ii) Is the architect under a duty to ascertain or to instruct the quantity surveyor to ascertain whether a loss and expense within the said clauses has indeed been incurred and if so its amount?
(iii) If the architect is under a duty as aforesaid, is that duty:

(a) independent of the supply of particulars as aforesaid; or
(b) dependent on the supply of particulars as aforesaid:

(iv) If the architect is under a duty as aforesaid, is the building owner liable in damages or otherwise or at all for breach thereof?
(v)   If the contractor is under a duty as aforesaid, is he liable in damages or otherwise or at all for breach thereof?'

This issue overlapped to some extent with other issues relating to whether Leach had in fact made written applications as required by clauses 11(6) and 24(1). What follows is a conflation of Mr Justice Vinelott's judgment in respect of all these issues.

Mr Justice Vinelott said:

'The common features of sub-clauses 24(1) and 11(6) are first that both are "if" provisions, that is provisions which only operate in the event that the contractor invokes them by making a written application, secondly, that if an application is made the architect must form an opinion whether the contractor has suffered direct loss and/or expense in the circumstances of the kind there set out, thirdly, that the written application must be made within a reasonable time after a stated event and, fourthly, that the architect must then ascertain or instruct the quantity surveyor to ascertain the amount of the loss or expense which is then to be added to the contract sum. They differ in that clause 24 is concerned with loss and/or expense which stems from an interruption in the regular progress of the work by one of the causes there set out and which would not be reimbursed under the provisions of the contract as a whole, whereas clause 11(6) is directed to loss or expense which stems from a variation or the execution of work for which a provisional or prime cost sum is included in the contract bills and for which the contractor would not be reimbursed under clause 11(4); in consequence the reasonable time within which written application can be made is measured in one case from the time when it becomes apparent that the progress of the work has been affected and in the other case from the time when the loss or expense is incurred.

'The question is whether certain documents were written applications under both clause 11(6) and 24(1) or in two instances under one or other of those sub-clauses alone. The question of principle is whether an application under clause 24(1) or 11(6) must contain sufficient information to enable the architect to form an opinion on the questions whether (in the case of clause 24) the regular progress of the works has been materially affected by an event within the numbered sub-paragraphs of clause 24 or (in the case of clause 11(6)) whether the variation has caused direct loss and/or expense of the kind there described and in either case whether the loss and/or expense is such that it would not be reimbursed by a payment under other provisions of the contract or (in the case of clause 11(6)) under clause 11(4). The arbitrator's answer to this question of principle is to be found in two paragraphs of the interim award which I should I think read in full. Having said that Merton submitted that the application must contain sufficient information on the matters which I have mentioned, the arbitrator continued:

"I am against [Merton] on this point for three reasons. First, although I accept that the architect's contact with the site is not on a day to day basis there are many occasions when an event occurs which is sufficiently within the knowledge of the architect for him to form an opinion that the contractor had been involved in loss or expense. Secondly, while it may be desirable for the contractor to give the fullest possible information as part of his original application, the contract does not, as it could so easily have done, *require* the contractor to do so. Finally, [Merton] make a specific submission in connection with this issue that the contract clearly anticipates (not 'requires') that the contractor will supply sufficient information to enable the architect to form his opinion. [Merton] emphasise that the word 'anticipates' is a better way of describing the situation than 'requires'. It must follow from this that the words 'must necessarily provide' in the first submission are inappropriate.

If the contractors' application under clause 11(6) or 24(1) is confined to the bare minimum requirements of the contract and the architect does not possess from his own sources sufficient information to form the requisite opinion then I agree with [Merton] that the contract 'anticipates' that the architect can and will seek further information from the contractor. There is no reason why this additional information should not be requested and given orally. But I emphasise that in my view any need for additional information does not negative or reduce the effectiveness of the original application.'

[Counsel for Merton] attacked this conclusion upon the ground that the planning of the work is the task of the contractor and that he alone can know whether the regular progress of the work has been affected (for the purpose of clause 24) or whether a variation will involve him in direct loss or expense which will not be reimbursed by a measurement and valuation in accordance with clause 11(4). The contractor alone will know whether, for instance, a delay in giving instructions is likely to cause him otherwise uncompensated loss or expense. He must then inform the architect so that the architect can consider whether he should issue an instruction forthwith or whether if it is impractical to do so he should ask the contractor to keep records to quantify the alleged loss. The contractor it is said must have had grounds for making the application under clause 24 or 11(6). It is reasonable therefore to construe these clauses as requiring him at least to make those reasons explicit in his application.

'This argument is at first sight an impressive one, but on further examination it appears to me to involve reading too much into these clauses. The contractor must act reasonably: his application must be framed with sufficient particularity to enable the architect to do what he is required to do. He must make his application within a reasonable time: it must not be made so late that, for instance, the architect can no longer form a competent opinion on the matters on which he is required to form an opinion or satisfy himself that the contractor has suffered the loss or expense claimed. But in considering whether the contractor has acted reasonably and with reasonable expedition it must be borne in mind that the architect is not a stranger to the work and may in some cases have a very detailed knowledge of the progress of the work and of the contractor's planning. Moreover, it is always open to the architect to call for further information either before or in the course of investigating a claim. It is possible to imagine circumstances where the briefest and most uninformative notification of a claim would suffice: a case, for instance, where the architect was well aware of the contractor's plans and of a delay in progress caused by a requirement that works be opened up for inspection but where a dispute whether the contractor had suffered direct loss or expense in consequence of the delay had already emerged. In such case the contractor might give a purely formal notice solely in order to ensure that the issue would in due course be determined by an arbitrator when the discretion would be exercised by the arbitrator in the place of the architect.

'I am not therefore persuaded that the arbitrator erred in principle in his approach to the documents relied on by the contractor.

Paragraphs (i), (ii) and (iii) overlap [the other issues]. However, they have been separately argued and I think that, at the risk of repetition, I should express my opinion on them.

'The arbitrator starts by summarising his conclusions [on the other issues] that:

"The conditions of contract only require the contractor to give a simple notice of application for loss and expense, indicating under which clause the application is made".

He adds that it is normal practice to give such additional information but that:

"... any such additional information is given voluntarily and not as a contract requirement".

'If the notice does not give the architect sufficient information for him to take the initial step of forming an opinion he must ask the contractor to furnish him with such further information as he requires for that purpose.

'This passage in the interim award is I think open to criticism in two respects. Clauses 11(6) and 24(1) do not require the contractor to make any application. They govern the steps to be taken if notice is given. I will return to this point later. Secondly, for the reasons I have already given, I think that if a written application is made under clauses 11(6) or 24(1) it should be made with sufficient particularity to enable the architect to know upon what question he is required to form an opinion. What in this context is a sufficient degree of particularity is a question of substance which cannot be determined in the abstract as a preliminary issue. It must be decided in the light of all the relevant circumstances including the knowlege of the architect as to the contractor's programme and any interruption in the planned progress of the work that has occurred. It may be that in some circumstances, as I have said, a very brief and uninformative notice will suffice. If a notice does sufficiently indicate the question on which the architect is required to form an opinion it is for the architect to obtain the information which he considers necessary to enable him to do so, whether from the contractor or from some other source. If the contractor on making an application under clauses 11(6) or 24(1) fails to identify with sufficient particularity the question on which the architect is required to form an opinion he cannot recover direct loss or expense under clause 24(1). It does not follow that he has no remedy. Again I will return to this point later.

'If the architect on application by the contractor forms an opinion favourable to the contractor it is his duty to ascertain or to instruct the quantity surveyor to ascertain the loss or expense suffered. The machinery of the contract for the payment of the contract sum and in particular the payment on issue of interim certificates then applies. The contractor must clearly co-operate with the architect or the quantity surveyor in giving such particulars of the loss or expenses claimed as the architect or quantity surveyor may require to enable him to ascertain the extent of that loss or expense; clearly the contractor cannot complain that the architect has failed to ascertain or to instruct the quantity surveyor to ascertain the amount of direct loss or expense attributable to one of the specified heads if he has failed adequately to answer a request for information which the architect requires if he or the quantity surveyor is to carry out that task.

'(iv) This is described by the arbitrator as the central issue. It will I think be more convenient to deal with it together with another issue.

'(v) I think the short answer to the question of whether the contractor was in breach of contract in making the application is that the contractor is not obliged to make a claim under clauses 11(6) or 24(1) at all. He is entitled to do so. If he makes a claim but fails to do so with sufficient particularity to enable the architect to perform his duty to or if he fails to answer a reasonable request for further information he may lose any right to recover loss or expense under those sub-clauses and may not be in a position to complain that the architect was in breach of his duty.'

These findings may be summarised as follows:

(1) The contractor has no duty to make a claim; it is an entitlement, not a duty. The contractor is therefore not in breach of contract if he fails to make an application for 'direct loss and/or expense' or to make it in the proper form, but he may lose his entitlement to recover under the contract (although, by virtue of clause 24(2), he will not lose his right to claim damages at common law for those matters which also constitute breaches of contract by the employer or the architect on his behalf).

(2) In order to preserve his entitlement to recovery under the contract the contractor must make an application at the proper time and in a form which will enable the architect to understand the nature of the claim; but the application itself need go no further than this.

(3) Again in order to preserve his entitlement the contractor in support of his application must provide the architect with sufficient futher information to enable the architect to form a judgment as to the validity of the claim and must further provide the architect and/or the quantity surveyor with sufficient further information to enable them properly to ascertain the amount of direct loss and/or expense incurred.

(4) However, the architect and/or the quantity surveyor cannot sit back and say 'we cannot form a judgment or carry out the ascertainment because the contractor has not volunteered the necessary further information'. They have a duty to request the contractor to provide the information necessary for the carrying out of their own duties.

(5) If the contractor fails to provide sufficient further information upon request he may again lose his entitlement to recovery under

the contract but not his entitlement to damages at common law for those matters which are also breaches of contract.

It will be seen that all the terms regarding the provision of further information by the contractor and the architect's/quantity surveyor's duty to request it are now express terms of JCT 80 clause 26.1.

As to the 'matters' giving rise to entitlement, sub-paragraphs (a), (b), (c), (d) and (e) of clause 24(1) correspond to the equivalent 'matters' set out in JCT 80, clause 26.2.1, .2, .3, .4.1 and .5, respectively. Clause 11(6) corresponds, with modifications, to clause 26.2.7 but the latter relates only to the effect upon regular progress of the works of the execution of variations and provisional sum work. There is no equivalent in JCT 63 of clauses 26.2.4.2 and 26.2.6.

Comparison between the wording of clause 24(1)(d) of JCT 63 and clause 26.2.4.1 of JCT 80 reveals significant differences. In JCT 63 the reference is to 'delay on the part of artists tradesmen or others' and this raises two points. The decision of the House of Lords in *Westminster Corporation* v. *J. Jarvis & Sons Ltd* (1970), on the interpretation of the phrase 'delay on the part of' nominated sub-contractors in clause 23(g), would seem to restrict the operation of clause 24(1) (d) to delay by such persons in the execution of their work and would not include, for example, delay caused by their returning to site to remedy defects; and this is in contrast with the revised wording in JCT 80, clause 26.2.4.1. Further, if the views expressed by Judge Edgar Fay QC in *Henry Boot Construction Ltd* v. *Central Lancashire New Town Development Corporation* (1980) are correct, the phrase 'artists tradesmen *or others*' is not to be construed *ejusdem generis* and so the word 'others' is not restricted to persons of the like kind to 'artists and tradesmen' and in that case was held apt to cover statutory undertakers carrying out work under contract to the employer.

The lack of any reference to work carried out by the employer himself should be noted in clause 24(1)(d). This yawning gap has been filled by the revised wording of clause 26.2.4.1 in JCT 80.

The preceding discussion deals only with the differences between money claims under JCT 63 and similar claims under JCT 80. In all other respects readers are referred to our discussion of clause 26 in chapter 5.

Chapter 7

Claims under GC/Works/1

INTRODUCTION

The General Conditions of Government Contracts for Building and Civil Engineering Works, commonly called Form GC/Works/1, are used by many government departments for construction works. The current version is Edition 2, published in September 1977, as amended to 17 November 1987. The conditions can be used as a full bill form of contract, as a schedule form of contract, or as a lump sum form. They differ basically from the JCT Standard Forms and, unlike the JCT contract, GC/Works/1 is not a negotiated document. It is drafted on behalf of the relevant government departments and with the employer's interests in mind. Accordingly, it is an employer's 'standard form of contract' for the purposes of the Unfair Contract Terms Act 1977, section 3, which is wide ranging in its effect on contractual responsibilities. The 1977 Act does not apply to the Crown, but the point would be applicable where GC/Works/1 is adopted by an employer who is not technically an emanation of the Crown. Moreover, any ambiguities in GC/Works/1 will be construed *contra proferentem* the employer. Thus, it is submitted that the liquidated damages clause [clause 29] and extensions of time clause [clause 28(2)] will be so construed in accordance with the views expressed by Lord Justice Salmon in *Peak Construction (Liverpool) Ltd* v. *McKinney Foundations Ltd* (1970) where he said: 'Liquidated damages and extension of time clauses in printed forms of contract must be construed *contra proferentem.*'

The principles involved in claims under GC/Works/1, Edition 2 are, however, identical with those in JCT claims, which have been discussed in earlier chapters. This chapter will examine the particular provisions in GC/Works/1 that may give rise to claims by the contractor.

210

CLAUSE 9 – VALUATION OF SUPERINTENDING OFFICERS' (SO's) INSTRUCTIONS

The text of this important clause reads as follows:

9 (1) 'The value of alterations in, additions to and omissions from the Works made in compliance with the SO's instructions shall be added to or deducted from the Contract Sum, as the case may be, and shall be ascertained by the Quantity Surveyor as follows:

(a) by measurement and valuation at the rates and prices for similar work in the Bills of Quantities or Schedules of Rates in so far as such rates and prices apply;

(b) if such rates and prices do not apply, by measurement and valuation at rates and prices deduced therefrom in so far as it is practicable to do so;

(c) if such rates and prices do not apply and it is not practicable to deduce rates and prices therefrom, by measurement and valuation at fair rates and prices; or

(d) if the value of alterations or additions cannot properly be ascertained by measurement and valuation, by the value of the materials used and plant and labour employed thereon in accordance with the basis of charge for daywork described in the Contract:

Provided that where an alteration in or addition to the Works would otherwise fall to be valued under sub-paragraph (a) or (b) above but the Quantity Surveyor is of the opinion that the instruction therefor was issued at such a time or was of such content as to make it unreasonable for the alteration or addition to be so valued, he shall ascertain the value by measurement and valuation at fair rates and prices.

(2) (a) If the Contractor –

(i) properly and directly incurs any expense beyond that otherwise provided for in or reasonably contemplated by the Contract in complying with any of the SO's instructions (other than instructions for alterations in, additions to or omissions from the Works), or

(ii) can reasonably effect any saving in the cost of the execution of the Works in or as a result of complying with any of the SO's instructions,

the Contract Sum shall, subject to sub-paragraph (b) of this paragraph and to Condition 23, be increased by the amount of that expense, or shall be decreased by the amount of that saving, as ascertained by the Quantity Surveyor.

(b) It shall be a condition precedent to the Contract Sum being increased under sub-paragraph (a) of this paragraph that –

(i) as soon as reasonably practicable after incurring the expense the Contractor shall have provided such documents and information in respect of the expense as he is required to provide under Condition 37(2); and

(ii) the instruction shall not have been rendered necessary as a result of any default on the part of the Contractor.

(3) If any alterations or additions (other than those authorised to be executed by daywork) have been covered up by the Contractor without his having given notice in pursuance of the provisions of Condition 22 of his intention to do so, the Quantity Surveyor shall be entitled to appraise the value thereof and his decision thereon shall be final and conclusive.'

This condition provides for the measurement and valuation of three separate things. First, variations instructed by the SO under clause 7(1)(b). Secondly, certain expenses 'properly and directly' incurred by the contractor in complying with any other instructions of the SO, and which are contractor's claims for the purposes of this book. Thirdly, any savings in the cost of the execution of the works consequent on any of the SO's instructions.

The clause assigns measurement and valuation to the quantity surveyor, but as clause 37(2) makes plain the contractor must 'provide to the quantity surveyor all documents and information necessary for the calculation of the Final Sum ... certified in such a manner as the Quantity Surveyor may require'.

Valuation of variations

The principles of valuation of variations are the same as those under the JCT contracts as explained in chapter 3. Clause 9(1) states that the value of such variations is to be ascertained by the quantity surveyor in accordance with the rules it contains, and these are set out in order of application. The valuation rules are:

(a) By measurement and valuation at the rates and prices for similar work in the bills of quantities or schedule of rates in so far as such rates and prices apply.

(b) If such rates and prices do not apply, by measurement and valuation at rates and prices deduced therefrom in so far as it is practicable to do so.

(c) By measurement and valuation at fair rates and prices if the rates and prices for similar work are inapplicable and it is impracticable to deduce rates and prices therefrom.

(d) Where the valuation of alterations or additions cannot properly be ascertained by measurement and valuation, then by the value of the materials used and the plant and labour employed thereon in accordance with the basis of charge for daywork described in the contract. Clause 24 deals with the contractor's obligation to produce daywork vouchers for verification.

There is a proviso that qualifies rules (a) and (b), and it confers a discretion on the quantity surveyor. He is entitled to value on the basis of 'fair rates and prices' where, in his opinion, the instruction for the variation was issued at such a time or was of such a content as to make it *unreasonable* to be valued in accordance with rules (a) and (b).

Expense incurred
Clause 9(2) is a two-edged sword and provides for the adjustment of the contract sum in two sets of circumstances.

Paragraph (a)(i) is a claims provision. The contract sum is to be *increased* by the amount of 'any expense beyond that otherwise provided for in or reasonably contemplated by the Contract in complying with any' instructions of the SO, other than variation instructions.

The wording of this paragraph raises considerable difficulties, which have been analysed competently by Mr I. N. Duncan Wallace (*Further Forms*, page 25). It is suggested that expense incurred consequent on complying with an SO's instruction to suspend the execution of the works would be reimbursable under the paragraph, as would expense consequent upon the issue of an SO's instruction under many headings set out in clause 7(1), which authorises the SO to issue instructions in regard to:

(a) The variation or modification of the design, quality or quantity of the works or the addition or omission or substitution of any work.
(b) Any discrepancy in or between the specification and/or bills and/or drawings.
(c) The removal from site of materials brought thereon by the contractor and the substitution therefor of other materials.
(d) The removal and/or re-execution of any work executed by the contractor.
(e) The order of execution of the works or any part thereof.
(f) The hours of working and the extent of overtime or nightwork to be adopted.
(g) The suspension of the execution of the works or part thereof.
(h) The replacement of any foreman or person below that grade employed in connection with the contract.
(i) The opening up for inspection of any work covered up.
(j) The amending or making good of defects.
(k) The execution in an emergency of work necessary for security.
(l) The use of materials obtained from excavations on site.
(m) Any other matter as to which it is necessary or expedient for the SO to issue instructions.

It is submitted, for example, that a claim would lie under clause 9(2)(a)(i) in respect of expense consequential under (f), for example, where the change in hours of working, etc. was not foreseeable. But the wording of the paragraph should be noted.

It may well be in practice that the difficulties envisaged by the commentators are more apparent than real.

Paragraph (a)(ii) deals with the converse case and provides that if the contractor can reasonably effect any saving in the cost of the execution of the works in or as a result of complying with *any* of the SO's instructions (including a variation instruction), the contract sum is to be *decreased* by the amount of that saving.

Two conditions precedent must be fulfilled before a claim is allowed under paragraph (a)(i). These are set out in clause 9(2)(b):

(1) The contractor must have provided the quantity surveyor with all necessary documents and information in respect of the expense claimed as soon as reasonably practicable after incurring the expense.

(2) The instruction must not have been rendered necessary as a result of any default on the contractor's part.

Alterations or additions covered up

Clause 9(3) deals with alterations or additions (other than those authorised to be executed by daywork) which have been covered up by the contractor without his having given the SO notice of his intention to do so as is required by clause 22. In such a case, the sub-clause empowers the quantity surveyor 'to appraise the value' of the work so covered up and states baldly that 'his decision thereon shall be final and conclusive'. In other words, the merits of the quantity surveyor's decision are not open to review on arbitration.

CLAUSE 53 – PROLONGATION AND DISRUPTION EXPENSES

This clause is the equivalent of JCT 80, clause 26 but, unlike that provision, it is more limited in its operation. Its objective is to reimburse the contractor for any *expense* in performing the contract as a result of regular progress of the whole or part of the works being 'materially disrupted or prolonged' as an unavoidable result of one or more of five specified matters.

The text of clause 53 reads as follows:

53 (1) 'If

    (a) complying with any of the SO's instructions;

    (b) the making good of loss or damage falling within Condition 26(2);

    (c) the execution of works pursuant to Condition 50; or

    (d) delay in the provision of any of the items specified in paragraph (2) of this Condition; or

    (e) any Unforeseeable Ground Conditions

unavoidably results in the regular progress of the Works or of any part thereof being materially disrupted or prolonged and in consequence of such disruption or prolongation the Contractor properly and directly incurs any expense in performing the Contract which he would not otherwise have incurred and which is beyond that otherwise provided for in or reasonably contemplated by the Contract, the Contract Sum shall, subject to paragraph (3) of this Condition and to Condition 23, be increased by the amount of that expense as ascertained by the Quantity Surveyor:

Provided that there shall be no such increase in respect of expense incurred in consequence of the making good of loss or damage falling within Condition 26(2) except where the Contractor is entitled to payment under that provision, and where his entitlement to payment under that provision is limited to a proportionate sum any such increase in respect of expense so incurred shall be limited in like manner.

(2) The items referred to in sub-paragraph (1)(d) of this Condition are –

    (a) any drawings, schedules, levels or other design information to be provided by the SO and to be prepared otherwise than by the Contractor or any of his sub-contractors;

    (b) any work the execution of which, or thing the supplying of which, is to be undertaken by the Authority or is to be ordered direct by him otherwise than from the Contractor and is to be so undertaken or ordered otherwise than in consequence of any default on the part of the Contractor; and

    (c) any direction from the Authority or the SO regarding the nomination or appointment of any person, or any instruction of the SO or consent of the Authority, to be given under Condition 38(4).

(3) It shall be a condition precedent to the Contract Sum being increased under paragraph (1) of this Condition –

    (a) in the case of expense incurred in consequence of an SO's instruction, that the instruction shall have been given or confirmed in writing and shall not have been rendered necessary as a result of any default on the part of the Contractor;

    (b) in the case of expense incurred in consequence of delay in the provision of any of the items specified in paragraph (2) of this Condition, that, except where a date for the provision of the relevant item was agreed with the SO, the Contractor shall, neither unreasonably early nor unreasonably late, have given notice to the SO specifying that item and the date by which it was reasonably required; and

(c) in any case that –

(i) the Contractor, immediately upon becoming aware that the regular progress of the Works or of any part thereof has been or is likely to be disrupted or prolonged as aforesaid, shall have given notice to the SO specifying the circumstances causing or expected to cause that disruption or prolongation and stating that he is or expects to be entitled to an increase in the Contract Sum under that paragraph;

(ii) as soon as reasonably practicable after incurring the expense the Contractor shall have provided such documents and information in respect of the expense as he is required to provide under Condition 37(2).'

The first point to note is that the clause refers only to 'expense'; and it must be an expense 'beyond that otherwise provided for in or reasonably contemplated by the Contract'. This is an objective test; it is *not* the contemplation of the contractor concerned. It must also be an expense which the contractor 'would not otherwise have incurred' and it must have been '*properly and directly*' incurred by the contractor. In other words, consequential loss is excluded and it would seem that the incurring of the expense must be wholly unexpected. In the first edition of this book, we expressed the view that the amount recoverable under clause 53 (and clause 9(2)(a)(i)) was limited to 'expense' in the sense of money paid out. On that view, loss of profit would clearly be excluded. We no longer think that this is necessarily the case, because in law the word 'expense' is not necessarily treated as excluding loss: see *Re Stratton's Deed of Disclaimer* (1957) where the phrase under consideration was 'at the expense of the deceased'. This, of course, is not the same as the GC/ Works/1 phrase 'incur any expense', and on different wording in a charterparty the Court of Appeal took a more limited approach in *Chandris* v. *Union of India* (1956) where the phrase 'any expense in shifting the cargo' was at issue. There were numerous clauses in the charterparty which drew a distinction between 'expense' or 'expenses' on the one hand and 'time occupied' on the other. In these circumstances, Lord Justice Denning was firmly of the opinion that 'expense' in the context meant 'money spent out of pocket and does not include loss of time'.

However, the other clauses in GC/Works/1 do not make a clear distinction between 'expense' and 'loss'. Clause 9(2)(a)(ii) refers to 'cost' and if this is to be distinguished from expense, it is probable that 'expense' has a wider meaning. Furthermore, in the PSA's *Notice to Tenderers* (C2041, July 1986 – *Valuations under Conditions 9 and 53*, it is recognised that 'expense' includes, *inter alia*, 'interest not earned if the contractor uses his own capital', and that is also support for the wider meaning. Expenses actually incurred would, in any event, include any true additional overhead costs to the contractor, for example, the cost of additional supervision, and the cost of keeping men on site, and on the wider interpretation the amount recoverable would extend to fixed overheads such as head-office rent and rates and so on.

There are five matters that may give rise to a claim for prolongation and disruption expenses under the clause. They are:

(1) Compliance with *any* of the SO's instructions.
(2) Making good of loss or damage that is the responsibility of the authority under clause 26(2), which is loss or damage caused by the neglect or default of Crown servants and the 'accepted risks'. This term is defined (clause 1(2)) as meaning the risks of:

'(a) pressure waves caused by aircraft or other aerial devices whether travelling at sonic or supersonic speeds,
(b) ionising radiations or contamination by radioactivity from any nuclear fuel or from nuclear waste from the combustion of nuclear fuel.
(c) the radioactive, toxic, explosive or other hazardous properties of any explosive nuclear assembly or nuclear compenent thereof, and
(d) war, invasion, act of foreign enemy, hostilities (whether or not war has been declared) civil war, rebellion, revolution, insurrection, or military or usurped power '.

(3) Execution of other works by the authority within clause 50. The latter clause empowers the authority to execute other works on site contemporaneously with the execution of the contract works.
(4) Delay in the provision of any the undermentioned items:

(a) Any drawings, schedules, levels or other design information to be provided by the SO or to be prepared otherwise than by the contractor or one of his sub-contractors;
(b) Work or the supply of goods or materials, etc., which is to be undertaken or ordered direct by the authority otherwise than from the contractor, unless this is done in consequence of some default on the contractor's part.
(c) Any direction of the authority or the SO 'regarding the nomination or appointment of any person', such as a

nominated sub-contractor or supplier or any instruction of the SO or consent of the authority relating to prime cost items.

(5) Any unforeseeable ground conditions. This ground was inserted by Amendment 4 (which became effective on 17 November 1987) as a result of a new clause 2A dealing with Unforeseeable Ground Conditions. The clause inserted reads:

'2A (1) If, during the execution of the works, the contractor becomes aware of ground conditions (excluding those caused by weather but including artificial obstructions) which he did not know of, or which he could not reasonably have foreseen having regard to any information which he had or ought reasonably to have had, he shall immediately give notice to the SO –
(a) specifying those conditions, and
(b) stating the measures which he proposes to take to deal with them.

(2) If the SO agrees that the ground conditions specified in the contractor's notice could not have been reasonably foreseen having regard to any information he should have had in accordance with the paragraph and Condition 2 (1), he shall certify those conditions to be Unforeseeable Ground Conditions. The SO shall inform the contractor in writing of his decision.

(3) If as a result of Unforeseeable Ground Conditions the Contractor in executing the Works properly carries out or omits any work which he would not otherwise have carried out or omitted then, without prejudice to any instruction given by the SO under condition 7, the value of the work carried out or omitted shall be ascertained in accordance with Condition 9 and the Contract Sum increased or decreased accordingly'.

This new provision thus provides a completely new head of claim and it is clearly and sensibly modelled on the corresponding provision in the ICE Conditions of Contract.

The abstract of particulars (which is one of the contract documents) is a vital document when considering claims under clause 53 since, among other things, it lists dates for the supply of certain information – which is relevant to a claim in respect of item (a) – and also gives the periods that the contractor requires for sub-contract nominations – which is relevant to a claim in respect of (c).

Merely because one or more of these events occur does not give rise to an automatic claim. The clause states that the amount of the expense is to be ascertained by the quantity surveyor and added to the contract sum only if:

(1) The matter relied upon unavoidably results in the *regular progress*

of the works being *materially disrupted or prolonged*, and there is no guidance in the contract conditions. At common law it is a term implied in every building contract that the contractor 'will proceed with reasonable diligence and maintain reasonable progress' (*Hudson*, 10th Edition, page 314), but as Mr Justice Megarry remarked in *London Borough of Hounslow* v. *Twickenham Garden Developments Ltd* (1970), when considering the contractor's express obligation under a JCT contract to proceed 'regularly and diligently' with the works, there is uncertainty as to the concept enshrined in such words.

(2) As a direct result the contractor properly and directly incurs expense in performing the contract which would not otherwise have been incurred; and

(3) The expense incurred must be beyond that otherwise provided for or reasonably contemplated by the contract.

Finally – as clause 53(3) makes plain – the contractor must have taken the steps specified in that sub-clause, and this is expressed to be a condition precedent to a valid claim. Unless the contractor can meet those requirements, his claim is doomed to failure; and the SO is entitled to reject the claim out of hand. The onus of proof is on the contractor.

The specified steps are as follows:

First, the contractor must give written notice to the SO, 'immediately upon becoming aware that ... regular progress ... has been or is likely to be disrupted or prolonged'. The notice must specify the circumstances causing or expected to cause disruption or prolongation. It must also state that the contractor is or expects to be entitled to an increase in the contract sum under clause 53(1).

This is an important requirement, as was emphasised by the court in *Tersons Ltd* v. *Stevenage Development Corporation* (1965), the notice provisions being for the benefit of both authority and contractor, and it is the service of notice that sets the machinery in motion.

Secondly, the contractor must have provided the quantity surveyor with 'all documents and information necessary for the calculation ... certified in such manner as the quantity surveyor may require': see clause 37(2). These two requirements are laid down by clause 53(3)(c).

Thirdly – but this applies only where the expense was incurred in consequence of an SO's instruction – the instruction must have been given or confirmed in writing. Moreover, the instruction must not have been made necessary as a result of any default by the contractor.

Fourthly, where the expense is incurred in consequence of delay in providing the items referred to in clause 53(2), the contractor must have applied in writing to the SO for the information and the contractor's application must not have been made too early or too late. The only exception is where a date for the provision of the relevant information was agreed with the SO: see clause 53(3)(b).

It cannot be too strongly emphasised that it is for the contractor to trigger off the claim under this clause. As soon as the contractor becomes aware that regular progress has been or is likely to be disrupted or prolonged then he must give written notice to the SO immediately. The wording suggests that one notice is sufficient; and a series of notices is not required. Contractors should not wait until they see exactly how far the regular progress of the works is affected, as otherwise they may find the notice rejected as being out of time.

There is no particular form of notice required, but it must specify the circumstances giving rise to the claim and state that the contractor is or expects to be entitled to an increase in the contract sum, and it is suggested that it should refer specifically to the provisions of clause 53.

There is an important proviso to clause 53(1), the effect of which is that no payment will be made in respect of any expense incurred in consequence of the making good of loss or damage falling under clause 26(2), unless the contractor is entitled to payment under that clause. Clause 26(2) deals with damage to the works, etc. and makes the authority liable for such loss or damage if it is caused by the neglect or default of Crown servants and by the accepted risks; in other cases the contractor is liable.

There is another contract provision under which financial claims may arise against the authority and that is under clause 44, which confers upon the authority a *discretionary* power to determine the contract at any time by notice to the contractor. This is a power additional to the authority's common law rights to determine for certain serious breaches of contract by the contractor or under clause 45 of GC/Works/1 for certain specific defaults of the contractor, or under clause 55 on account of corrupt gifts or payments. Clause 44 sets out the various amounts payable to the contractor when the contract is so specially determined, and the only sub-clause that need comment is clause 44(5), which reads as follows:

44 (5) 'If upon the determination of the Contract under this Condition the Contractor is of the opinion that he has suffered hardship by reason of the operation of this Condition he may refer the circumstances to the Authority, who, on being satisfied that such hardship exists, or has existed, shall make such allowance, if any, as in his opinion is reasonable, and his decision on that matter shall be final and conclusive.'

As is apparent from the wording, such a hardship payment is wholly discretionary, and the writers share the view expressed by Mr I. N. Duncan Wallace (*Further Forms*, page 59) that 'the words "hardship" and "allowance" ... are ... deplorably vague, and certainly not the equivalent ... of "damage" or "expense" and "damages" ...'. Payment of any allowance under sub-clause (5) is entirely within the authority's discretion, and the authority's decision is made 'final and conclusive'. The dictionary defines 'hardship' as 'hardness of fate or circumstances; severe suffering or privation', and effectively the provision merely empowers the authority to make *ex gratia* payments if it so decides. It is understood that, in practice, any allowance made for hardship suffered by the contractor as a result of the exercise of the special powers of determination does, in fact, include something for loss of profit.

EXTENSIONS OF TIME AND LIQUIDATED DAMAGES

Clause 28(2) is the provision under which any alteration to the date for completion is made. The 'date for completion' is the date set out in or ascertained in accordance with the abstract of particulars or the date on which any extensions of time which the contractor is allowed under clause 28(2) expire.

The text of clause 28(2) is as follows:

28 (2) 'The Contractor shall be allowed by the Authority a reasonable extension of time for the completion of the Works or of any section for which a separate date for completion is specified in the Abstract of Particulars in respect of any delay in such completion which has been caused or which the Authority is satisfied will be caused by any of the following circumstances –

  (a) the execution of any modified or additional work;
  (b) weather conditions which make continuance of work impracticable;
  (c) any act or default of the Authority;
  (d) strikes or lock-outs of workpeople employed in any of the building, civil engineering or analogous trades in the district in which the Works are being executed or employed in the preparation or manufacture of things for incorporation;
  (e) any of the accepted risks or any Unforeseeable Ground Conditions; or
  (f) any other circumstance which is wholly beyond the control of the Contractor:

Provided that –
  (i) except in so far as the Authority shall otherwise decide, it shall be a condition upon the observance of which the Contractor's right to any such extension of time shall depend that the Contractor shall, immediately upon becoming aware that any such delay has been or will be

> caused, give notice to the SO specifying therein the circumstances causing
> or likely to cause the delay and the actual or estimated extent of the delay
> caused or likely to be caused thereby;
> (ii) in determining what extension of time the Contractor is entitled to the
>   Authority shall be entitled to take into account the effect of any
>   authorised omission from the Works; and
> (iii) the Contractor shall not be entitled to an extension of time if any such
>   delay is attributable to any negligence, default or improper conduct on his
>   part.'

The initiative for taking action under this provision lies on the contractor when he realises that the works are running behind time. This is made clear by proviso (i), which states '*except in so far as the Authority shall otherwise decide*, it shall be a condition upon the observance of which the Contractor's right to any such extension of time shall depend that the Contractor shall ... give notice to the SO' *immediately* he becomes aware that delay *has been or will be caused.* In practical terms this means that the contractor must give written notice immediately he becomes so aware. The notice must be specific in its terms. It should identify one or more of the specified causes and must also give the actual or estimated period of delay.

The authority must then consider the matter. The duty imposed upon the authority by the clause is to allow the contractor a *reasonable* extension of time for completion in respect of any delay in completion that has been caused or which the authority is satisfied will be caused by one or more of the seven specific causes. The delay in progress must mean a failure or likely failure to achieve the date for completion, and the three provisos to clause 28(2) are important. In determining to what extension of time the contractor is entitled (if any), the authority is entitled to take into account the effect of any authorised omission from the works: see proviso (ii). An omission may, and often will, have the effect of saving time.

The terms of proviso (iii) should be noted. The contractor is not entitled to any extension of time if the delay is attributable to any negligence, default or improper conduct on his part.

It is sometimes questioned whether the authority can defer its decision as to extensions of time until it sees how the works progress, or whether the authority must grant an extension of time once it is satisfied that 'any delay in completion ... has been caused or which the authority is satisfied will be caused' by any of the specified events.

The case of *Amalgamated Building Contractors Ltd* v. *Waltham Holy Cross UDC* (1952) suggests that where the delaying event is one outside the control of the authority – for example, weather conditions, labour disputes, etc. – or is within the contractor's control, then the authority need not decide on whether or not to make an extension of time until or even after the works have been completed, even though the original date for completion has passed. In other words, an extension of time may be granted even after the works have been completed if the cause of delay operates until the completion.

On the other hand, if the event causing the delay is one within the control of the authority or of the SO, e.g. 'any act or default of the authority', it seems that in those circumstances the authority must then decide whether or not to grant an extension before or on the date for completion as set out in the abstract of particulars, just as it must do if the cause of the delay has ceased to operate before completion. If it fails so to do, then the date for completion may become at large: see *Miller* v. *LCC* (1934) and *Anderson* v. *Tuapeka County Council* (1900).

The cause or causes of delay of which the contractor must give written notice must fall within one or more of paragraphs (a) to (f). If the authority is not satisfied that the delay is caused by one or more of the circumstances specified, the contractor's only method of challenging that decision is by way of arbitration under clause 61.

The specified circumstances are:

(a) *The execution of any modified or additional work.* (For example, pursuant to an instruction from the SO under clause 7(1)(a).) This ground may, and independently, also give rise to a money claim under clause 53(1)(a).

(b) *Weather conditions which make continuance of the work impracticable.* The weather conditions relied on must make continuance of the work *impracticable*, which means, according to the *Concise Oxford Dictionary*, 'impossible in practice'. The weather conditions must therefore, interfere with the work at the particular stage it has reached and make it impossible in practice to continue with that work.

This form of contract also confers on the SO an express power to order suspension of the works or part thereof in order to avoid risk of damage from frost, inclement weather 'or other like causes'. This power is contained in clause 23, in which case any extra cost involved as a result of the suspension may be recoverable under clauses 9(2) or 53(1).

(c) *Any act or default of the authority.* In our view, this ground would extend to cover the acts or defaults of those for whom the authority is responsible vicariously in law. 'Default' does not have a limited meaning as is sometimes contended: see *City of Manchester* v. *Fram Gerrard Ltd* (1977), discussed in chapter 8, page 233.

(d) *Strikes or lock-outs of workpeople employed in any of the building, civil engineering or analogous trades in the district in which the works are being executed or employed in the preparation or manufacture of things for incorporation.* This ground applies to strikes or lock-outs in two kinds of trades : first, those employed in any of the building and allied trades in the district; secondly, those engaged in preparing or manufacturing any goods or materials required for the works. It does not cover non-building-type trades, for example, a strike of lorry-drivers engaged in transporting materials to site, and this would fall to be dealt with under paragraph (f).

(e) *Any of the accepted risks or any unforeseeable ground conditions.* The 'accepted risks' are defined in clause 1(2), and are similar to those in other construction industry contracts. The full list of accepted risks is set out on page 217. 'Unforeseeable ground conditions' means those ground conditions certified by the SO under clause 2A which is set out on p. 218.

(f) *Any other circumstance which is wholly beyond the control of the contractor.* The word 'wholly' is important, but the wording is wide and is generously interpreted (at least by the PSA) in practice, although it is probably aimed at what is usually called Act of God, which is an overwhelming superhuman event, and also at circumstances covered in other forms of contract by the term *'force majeure'*. This is a French law term which in English law 'is used with reference to all circumstances independent of the will of man, and which it is not in his power to control': *Lebeaupin* v. *Crispin* (1920).

In *Matsoukis* v. *Priestman & Co.* (1915) the term *'force majeure'* was held to apply to dislocation of business caused by a nation-wide coal strike and also accidents to machinery. It did not cover delays caused by bad weather, football matches or a funeral, on the basis that these were quite usual incidents interrupting work and the contractors ought to have taken them into account in making the contract.

A question commonly asked is whether delays caused by suppliers and sub-contractors, nominated or domestic, are covered by the paragraph. So far as domestic sub-contractors and suppliers are concerned, it is our view that delays caused by them are at the risk of the contractor and so do not fall within paragraph (f). Clause 31(3) states that the contractor must 'make good any loss suffered or expense incurred by the Authority by reason of any default or failure, whether total or partial, on the part of any sub-contractor or supplier'. In our view, the position is the same as far as delays caused by nominated sub-contractors and nominated suppliers are concerned, and consequently the contractor cannot use delay by sub-contractors, etc. as the basis for a claim for extension of time under this paragraph.

Delays caused by persons with whom the authority contracts direct under clause 38(4) do fall within the paragraph.

Liquidated damages are dealt with by clause 29 which provides for the payment of such damages by the contractor if he fails to complete the works and clear the site on or before the date for completion or any extension of that date authorised by the authority under clause 28(2).

Clause 29 reads as follows:

29 (1) 'If –
   (a) the Works shall not be completed and the Site cleared and delivered up on or before the date for completion to the satisfaction of the SO, or
   (b) any section (in respect of which a rate of liquidated damages is specified in the Abstract of Particulars) shall not be completed and any relevant part of the Site is not so delivered up by the due date for completion.

the Contractor shall pay to the Authority liquidated damages in respect of the delay in due completion calculated in accordance with the Abstract of Particulars for the period during which the Works, or any section, shall remain uncompleted and the Site, or any relevant part, is not duly delivered up to the satisfaction of the SO.'

(2) No payment or concession to the Contractor or order for modified or additional work at any time given to the Contractor or other act or omission of the Authority or his servants shall in any way affect the rights of the Authority to recover the said liquidated damages or shall be deemed to be a waiver of the right of the Authority to recover such damages unless such waiver has been expressly stated in writing signed by or on behalf of the Authority.

(3) If at any time the Authority (whether or not he has previously allowed the Contractor any extension of time under Condition 28) gives notice to the Contractor that, in the opinion of the Authority, the Contractor is not entitled to any or (as the case may be) any further extension, then any sum which at that time would represent the amount of liquidated damages payable by the Contractor under this Condition or this Condition as modified by Condition 28A(4) (as the case may be) shall be treated for the purposes of Condition 43 as a sum recoverable from or payable by the Contractor.'

Liquidated damages will not be recoverable by the authority if the authority is at all responsible for failure to achieve the completion date. This point was emphasised by Mr Justice Staughton in *Astilleros Canarios SA* v. *Cape Hatteras Shipping Co.* (1981):

'[The] cases show that if completion by the specified date was prevented by the fault of the employer, he can recover no liquidated damages unless there is a clause providing for extension of time in the event of delay caused by him.'

In other words, where completion of the contract works or any section (if sectional completion applies) in due time has been prevented by the authority's act or default, the authority cannot recover liquidated damages from the contractor, unless the authority has granted an extension of time on that ground: see clause 28(2)(c). It seems also that if no extension of time is granted under clause 28 the contractor might, in such circumstances, argue that the delay was not caused by him but by the authority and therefore no liquidated damages are payable. This would also be the case where there is power to extend time but it has not been properly exercised: see *Peak Construction (Liverpool) Ltd* v. *McKinney Foundations Ltd* (1971).

GC/Works/1 is not a negotiated contract, but is one drawn up on behalf of the government departments that use it. Accordingly, as indicated earlier, it is to be construed *contra proferentem* the authority, whose document it is. To quote Lord Justice Salmon in *Peak Construction (Liverpool) Ltd* v. *McKinney Foundations Ltd*:

'The liquidated damages and extension of time clauses in printed forms of contract must be construed strictly *contra proferentem*. If the employer wishes to recover liquidated damages for failure by the contractor to complete on time in spite of the fact that some of the delay is due to the employer's own fault or breach of contract, then the extension of time clause should provide, expressly or by necessary inference, for an extension on account of such a fault or breach on the part of the employer...'

His lordship added that failure by the employer to extend time where the contract provided for an extension of time on grounds of employer's fault 'would be fatal to the claim for liquidated damages'. No liquidated damages are recoverable where the authority has failed to extend time when it should do so.

An earlier illustration of this principle is to be found in the case of *Miller* v. *London County Council* (1934). There, a building contract provided that the whole of the work should be completed by 15 November 1931. Clause 31 provided that 'it shall be lawful for the engineer, if he shall think fit, to grant from time to time, and at any time or times, by writing under his hand such extension of time for completion of the work and that either prospectively or retrospectively, and to assign such other time or times for completion as to him may seem reasonable'. Clause 37 provided that should the contractor fail in due completion of the work, he should pay liquidated damages for delay at a specified rate.

The work was not completed until 25 July 1932. Some four months after completion of the work the engineer issued a certificate granting an extension of time to 7 February 1932, and subsequently certified a sum of £2625 as payable by the contractor to the building owner under clause 37 for the delay from 7 February to 25 July 1932.

Mr Justice du Parcq, who construed the relevant clause *contra proferentem* the employer, 'on the ground that it was [they] who prepared and put forward the contract', held that the words 'either prospectively or retrospectively' in clause 31 did not give the engineer a right to fix a new date for completion *ex post facto* after the entire work had been completed. They only empowered him, if a delay occurred during the progress of the work, to wait until the cause of the delay had ceased to be operative, and then within a reasonable time after the delay had come to an end 'retrospectively' with regard to the cause of the delay to assign to the contractor a new date for completion. The power to extend the time had not, therefore, been exercised within the time limited by the contract, and so the building owner had lost the benefit of the clause. There was therefore no date from which liquidated damages could run and none were recoverable.

Chapter 8

Claims under the ACA Form

INTRODUCTION

In October 1982 the Association of Consultant Architects published a 'Form of Building Agreement' ('the ACA Form'), together with an associated Form of Sub-Contract. A second and substantially revised edition of the ACA Form was published in 1984. This second edition took account of criticisms made of the first edition, and in parts was substantially redrafted. The ACA Form can be used for 'design, develop and construct' contracts, as well as more normally where the architect produces all the design and construction information. It can be used with or without bills of quantities but, rather oddly, the use of the Standard Method of Measurement has been ignored. It contains a number of alternative clauses, and is highly flexible in use.

The ACA Form has been the target of much criticism from the contracting side of the industry and, fortunately or unfortunately, it has not become as widely used as the ACA had hoped, despite the fact that a British Property Federation (BPF) edition was published in 1984. The edition is especially suitable for use in connection with the BPF system of building procurement described in the *Manual of the BPF System* published in 1983. Since the ACA Form is not a negotiated document (unlike the JCT Forms) it will be construed by the courts *contra proferentem*. This means that any ambiguities in it could be construed against the employer, whose document it is. The JCT Forms are agreed by the whole industry; the ACA Form is not. When a contractor enters into a contract in the ACA Form, he will be entering into a contract on the employer's 'written standard terms of business' for the purposes of s.3 of the Unfair Contract Terms Act 1977, because any employer who utilises the ACA Form makes it his own document in law, just as if he had employed lawyers to draft a special contract for him.

228

The claims provisions of the ACA Form – both as regards money and extensions of time – are different from the corresponding JCT provisions or, indeed, the provisions of other standard forms. In its first alternative, the extension of time provision is narrower than under JCT Forms, to the extent that such things as adverse weather conditions, strikes and delays or unforeseeable shortages in the available ability of labour and materials are not expressly mentioned as grounds for extension of time. However, it covers 'any act, instruction, default or omission of the Employer, or of the Architect on his behalf, whether authorised by or in breach of this Agreement', which is more widely cast than the JCT equivalent. The second alternative is along more traditional lines and includes *force majeure* as a ground for extension of time, as well as other risks which are the fault of neither party. There is, however, an optional provision in the ACA Form for adjudication on disputes related to money and other claims, thus (in theory at any rate) allowing for speedy settlement of disputed claims. The contract deals separately with money claims arising in consequence of 'any act, omission and default of the Employer or of the Architect' and those arising as a consequence of architect's instructions, but in both cases the contractor is required to submit an estimate of the money involved.

The principles involved in assessing claims under the ACA provisions, whether for time or for money, are of course identical with those involved in claims under JCT provisions, which have been discussed earlier. This chapter will examine the particular provisions in the ACA form that may give rise to claims by the contractor.

MONETARY CLAIMS UNDER ACA FORM

There are two sets of provisions that enable the contractor to make a money claim. First, clause 7, which is concerned with disruption of 'the regular progress of the Works or of any Section' of them or which 'delays the execution of them in accordance with the dates stated in the Time Schedule', where the disruption or delay is caused by 'any act, omission, default or negligence of the Employer or of the Architect' (other than architect's instructions). Secondly, clauses 8 and 17, which deal with architect's instructions and their valuation. Architect's instructions, whether in respect of variations or otherwise, may have a serious disruptive effect.

(a) Clause 7 – Employer's liability

The text of this provision reads as follows:

7. EMPLOYER'S LIABILITY

Disturbance to regular progress

7.1 Save in the case of Architect's instructions (to which the provisions of Clause 17 shall apply), if any act, omission or default or negligence of the Employer or of the Architect disrupts the regular progress of the Works or of any Section of delays the execution of them in accordance with the dates stated in the Time Schedule and, in consequence of such disruption or delay, the Contractor suffers or incurs damage, loss and/or expense, he shall be entitled to recover the same in accordance with the provisions of this Clause 7.

Notice of Claim

7.2 Upon it becoming reasonably apparent that any event giving rise to a claim under Clause 7.1 is likely to occur or has occurred, the Contractor shall immediately give notice to the Architect of such event and shall, on presentation of his interim application pursuant to Clause 16.1 next following the giving of such notice, submit to the Architect an estimate of the adjustment to the Contract Sum which the Contractor requires to take account of such damage, loss and/or expense suffered or incurred by him in consequence of such event prior to the date of submission of his estimate.

Submission of estimates

7.3 Following the submission of an estimate under Clause 7.2, the Contractor shall, for so long as the Contractor suffers or incurs damage, loss and/or expense in consequence of such event, on presentation of each interim application pursuant to Clause 16.1, submit to the Architect an estimate of the adjustment to the Contract Sum which the Contractor requires to take account of such damage, loss and/or expense suffered or incurred by him since the submission of his previous estimate.

Agreement of estimates

7.4 Any estimate submitted by the Contractor pursuant to Clause 7.2 or 7.3 shall be supported by such documents, vouchers and receipts as shall be necessary for computing the same or as may be required by the Architect. Within ⎡ 20 ⎤ * working days of receipt of any such estimate duly supported as aforesaid, the Architect shall either give notice that he accepts it or he shall give notice of his wish to negotiate the adjustment to the Contract Sum. Upon agreement being reached as to the amount of any damage, loss and/or expense, the Contract Sum shall be adjusted accordingly and no further or other additions or payments shall be made in respect of the damage, loss and/or expense suffered or incurred by the Contractor during the period and in consequence of the event to which such agreement relates.

Failure by Contractor to submit estimates

7.5 If the Contractor fails to comply with the provisions of Clause 7.2 or 7.3, then the Architect shall have no power or authority to make, and the Contractor shall not be entitled to any adjustment to the Contract Sum in respect of the damage, loss and/or expense to which such failure relates on any certificate issued under this Agreement prior to the Final Certificate. Such adjustment shall not in such event include an addition in respect of loss of interest or financing charge suffered or incurred by the Contractor between the date of the Contractor's failure so to comply and the date of the Final Certificate.

Adjudication

7.6 If agreement cannot be reached within [20] working days after the Architect's notice under Clause 7.4, either party may refer the Contractor's estimates to the Adjudicator for his decision under Clause 25. *

This clause entitles the contractor to claim reimbursement for any 'damage, loss and/or expense' which he suffers or incurs in consequence of delays and disruptions caused by 'any act, omission or default' (save architect's instructions) of the employer or the architect. Delays and disruptions occasioned by architect's instructions – which are by far the commonest ground of claim – are dealt with separately by clauses 8 and 17. The provisions of clause 7 bear some resemblance to the equivalent provisions in the JCT Forms (e.g., JCT 80, clause 26) but that resemblance is only superficial. In issuing the contract form, the ACA stated that under it 'the contractor cannot claim ... additional money for a series of things that most clients consider to be normal building risks'. The scope of this clause is limited.

Moreover, the contractor is only entitled to have the contract sum adjusted, i.e. to payment for claims by way of inclusion of the amount in interim certificates, if he complies exactly with the provisions of clauses 7.2 and 7.3. If he fails to comply with those provisions – which lay down procedures for the giving of notice and the submission of estimates – his entitlement to an adjustment to the contract sum is removed until the final certificate. This is the result of clause 7.5, which has the side-heading 'Failure by Contractor to submit estimates'. It may also be noted that if the optional provision for adjudication forms part of the contract, any dispute under the clause as to the contractor's claims is to be decided by the named adjudicator: clause 7.6.

Each word of clause 7 is important, and the wording used raises several interesting points. Arguments can be anticipated as to what is properly claimable under the clause, particularly as regards the 'damage, loss and/or expense' that is recoverable. There is an important difference in the wording used in this Form and in the equivalent provision of JCT Forms, since under ACA clause 7 the words 'damage, loss and/or expense' are not limited by the word 'direct'. The qualifying phrase is 'in consequence of such disruption or delay' and on one view, a claim under clause 7 will also extend to consequential loss and cover those heads of claim which, if made as damages at common law, are not excluded if the employer, at the time of entering into the contract, knew or must be taken to have known were liable to result from his or his architect's 'act, omission, default or negligence': see *Hadley* v. *Baxendale* (1854).

The common law position as regards damages is quite simple in essence, and was put tersely by Lord Justice Asquith in these words:

> 'The governing purposes of damages is to put the party whose rights have been violated in the same position, so far as money can do, as if his rights had been observed.': *Victoria Laundry Ltd* v. *Newman Industries Ltd* (1949).

However, the defaulting party is not liable 'for all loss *de facto* resulting from a particular breach however improbable, however unpredictable'. The law therefore sets a limit to the loss for which damages are recoverable – sometimes called the general rule as to 'foreseeability'. In both practical and legal terms the contractor's entitlement is to recover only that part of the resulting loss as was reasonably foreseeable as liable to result from the breach relied on. This is to be judged at the time the contract was entered into. Under clause 7.1, therefore the amount claimable includes all foreseeable consequential loss. Loss of profits is included (*Wraight Ltd* v. *P. H. & T. Holdings Ltd* (1968)).

All that is necessary to give rise to a claim under clause 7 is some 'act, omission, default or negligence of the Employer or of the Architect' (other than an architect's instruction). If such an act or omission, etc. disrupts regular progress of the works or delays their execution in accordance with the dates stated in the time schedule, and the contractor suffers or incurs damage, loss and/or expense in consequence of the delay or disruption, he is entitled to recover the amount of the damage, loss and/or expense.

The words 'act, omission, default or negligence' are very important because some of the concepts enshrined in them are very difficult to express. Although the reference is only to employer and architect, it is probable that the clause covers others for whom the employer is vicariously responsible in law. In our view, the first three words must be interpreted without reference to the question of whether or not any relevant act or omission could also have provided the foundation for a claim in tort or in contract against the person directly concerned: it is not necessary for there to have been a breach of some legally enforceable duty. 'Negligence' presents very little practical difficulty because once the facts are established it is usually clear whether a duty of care in the legal sense arises and, if it does, whether it has been broken. In the vast majority of situations covered by clause 7, the contractor *would* have a right of action against the defaulting party, but the scope of this phrase is not to be limited by considering whether the contractor could sue employer or architect direct.

In *In re Bayley-Worthington & Cohen's Contract* (1909), Mr Justice Parker considered, for example the legal meaning of 'default', albeit in the very different context of a contract for the sale of real property. He said there:

> 'Default must, I think, involve either not doing what you ought or doing what you ought not, having regard to your relations with the other parties concerned in the transaction; in other words, it involves the breach of some duty you owe to another or others. It refers to personal conduct and is not the same thing as breach of contract.'

In the context of a construction industry contract – Mr Justice Kerr held (in *City of Manchester* v. *Fram Gerrard Ltd* (1977)), in construing similar words to the present in an indemnity clause, and having cited with approval Mr Justice Parker's statement said that 'default would be established if one of the persons covered by the clause either did not do what he ought to have done, or did what he ought not to have done in all the circumstances, provided of course ... that the conduct in question involves something in the nature of a breach of duty so as to be properly describable as a default'. In our view, this is the correct interpretation to be put upon the wording of clause 7, and this is reinforced by *Greater London Council* v. *The Cleveland Bridge and Engineering Co. Ltd* (1986), which emphasises that 'default' is a narrower term than breach of contract.

This is not to suggest, of course, that it is easy to establish a claim under the clause, and it is important to note that the contractor must be able to show that he 'suffers or incurs damage, loss and/or expense' *in consequence* of the disruption or delay occasioned by the employer's (or architect's) act, omission, etc. The position is neatly summarised by Dr Parris in *The Standard Form of Building Contract: JCT 80*, 2nd edition, 1985, where he points out that the damage, loss and/or expense,

> 'must have been *caused* by the breach and not merely be the occasion for it: *Weld-Blundell* v. *Stephens* (1920). It must be a *causa causans* and

not a *causa sine qua non*, some precedent event but for which a *causa causans* would not have operated'.

In other words, the loss, etc. must follow directly and in the natural course of things from the event that gives rise to it; and the event giving rise to the claim is the 'act, omission, default or negligence of the employer or of the architect' resulting in delay or disruption.

There is a further limitation, because the disruption or delay must be referable to the dates stated in the time schedule. There must be disruption to 'the regular progress of the Works or of any Section' or delays to 'the execution of them in accordance with the dates stated in the Time Schedule', which is thus the yardstick against which delays and disruption are to be measured.

The time schedule is a feature peculiar to the ACA Form, although similar in some respects to the abstract of particulars under Form GC/ Works/1, and, indeed, is described by the ACA as 'an essential part of the ACA Form of Agreement'. The time schedule is a contract document and is not the same as the contractor's programme. It is expressly referred to in several of the contract clauses and, as one of the ACA's own guidance notes points out, 'the architect must make a special point of adhering to [it], take every care in its preparation, and issue drawings in accordance with it, otherwise he may be responsible for delaying the Works'.

The time schedule is printed at the back of the form of agreement, and is in two alternative versions, one providing for normal single completion and the other for sectional completion. For ordinary completion, it contains the following information: (a) date for possession (clause 11.1); (b) taking-over and commencement of maintenance period ('taking-over' is described by the ACA as 'similar to "practical completion" which has been described as "when the building is reasonably safe and not unreasonably inconvenient"'); (c) weekly rate of liquidated damages (clause 11.3) (this is, however, to be deleted where the employer wishes to exercise his option of recovering 'unliquidated damages' for late completion and based on actual loss, and is one alternative open to him under the contract, as the alternative clause 11.3 so provides and entitles the employer to deduct such unliquidated damages from amounts otherwise payable to the contractor); (e) the maintenance period.

The same information is required as regards the alternative version for sectional completion, with appropriate adjustments.

The final part of the time schedule is headed 'Issue of Information'. Under the normal contract procedure, where the architect is to be responsible for the preparation and issue of all drawings, etc., the architect may set out under this heading the items he proposes to issue and when, to the intent that the contractor can then prepare his construction programme taking this into consideration. (An alternative version is for use where the contractor is to supply drawings, etc., in which case he completes it appropriately.)

The dates stated in the time schedule are those against which 'regular progress of the Works' is to be judged and, under clause 7, failure by the employer or the architect to adhere to those dates may give rise to a claim and will do so if delay or disruption results.

Clause 7.2 and clause 7.3 lay down the actual claims procedure, and exact adherence to it is essential if the contractor is to be reimbursed as the contract proceeds. The procedural steps may be summarised in this way:

(1) The contractor must give written notice to the architect of any event giving rise to a claim, i.e. 'any act, omission, default or negligence' of the employer or his architect. The notice must be specific and identify the event(s) relied on.

(2) This notice must be given *immediately* 'upon it becoming reasonably apparent that any event giving rise to a claim under clause 7.1 *is likely to occur or has occurred*'. This means that the notice must be given as soon as regular progress is likely to be disrupted or delayed.

(3) When he makes his next interim application for payment after the issue of his notice, the contractor must submit to the architect a written estimate of the adjustment to the contract sum that he requires to take account of the claim, in respect of the damage, etc., which he has suffered prior to the date of submission of the estimate. The use of the word 'estimate' is probably misleading for the principal meaning of the word 'estimate' is 'an approximate judgment'. If the contractor's 'estimate' is accepted by the architect or subsequently agreed, then, as will be seen, the contract sum is to be adjusted accordingly 'and no further or other additions or payments shall be made in respect of such claim'. The contractor's estimate is to be supported 'by such documents, vouchers and receipts as shall be necessary for computing the same *or as may be required by the architect*': see clause 7.4. In practical terms the clause requires 'moneyed-out' claims supported by substantiating documentation. The italicised phrase is not qualified in any way by the word 'reasonably' or otherwise and therefore it seems that the architect can call for whatever 'documents, vouchers and receipts' as he may in his absolute discretion require. Clause 7.3 is important

since it covers continuing losses. The contractor is to submit further estimates with each subsequent interim application for payment in respect of damage, loss and/or expense which he has suffered or incurred since the submission of his previous estimate. This provision did not appear in the first edition which contemplated a once-for-all payment.

(4) The onus then passes to the architect. Within 20 working days from receipt of the contractor's estimate and supporting documentation, the architect must either give written notice to the contractor that he accepts the estimate of quantum *or* 'give notice of his wish to negotiate the adjustment to the contract sum'. If the adjudication option applies (Alternative 1, clause 25) and the contractor's estimate cannot be agreed within 20 working days after the architect's notice, either contracting party may call upon the adjudicator to decide the matter.

(5) The contract sum is to be adjusted – and the amount of the claim included in the next interim certificate – as soon as agreement is reached as to the amount of the claim, i.e. by the acceptance of the contractor's estimate or, more usually, by agreement after negotiations, which, in the nature of things, could be quite protracted. Clause 7.4 says that 'the Contract Sum is to be adjusted accordingly *and no further or other additions or payments shall be made in respect of such claim*'.

(6) If the contractor fails to submit estimates as required by clauses 7.2 and 7.3 then, by virtue of clause 7.5, he loses any entitlement to reimbursement in respect of his claim until final certificate. Furthermore, he is disentitled to any interest or financing charges element in his claim which he suffers or incurs in the period between the date of his failure to submit the estimate and the date of the final certificate.

In contrast with the JCT Forms of Contract it would seem that, under clause 7, the architect also has power to settle common law claims, provided that such arise from 'any act, omission, default or negligence of the Employer or of the Architect'.

The effect of clause 7.5 is straightforward. If the contractor fails to comply with the procedures of clauses 7.2 and 7.3 as to the giving of notice and the submission of his estimate, he loses his entitlement to an adjustment of the contract sum until the final certificate, as well as any interest or financing charges which might otherwise form part of his claim. Failure to so comply with these provisions means that 'the

Architect shall have no power or authority to make, and the Contractor shall not be entitled to, any adjustment to the Contract Sum in respect of [his claim] on any certificate issued ... prior to the Final Certificate'.

Clause 7.6 is optional and will be deleted if there is no adjudicator named in clause 25, which provides three optional methods of settling disputes, viz adjudication, arbitration or litigation. Only one of these options can apply in any particular contract. Where an adjudicator is appointed, if the contractor's estimates cannot be agreed within 20 days after the architect's notice under clause 7.4, either party may refer the matter to the adjudicator for decision.

If properly operated, these claims provisions should prove of benefit to contractors and employers alike although, where the adjudication clause is deleted, clause 7 procedures lose some of their attractiveness from the contractor's point of view. Clearly, there is room for argument as to whether it is an 'act, omission, default or negligence' of employer or architect that is the cause of the delay; but the existence of the time schedule as a measure of progress does away with some of the practical difficulties encountered under the money claims clauses of other contract forms.

(b) Architect's instructions

Clause 8 deals with the issue of architect's instructions (which are normally to be in writing), and gives the extent of the architect's authority in this respect. (The provisions for the confirmation of oral instructions are more satisfactory than those under JCT Forms since they must be confirmed in writing by the architect within 5 working days of being issued. Oral instructions can only be issued in an emergency, the primary meaning of which, according to *Collins English Dictionary* is 'an unforeseen or sudden occurrence, especially of a danger demanding immediate remedy or action'.) The cost of complying with architect's instructions is to be settled under clause 17.

The text of clauses 8 and 17 is as follows:

8. ARCHITECT'S INSTRUCTIONS

Architect's instructions

8.1 The Architect shall have authority to issue instructions at any time up to the Taking-Over of the Works (save as otherwise provided in the proviso to this Clause 8.1 and in Clause 12.2) and the Contractor shall (subject to Clause 17.1) immediately comply with all instructions issued to him by the Architect in regard to any of the following matters:

(a) the removal from the Site of any work, materials or goods which are not in accordance with this Agreement;

(b) the dismissal from the Works of any person employed on them if, in the opinion of the Architect, such person misconducts himself or is incompetent or negligent in the performance of his duties;

(c) the opening up for inspection of any work covered up or the carrying out of any test of any materials or goods or of any executed work;

(d) the addition, alteration or omission of any obligations or restrictions in regard to any limitations of working space or working hours, access to the Site or use of any parts of the Site;

(e) the alteration or modification of the design, quality or quantity of the Works as described in the Contract Documents, including the addition, omission or substitution of any work, the alteration of any kind or standard of any materials or goods to be used in the Works and the removal from the Site of any materials or goods brought on to it by the Contractor for the Works;

(f) on any matter connected with the Works; and

(g) pursuant to Clauses 1.5, 1.6, 1.7, 2.6 (if applicable), 3.5, 9.4, 9.5, 10.2, 11.8, 12.2 and 14.

Provided that the Architect shall have the authority to issue instructions at any time up to completion by the Contractor of his obligations under Clause 12.2 and the Contractor shall (subject to Clause 17.1) immediately comply with all instructions issued to him by the Architect in regard to any of the matters referred to in Clauses 8.1(a), (b), (c) and (d).

Valuation of Architect's instruction

8.2 If any instruction issued under Clauses 1.6, 3.5, 8.1(c), (d), (e) or (f) or 14 or any instruction issued under Clause 1.5 or 2.6 (if applicable) to which this Clause 8.2 shall apply, shall require the Contractor to undertake work or do any other thing not provided for in, or to be reasonably inferred from, the Contract Documents, or shall require the omission of any work or of any obligation or restriction, and provided the same shall not have arisen out of or in connection with, or shall not reveal, any negligence, omission or default of the Contractor or of any sub-contractor or supplier or his or their respective servants or agents, the provisions of Clause 17 shall apply. Otherwise, no adjustment shall be made to the Contract Sum in respect of compliance by the Contractor with any such instruction.

Oral instructions

8.3 Notwithstanding the provisions of Clauses 17 and 23, in an emergency the Architect may issue an oral instruction under Clause 8.1. Such oral instruction shall be confirmed in writing by the Architect within ⟨5⟩ working days of* being issued. The Contractor shall immediately comply with such an oral instruction.

17. VALUATION OF ARCHITECT'S INSTRUCTIONS

Submission of estimates by Contractor

17.1 Where, in the opinion of the Contractor or of the Architect, any instructions issued by the Architect to the Contractor under Clause 1.6, 3.5, 8.1(c), (d), (e) or (f) or 14 or any instructions issued under Clause 1.5 or 2.6 (if applicable) to which Clause 8.2 shall apply, will require an adjustment to the Contract Sum and/or affect the Time Schedule, the Contractor shall not comply with them (subject to Clauses 8.3 and 17.5) but shall first furnish the Architect within ☐ 10 working days (or within such other period as may be agreed* between the Contractor and the Architect) of receipt of the instruction with estimates of:

(a) the value of the adjustment (providing him with all necessary supporting calculations by reference to the Schedule Rates or otherwise); and

(b) the length of any extension of time to which he may be entitled under Clause 11.5; and

(c) the amount of any damage, loss and/or expense which may be suffered or incurred by him arising out of or in connection with such instruction.

Agreement of Contractor's estimates

17.2 The Contractor and the Architect shall then take reasonable steps to agree the Contractor's estimates and any agreement so reached shall be binding upon the Contractor and the Employer. The Contractor shall immediately thereafter comply with the instruction and the Architect shall grant an extension of time under Clause 11.6 of the agreed length (if any) and the agreed adjustments (if any) in relation to the Contractor's estimates under Clauses 17.1(a) and/or 17.1(c) shall be made to the Contract Sum.

Failure to agree Contractor's estimates

17.3 If agreement cannot be reached within ☐ 5 working days of receipt by* the Architect of the Contractor's estimates on all or any of the matters set out in them, then

(a) the Architect may nevertheless instruct the Contractor to comply with the instruction in which case the provisions of Clause 17.5 shall apply as if the Architect had dispensed with the Contractor's obligation under Clause 17.1; or

(b) the Architect may instruct the Contractor not to comply with the instruction; or

(c) the Architect may refer the Contractor's estimates to the Adjudicator for his decision.

Instruction not to comply

17.4 If the Architect instructs the Contractor not to comply under Clause 17.3(b), the Contractor shall have no claim arising out of or in connection with such instruction or with any failure to reach agreement.

Valuation if no agreement of estimates

17.5 The Architect may, by notice to the Contractor before or after the issue of any instruction, dispense with the Contractor's obligation under Clause 17.1, in which case the Architect shall, within a reasonable time after the issue of such instruction, ascertain and certify a fair and reasonable adjustment to the Contract Sum based on (where appropriate) the Schedule of Rates in respect of compliance by the Contractor with such instruction and any damage, loss and/or expense suffered or incurred by the Contractor arising out of or in connection with it and a fair and reasonable extension of time shall be granted under Clause 11.6.

Non-compliance by Contractor
17.6 If the Contractor fails to comply with any one or more of the provisions of Clause 17.1 where the Architect has not dispensed with compliance under Clause 8.3 or Clause 17.5, the Architect shall have no power or authority to make, and the Contractor shall not be entitled to, any addition to the Contract Sum in respect of any instructions issued by the Architect to which this Clause 17 relates on any certificate issued under this Agreement prior to the Final Certificate. Such addition shall not in any such event include any adjustment in respect of loss of interest or financing charges suffered or incurred by the Contractor prior to the issue of the Final Certificate.

Only compliance with architect's instructions relating to the following matters may give rise to payment.

(1) Opening up of work for inspection or testing [clause 8.1(c)], where such inspection and testing is in the contractor's favour.
(2) Additions, alterations or omission of any obligations or restrictions to working space or working hours, access to the site or parts of the site [clause 8.1(d)].
(3) The alteration or modification of the design, quality or quantity of the works as described in the Contract Documents, including the addition, omission or substitution of any work, alteration of any kind or standard, or the removal or bringing on to site of any materials or goods brought thereon by the contractor for the works, i.e. variations *eo nomine* [clause 8.1(e)].
(4) On any matter connected with the Works [clause 8.1(f)].
(5) Relating to any ambiguity or discrepancy falling within Clause 1.5. This provision relates to ambiguities and discrepancies in the contract documents which could not reasonably have been foreseen or found at the date of the making of the contract by a contractor of the prescribed degree of competence [clause 8.1(g).]
(6) Compliance with statutory requirements under clause 5.1.6 [Clause 8.1(g).]
(7) Where applicable, in respect of adverse ground conditions or artificial obstructions at the site as referred to in the optional clause 2.6, [Clause 8.1(g).]
(8) Provision of samples of the quality of any goods, materials or standards of workmanship under clause 3.5 [Clause 8.1(g).]
(9) Relating to the execution of work or installation of materials, etc, not forming part of the contract by the employer's direct

contractors in accordance with clause 10.2 [Clause 8.1(g).]
(10) Acceleration or postponement instructions under clause 11.8 [Clause 8.1(g).]
(11) Relating to the discovery of antiquities, etc. under clause 14.2 [Clause 8.1(g).]

However, there is a very important limitation on the contractor's entitlement to payment for compliance with these architect's instructions and it is found in clause 8.2. First, the instruction must require 'the Contractor to undertake work or do any other thing not provided for in, *or to be reasonably inferred from*, the Contract Documents' *or* 'shall require the omission of any work or of any obligation or restriction'. Secondly, the need for the instruction 'shall not have arisen out of or in connection with, or shall not reveal, any negligence, omission or default of the Contractor or of any *sub-contractor or supplier of his or their respective servants or agents*'. Only if these conditions are satisfied will compliance with an architect's instruction rank for payment.

As regards the valuation provisions in clause 17, the peculiar position thereunder should be carefully noted. *Clause 17.1* provides that if the architect issues an instruction ranking for payment (i.e. one related to those matters listed above) which, in the opinion of the architect *or* the contractor, requires an adjustment to the contract sum under clause 8.2 and/or will affect the time schedule, the contractor must provide to the architect the following estimates before complying with the instruction:

(1) 'The value of the adjustment (providing [the architect] with all necessary supporting calculations by reference to the schedules of rates or otherwise.)'
(2) 'The length of any extension of time to which he may be entitled under Clause 11.5.'
(3) 'The amount of any damage, loss and or expense which may be suffered or incurred by him arising out of or in connection with such instruction.'

In principle these estimates must be provided with 10 working days of receipt of the relevant instruction, or such other period as the architect and the contractor shall agree.

Moreover, there is a saving provision in clause 17.5 (below), which provides that the architect may waive the contractor's obligation to provide estimates and himself make a fair and reasonable adjustment to the contract sum and a fair and reasonable extension of time and, in any case, an emergency oral instruction under clause 8.3 is to be excluded from this 'estimate' procedure. It seems to us curious, to say the least, that the draftsman of this form has linked time and money claims in this way, as the two are not necessarily correlated, as is made clear under JCT procedures.

Assuming that the contractor is required to submit these estimates – which it is obviously practicable to do where a reasonable time is allowed for compliance with the instruction – *clause 17.2* imposes on architect and contractor a duty to take *reasonable steps* to agree the contractor's estimate. Any agreement so reached is binding upon both employer and contractor, and thereupon the contractor is to comply with the instruction immediately.

If agreement cannot be reached with 5 working days of receipt of the contractor's estimates by the architect – an unusually short time period, although of course this and all other time provisions can be amended when the contract is made – *'on all or any of the matters set out in'* the estimates then:

(1) The architect may nevertheless instruct the contractor to comply with the instruction, in which case it is to be valued by the architect under clause 17.5; *or,*
(2) The architect may instruct the contractor *not* to comply; *or,*
(3) The architect may refer the contractor's estimate to the ajudicator, if the adjudication provision applies.

Where the architect withdraws his instruction, the contractor has no claim for reimbursement of any loss or expense incurred and this could, of course, be considerable: *clause 17.4.*

Clause 17.5 applies where the architect waives the contractor's obligation to submit estimates of cost, etc. and also where he decides, failing agreement as to price, etc., to instruct compliance in any event. The architect's duty then is to ascertain and certify 'a fair and reasonable adjustment to the Contract Sum based on (where appropriate) the Schedule of Rates', (and presumably in other cases on the basis of 'fair valuation'). This ascertainment is to include any damage, loss or expense suffered or incurred by the contractor 'arising out of or in connection with it'. The architect is also bound to grant 'a fair and reasonable extension of time' under clause 11.5.

The terms of clause 17.6 are important. If the contractor fails to submit estimates under clause 17.1, and the architect has not waived compliance under clause 17.5 or 8.3 (emergency oral instructions), the contractor is deprived of any entitlement to payment until the final certificate. In other words, he loses his right to payment for compliance with the architect's instructions on an interim certificate basis. The contractor's non-compliance also means that he forfeits any right to interest or finance charges for the period prior to the issue of the final certificate.

These provisions seem extremely complex but are, in fact, based on similar provisions in certain specialist forms of contract and sub-contract. If it is practicable for the contractor to submit estimates and these can be agreed, this is to his immediate benefit. If not, then provided the provisions of clause 17.5 are operated fairly and properly, there should be no problem, and it is believed that few difficulties have been encountered in practice. The long-stop is payment at final certificate stage.

Under ACA terms, there is a provision (clause 10) whereby the contractor must permit work to be done by others on the site: it has the head-note 'Employer's Licencees' and covers work, etc., to be done on site 'by the Employer or his employees, agents and contractors as provided in the Contract Documents' as well as that done by statutory undertakers such as water, gas and electricity boards. Clause 10.4, then provides that if the regular progress of the works or any section is disrupted or delayed by the employer's licencees, the contractor is entitled to recover any loss, damage or expense under the provisions of clause 7.4. It is important to note, that there is no claim in respect of statutory undertaker's work carried out under clause 10.3. The case of *Henry Boot Construction, Ltd* v. *Central Lancashire New Town Development Corporation* (1980), which was decided under JCT terms, is relevant here. If the statutory undertakers are acting under their statutory powers they fall under clause 10.3. If, on the other hand, they are acting under contract with the employer, they fall under clause 10.2, in which case the contractor will have a disturbance claim. The point is both important and significant.

A monetary claim may also arise as a result of the operation of clause 11.8, which in broad terms entitles the architect to issue an instruction to bring forward or postpone dates shown on the time-schedule for the taking over of any part of the works. It is then provided that 'the architect shall ascertain and certify a fair and reasonable adjustment (if appropriate) to the Contract Sum in respect of compliance by the Contractor with such instruction and any damage, loss and/or expense suffered or incurred by the Contractor arising out of or in connection with it. Provided that if prior to giving any such instruction the Architect requires the Contractor to give an estimate of the adjustment to the Contract Sum, the provisions of clause 17 (other than the provisions relating to extensions of time therein contained) shall apply as if an instruction given under this clause 11.8 were included in clause 17.1.'

(c) Extensions of time and liquidated damages

The important related matters of extensions of time and liquidated damages are dealt with in the lengthy clause 11, and it should be noted that the provision for damages is in the alternative. Alternative 1 of clause 11.3 is an ordinary liquidated damages clause; alternative 2 provides for unliquidated damages and gives the employer power to deduct such sums from moneys otherwise due to the contractor. There are also alternative provisions as to extensions of time.

The full text of clause 11 is as follows:

11. COMMENCEMENT AND DELAYS IN THE EXECUTION OF THE WORKS

11.1 Subject to Clauses 11.6 and 22.4 and any provisions to the contrary referred to in Clause 1.3, the Employer shall give to the Contractor possession of the Site, or such part or parts of it as may be specified, on the date or dates stated in the Time Schedule. The Contractor shall then immediately commence the execution of the Works and shall proceed with the same regularly and diligently and in accordance with the Time Schedule so that the Works and each Section are fit and ready for Taking-Over by the Employer in accordance with the provisions of Clause 12.1 on the date or dates for the Taking-Over of the same stated in the Time Schedule, subject to the provisions of Clauses 11.6 and 11.7, to the Architect's powers pursuant to Clause 11.8 and to the Adjudicator's powers pursuant to Clause 25.2 (where applicable).

11.2 If any Section is, or the Works are, not fit and ready for Taking-Over by the Employer in accordance with Clause 11.1, the Architect shall issue a certificate to that effect.

Alternative 1
Damages for delay

11.3 If the Architect issues a certificate under Clause 11.2 in respect of any Section or of the Works, the Contractor shall pay or allow to the Employer liquidated and ascertained damages at the rate or rates stated in the Time Schedule for the period between the date stated in the Time Schedule for the Taking-Over of such Section or of the Works, or such other date as may have been adjusted or fixed under Clauses 11.6 or 11.8 or 25.2 (where applicable), and the Taking-Over of the same and, if the Employer so requires, the Architect may deduct such damages from the amount which would otherwise be payable to the Contractor on any certificate or the Employer may recover them from the Contractor as a debt.

Alternative 2
Damages for delay

11.3 If the Architect issues a certificate under Clause 11.2 in respect of any Section or of the Works, the Employer shall be entitled to recover from the Contractor such damage, loss and/or expense as may be suffered or incurred by him arising out of or in connection with the Contractor's breach of his obligations under Clause 11.1. The Employer may deduct such damage, loss and/or expense from the amount which would otherwise by payable to the Contractor on any certificate.

Adjustment of damages for delay

11.4 If, after the issue of a certificate under Clause 11.2, the Architect fixes a date for the Taking-Over of any Section or of the Works under Clause 11.6 or 11.7 or if the Adjudicator fixes a date pursuant to Clause 25.2 (where applicable) which is later than the date named in such certificate, the Employer shall pay or repay to the Contractor any amounts paid, allowed or recovered by the Employer under Clause 11.3, together with interest on such amounts at the rate stated in the Contract Documents, for the period between the date named in the certificate under Clause 11.2 and the later date fixed by the Architect or the Adjudicator.

Alternative 1
Grounds for extension of time

11.5 Subject to Clause 11.8 and 25.2 (where applicable), no extension of time shall be granted to the Contractor except in the case of any act, instruction, default or omission of the Employer, or of the Architect on his behalf, whether authorised by or in breach of this Agreement, which in the reasonable opinion of the Architect causes the Taking-Over of the Works or of any Section by the date or dates for taking-over stated in the Time Schedule to be prevented. The Contractor shall immediately upon it becoming reasonably apparent that the Taking-Over of the Works or of any Section is being or is likely to be so prevented submit to the Architect a notice specifying such act, instruction, default or omission and, as soon as possible thereafter, submit full and detailed particulars of the extension of time to which the Contractor may consider himself entitled and the Contractor shall keep such particulars up-to-date by submitting such further particulars as may be necessary or may be requested from time to time by the Architect, so as to enable the Architect fully and properly to discharge his duties under Clause 11.6 at the times specified for the discharge of the same.

Alternative 2
Grounds for extension of time

11.5 Subject to Clauses 11.8 and 25.2 (where applicable), no extension of time shall be granted to the Contractor except in the case of:

(a) *force majeure*;
(b) the occurrence of one or more of the contingencies referred to in Clause 6.4;
(c) war, hostilities (whether war be declared or not), invasion, act of foreign enemies, rebellion, revolution, insurrection, military or usurped power, civil war, riot, commotion or disorder;
(d) delay or default by a governmental agency, local authority or statutory undertaker in carrying out work in pursuance of its statutory obligations in relation to the Works or the exercise after the date of this Agreement of any statutory power which restricts the availability or use of labour, or prevents or delays the Contractor obtaining goods, materials, fuels or energy;
(e) any act, instruction, default or omission of the Employer, or of the Architect on his behalf, whether authorised by or in breach of this Agreement;

and only then to the extent that the Contractor shall prove to the satisfaction of the Architect that the taking-over of the Works or of any Section by the date or dates stated in the Time Schedule is prevented.

Provided that no account shall be taken of any of these circumstances (except in the case of the circumstances referred to in Clause 11.5 (e)) unless the Contractor: immediately upon it becoming reasonably apparent that the taking-over of the Works or of any section is being or is likely to be so prevented, shall have submitted to the Architect a notice specifying the circumstance or circumstances; and

as soon as possible thereafter, shall have submitted full and detailed particulars of the extension of time to which the Contractor may consider himself entitled; and

shall have kept such particulars up-to-date by submitting such further particulars which may be necessary or may be requested from time to time by the Architect; so as to enable the Architect fully and properly to discharge his duties under Clause 11.6 at the times specified for the discharge of the same.

Extensions of time

11.6 Either:
    (a) so soon as may be practicable, but in any event not later than $\boxed{60}$ * working days after receipt of all the particular referred to in Clause 11.5; or
    (b) in the case of any act, instruction, default of omission of the Employer, or of the Architect on his behalf, and where the Contractor has failed to provide such particulars, at any time,

the Architect shall grant to the Contractor such extension of time for the taking-over of the Works and/or of any Section as he then estimates to be fair and reasonable: Provided always that an extension of time for the taking-over of one Section shall not as a necessary consequence entitle the Contractor to an extension of time for the taking-over of any other Section and/or of the Works and provided further that the Contractor shall not be entitled to any extension of time in respect of any delay attributable to any negligence, default or improper conduct by him or by his sub-contractors or suppliers or his or their respective servants or agents. The Architect shall be entitled to take into account at any time before the taking-over of any Section of the Works, the effects of any omission from such Section or from the Works.

Review of extensions of time granted

11.7 Within a reasonable time after the taking-over of the Works, the Architect shall confirm the dates for the taking-over of the Works or of any Section previously stated, adjusted or fixed or may fix a date for the taking-over of the Works or of any Section which is later than previously stated, adjusted or fixed, whether as a result of reviewing all or any previous decisions under Clause 11.6 given prior to the date stated in the certificate under Clause 11.2 or as a result of any act, instruction, default or omision of the Employer, or of the Architect on his behalf, whether authorised by or in breach of this Agreement, having occurred after the date stated in the certificate issued under clause 11.2. The Architect shall notify the Contractor of his final decision under this Clause 11.7.

Acceleration and postponement

11.8 The Architect may at any time, but not unreasonably, issue an instruction to the Contractor to bring forward or postpone the dates shown on the Time Schedule for the taking-over of the Works, any Section or any part of the Works and the Contractor shall immediately take such measures as are necessary to comply with such instruction and the provisions of Clause 11.3 shall apply to the adjusted date. The Architect shall ascertain and certify a fair and reasonable adjustment (if appropriate) to the Contract Sum in respect of compliance by the Contractor with such instruction: Provided that if prior to giving any such instruction the Architect requires the Contractor to give an estimate of the adjustment to the Contract Sum, the provisions of Clause 17 (other than the provision relating to extensions of time therein contained) shall apply as if an instruction given under this Clause 11.8 were included in clause 17.1.

Revisions to the Time Schedule

11.9 If the Architect shall adjust the date for the taking-over of the Works or any Section under Clause 11.6 or shall issue an instruction under Clause 11.8 or if the Adjudicator shall adjust any such date pursuant to Clause 25.2 (where applicable), the Contractor shall submit to the Architect a time schedule revised to take account of such adjustment or instruction for the Architect's consent within ☐ 10 ☐ working days of the date of the Architect's notice or* instruction or the Adjudicator's decision (as the case may be) and, upon the Architect giving his consent to the same, such revised time schedule shall be the Time Schedule.'

Clauses 11.1 and 11.2 call for little comment in this book. Subject to any provision to the contrary, the employer must give the contractor possession of the site as set out in the time schedule. Breach of this requirement may give rise to a claim at common law or under clause 11.5 in either alternative. The contractor is then to commence and proceed with the works 'regularly and diligently and in accordance with the Time Schedule' until they are ready for taking-over. If the works (or a section of them) are not ready by the date shown in the time schedule (or as extended under clause 11 or by the adjudicator under clause 25.2) the architect is to certify to that effect in writing.

(A) Liquidated damages

Clause 11.3, alternative 1, is a common-form provision for 'liquidated and ascertained damages'. Where alternative 1 is used, the figure stated with be exhaustive of the employer's rights arising out of delay in completion, even if third-party claims are made against the employer: *Temloc Ltd* v. *Errill Properties Ltd* (1987). Deduction of liquidated damages is subject to the condition precedent of the issue by the architect of a certificate that the works (or section) are not fit and ready for taking-over. Subject to the issue of the certificate, the clause permits the employer to deduct liquidated damages at the rate or rates stated in the time schedule. The period for deduction of liquidated damages runs from the issue of the clause 11.2 certificate and the date of issue of the certificate for taking-over (clause 12) or under the provisions of clause 13. *If the employer so requires*, the architect may deduct liquidated damages from the amount that would otherwise be payable to the contractor, or the employer may recover them from the contractor as an ordinary debt by legal action.

(B) Unliquidated damages

Alternative 2 of clause 11.3 is a curious provision. It says that, subject to the issue of a clause 11.2 certificate, the employer is entitled to recover from the contractor 'such damage, loss and/or expense as may be suffered or incurred by him' arising out of the contractor's failure to meet his obligations under clause 11.1 . At first sight, it would appear that if the contractor is in breach of *any* of his obligations under clause 11.1, so that he is liable to the employer for damages, these are recoverable by deduction under this clause and without resort to litigation. However, the side-note refers to 'damages for delay', and it is clearly the draftsman's intention that the employer's right to set-off unliquidated damages is limited to the breach of late completion. *How* such damages are to be assessed is not stated; but they are the equivalent of unliquidated damages at common law, which are recoverable *on proof of actual loss*. What this version of clause 11.3 does, however, is to confer on the employer a right to 'deduct such damage, loss and/or expense from the amount which would otherwise be payable to the Contractor in any certificate', i.e. it confers an express right of set-off on the employer who, presumably, will quantify the amount himself or through his professional advisers. The wording of the clause is very broad; and in our view the use of this optional provision is contrary to the interests of contractors and should be resisted. It represents a startling departure from the accepted procedures in the construction industry and is an open invitation to litigation. Even if the optional provision for adjudication (clause 25) is one of the contract terms, it is not clear whether a dispute as to the amount deducted under this clause is referable to the adjudicator for decision; presumably it is, on the basis that it is a 'dispute or difference ... concerning ... adjustment or alteration of the Contract Sum' [clause 25.2(a)], although the contrary is arguable. The same thing goes if the alternative arbitration clause applied, since the wording is the same there. The third version of clause 25 merely provides for litigation in the ordinary courts.

(C) Adjustment of damages for delay

Clause 11.4 applies whichever of the foregoing alternative versions of clause 11.3 is used. If the architect grants extensions of time and adjusts the taking-over date to a later date (or the adjudicator does so), and damages have been deducted from sums due to the contractor, the employer is to repay any excess damages so deducted for the period between the original take-over date and the later date as adjusted, together with interest thereon at the rate stated in the contract documents.

(D) Grounds for extension of time

Clause 11.5 is given in alternative forms.

Alternative 1. In this form, clause 11.5 provides that an extension of time shall be granted to the contractor only where there is 'any act, instruction, default or omission of the Employer, or of the Architect on his behalf, whether authorised by or in breach of this Agreement'. Moreover, the contractor's entitlement to an extension of time on these grounds is qualified: the act, etc. relied on must '*in the reasonable opinion of the Architect [cause] the taking-over of the Works ... by the date ... stated in the Time Schedule to be prevented*'. Obviously this is a limiting factor since the contractor must not only establish that there is a cause of delay, i.e. some 'act [etc.] of the Employer, or of the Architect on his behalf' but also that this is causing delay 'in the reasonable opinion' of the architect, i.e., the subjective opinion of the particular architect in question. However, the reasonableness or otherwise of the architect's opinion is open to review on adjudication or arbitration as appropriate and, indeed, in litigation. 'Prevented' means 'hindered or stopped'; it has no special meaning in this context.

This clause also contains provisions for notices by the contractor. 'Immediately upon it becoming reasonably apparent that the taking-over ... *is being or is likely to be so prevented*' by the act, etc. of the employer or his architect, the contractor must serve written notice on the architect. The notice must *specify* the particular act, instruction, default or omission relied on. As soon as possible after that notice, the contractor must submit to the architect full and detailed particulars of the extension of time to which he thinks he is entitled. The contract wording is 'full and *detailed* particulars of the extension of time to which the Contractor may consider himself entitled', and it is suggested that this must be by reference to the time schedule and the contractor's own programme. The contractor is under a further duty; he must keep the particulars up to date, by submitting 'such further particulars which may be necessary or may be requested from time to time by the Architect, so as to enable the Architect fully and properly to discharge his duties' as to extension of time 'at the times specified for the discharge of the same'.

Under this version of clause 11.5 the grounds on which extension of time can be claimed are, broadly speaking, all 'defaults' of the employer or his agent, the architect. Normally, failure by the architect properly to exercise his duty to extend time will undoubtedly mean that time under the contract will be at large; in other words, the date fixed for completion will cease to be applicable and the contractor's obligation will then be to complete 'within a reasonable time': see *Percy Bilton Ltd* v. *Greater London Council* (1982). This is so under this form also, save to the extent that clause 11.6(b) enables the architect to grant an extension 'at any time' where the contractor has failed to provide the necessary information. In such cases, he can delay his decision right up until he is *functus officio*, where no notice is given. The architect must act if the contractor fails to give the necessary particulars in order to preserve the employer's right to liquidated damages and present time becoming 'at large'.

This version of clause 11.5 is limited in its extent since it does not cover events outside the control of the employer or the architect, and it has been criticised as being much narrower than is felt to be reasonable. Under it, no extensions of time are available for such things as adverse weather conditions, strikes and delays or unforeseeable shortages in the availability of labour or materials, etc. These eventualities are beyond the control of the contractor but no doubt contractors invited to tender under ACA terms with this version of clause 11.5 in force will adjust their tender price accordingly.

It is possible that the clause does not cover default, etc., by anyone (other than the architect) for whom the employer is vicariously responsible in law, although the contrary is arguable. If a strict interpretation is adopted, this could act seriously to the detriment of the employer, in that it could lead to the completion date being rendered unenforceable.

Alternative 2. The second version of clause 11.5 is more traditional in its drafting and is wider than the first alternative and is akin to the JCT provisions for extension of time.

The matters for which the contractor is entitled to claim an extension of time are six in number and, as in the case of alternative 1, the architect is expected to adjudicate upon matters which may be his own default. The six causes or matters giving rise to an extension of time are:

(a) *Force majeure.*

(b) The list of events set out in the insurance clause (clause 6.4), viz 'those contingencies covered by the Contractor's policy' referred to (or by the employer's policy, as appropriate).

(c) War, hostilities (whether war be declared or not), invasion, act of foreign enemies, rebellion, revolution, insurrection, military or usurped power, civil war, riot, commotion or disorder.

(d) Delay or default by governmental agency, local authority or statutory undertaker in carrying out work in pursuance of its statutory obligations in relation to the works, i.e. there is no extension of time where a statutory undertaker, such as an electricity board, is carrying out work pursuant to contract: see *Henry Boot Construction Ltd* v. *Central Lancashire New Town Development Corporation* (1980). Delay that is caused by a statutory undertaker carrying out work 'in pursuance of its obligations in relation to the Works' will come under this heading, but not otherwise.

(e) The exercise after the date on which the contract is made of any statutory power restricting the availability or use of labour or preventing or delaying the contractor obtaining goods, materials, fuels or energy.

(f) Any act, instruction, default or omission of the employer or of the architect on his behalf, whether authorised by or in breach of the contract. Thus, failure to give possession of the site (which is a breach of contract at common law) is within this provision.

From the contractor's point of view, this alternative is to be preferred to alternative 1. As regards *force majeure*, it must be some matter not within the control of the person relying on it and it is certainly wider than the English law term 'Act of God'. In *Lebeaupin* v. *Crispin* (1920), Mr Justice McCardie quoted with approval the definition of the French writer Goirand and held that:

'This term is used with reference to all circumstances independent of the will of man, and which it is not in his power to control .... Thus, war, inundations and epidemics are cases of *force majeure*; it has even been decided that a strike of workmen constitutes a case of *force majeure*'.

His lordship added that 'any direct legislative or administrative interference would, of course, come within the term: for example, an embargo'.

Force majeure in the context of ACA contracts has a rather more restricted meaning that might seem to be the case at first sight because many matters – such as war, governmental delays, etc., which are otherwise dealt with in the term – are covered expressly by the provisions of this clause. In our view, severe weather conditions, which are not foreseeable at the time of year in the place in which the work is being carried out, are within the term *'force majeure'* as are major strikes: see *Matsoukis* v. *Priestman & Co.* (1915), where it was held to include the general coal strike and the breakdown of machinery.

As in the former case, there is an important limitation; the onus of proof is on the contractor. He is stated to be entitled to an extension of time on the foregoing grounds (or any of them) only 'to the extent that [he] *shall prove* to the satisfaction of the Architect that the taking-over of the Works ... by the date ... stated in the Time Schedule is prevented'. The change in wording is noteworthy; *'to the satisfaction* of the Architect'; and not to his 'reasonable satisfaction', and the standard of proof required is that of the balance of probabilities. An unreasonable architect's opinion would be overruled on adjudication or in arbitration.

The proviso is important and governs all those events listed above *except clause 11(e)*, i.e. it does not apply where the delay is caused by acts or omissions of the employer or his architect acting on his behalf. (The reason for this is obvious: without this provision the employer would be liable to forfeit his right to liquidated damages: see, for example, *Dodd* v. *Churton* (1897)). Except in that special case, no account is to be taken of any of the other listed circumstances unless the contractor shall have given written notice to the architect as soon as it becomes reasonably apparent that the taking-over is being or going to be prevented. *No notice is required where the delaying cause falls within clause 11.5(e)*. The notice must be given 'immediately upon it becoming apparent that the taking-over ... is being or is likely to be so prevented'; and the notice must be specific. It must specify 'the circumstance or circumstances' relied on and must be followed up as soon as possible by 'full and detailed particulars of the extension of time to which the Contractor may consider himself entitled'. The contractor must keep the particulars up to date as necessary and also supply, on request, any further particulars that the architect may require to enable him fully and properly to discharge his duties under this clause. In four cases, therefore, the giving of notice, etc. appears to be a condition precedent to the contractor's entitlement to extension of time during the running of the contract. In the case of delay occasioned by 'any act, default or omission of the Employer, or of the Architect on his behalf' it is not; and this suggests strongly the need for early notice.

Moreover, the change in requirement emphasises that if the event causing delay is one outside the control of employer and architect, the architect need not decide on whether or not to make an extension of time until or even after the works are actually completed even though the original completion date is passed: see *Amalgamated Building Contractors Ltd* v. *Waltham Holy Cross UDC* (1952), the principle of which is clearly applicable to claims under this clause. If the cause of delay falls within clause 11.5(e), however, i.e. results from acts or omissions, etc. of the employer or his architect, then there is equally no obligation on the architect to make any decision as to extension of time before or on the completion date stated in the time schedule because the provisions of clause 11.6(b) (below) effectively prevent time becoming 'at large'; and the architect can exercise his duty to grant extensions of time 'at any time' before he becomes *functus officio*. 'The times specified for the discharge of' his duties are laid down in *clause 11.6*.

There are two situations to be considered as to when the architect must exercise his duty to grant an extension of time. The first and normal case is dealt with in clause 11.6(a). When the architect has received the contractor's written notice and he has received all the particulars that he requires to enable him to form an opinion, he must make a decision about an extension of time 'as soon as may be practicable, but in any event not later than 60 working days after *receipt*' of the contractor's particulars. The wording is unhappy; but we take it that the period of 60 working days does not begin to run until the receipt of the later particulars referred to in clause 11.5, i.e. those submitted on request by the architect, or which are necessary to update the position.

The second situation is where the circumstance relied on is 'any act, instruction, default or omission of the Employer, or of the Architect on his behalf and where the Contractor has failed to provide' the particulars in clause 11.5. As regards the second case, it is interesting that the reference is only to 'particulars' and not to 'notice'. We suggest that notice should be given in any event, but that the contractor's failure to submit the required particulars is not fatal to his claim for an extension. In these two cases, the architect may exercise his duties as regards extending the contract period '*at any time*', i.e. so long as he is not *functus officio*, which is the case after the issue of the final certificate under the contract.

The architect's duty is to 'grant to the Contractor such extension of time … as he *then* estimates to be fair and reasonable'. The first proviso is of great importance. Where there is a sectional completion, an extension of time for the taking-over of one section does not necessarily entitle the contractor to an extension for the taking-over of another section or of the works as a whole. There is a second proviso to the effect that the contractor cannot rely on his own breach to claim an extension of time. 'The Contractor shall not be entitled to any extension of time in respect of any delay attributable to any negligence, default or improper conduct by him *or his sub-contractors or suppliers or his or their respective servants or agents.*'

The italicised phrase is important. It means that the contractor is not entitled to any extension of time for delays caused by sub-contractors or suppliers (nominated or domestic) even to the limited extent laid down by the House of Lords in *Westminster Corporation* v. *J. Jarvis & Sons Ltd* (1970), as regards nominated sub-contractors under the 63 JCT Form. In our view, the words 'his or their respective servants or agents' would not extend to cover sub-sub-contractors (see *City of Manchester* v. *Fram Gerrard Ltd* (1977)), and a very limited meaning must be given to these words. However, delays caused by sub-sub-contractors might equally well not rank for an extension of time unless they could be proved to fall within the meaning of the term *force majeure* [clause 11.5(a)], which we do not think can be the case, or alternatively be shown to fall within clause 11.5(e).

The final sentence of clause 11.6 establishes that the architect is entitled to take into account any omission instructions which he has issued. An omission instruction may, of course, and usually will, effect a saving of time; and he can do this 'at any time before the taking-over of any Section or of the Works'. It is the *effect* on time of the omission instruction that is important.

Clause 11.7 – with the side-note 'Review of extensions of time granted' – imposes on the architect a mandatory duty to 'confirm the dates for the taking-over of the Works or any Section previously stated, adjusted or fixed ...'. He must exercise this duty 'within a reasonable time after the taking-over of the Works' as a whole; what is a reasonable time is a question of fact, but clearly the power must be exercised before the architect is *functus officio*. Alternatively, the architect may fix a later date than previously fixed, whether as a result of reviewing any clause 11.6 decisions *or* because there has been some act, instruction, default or omission of the employer or the architect on his behalf which has 'occurred after the date stated in the' clause 11.2 certificate. He must then notify the contractor of his *final* decision. This provision differs from the analogous provision under JCT 80 in so far as under it the architect cannot reduce an extension of time already granted; he may only 'fix a date ... which is later than previously stated, adjusted or fixed'; but he has powers under the next sub-clause to order acceleration.

Clause 11.8 is an unusual provision to find in a construction contract, although its rationale is easy to understand. Under its terms the architect may, at any time, issue an instruction to bring forward or postpone dates shown on the time schedule 'for the taking-over of the Works, any Section or any part of the Works'. If the architect issues such an acceleration or postponement instruction, the contractor must comply with it 'immediately'; and the clause 11.3 provision as to liquidated or unliquidated damages applies as appropriate from the adjusted date.

Any acceleration or postponement is *prima facie* at the employer's cost: 'The Architect shall ascertain and certify a fair and reasonable adjustment (if appropriate) to the Contract Sum' in respect of the contractor's compliance with such an instruction, along with any damage, loss and/or expense which the contractor suffers or incurs as a direct result of the instruction. In fact, the proviso states that the architect may require the contractor to give an estimate of the cost of complying with the instruction before he issues it, and if he exercises this option, the relevant provisions of clause 17 apply: i.e. contractor's written estimate of cost of compliance, acceptance or negotiation, etc.: see page 241.

Clause 11.9 deals with revisions to the time schedule where the architect adjusts the completion date by granting an extension of time under clause 11.6 or issues an instruction for postponement or acceleration under clause 11.8 or where the adjudicator adjusts the date under clause 25.2. The contractor must then submit a revised time schedule to the architect within 10 working days of the architect's notice or instruction or the adjudicator's decision for the architect's consent. The revised time schedule then takes the place of the original time schedule. This is a sensible and workmanlike provision.

CLAIMS ON FINAL CERTIFICATE

If the contractor fails to comply with the procedural provisions of clauses 7.2 and 7.3 then he loses his entitlement to settlement of his claim until the final certificate (clause 7.5).

The issue of the final certificate is provided for by clause 19.2 and is purely financial in its effect. It is to be issued by the architect within 60 working days after completion by the contractor of *all* his obligations under the agreement.

Before the final certificate is issued, the contractor must submit to the architect within 60 working days of the expiry of the maintenance period his final account for the Works, and this will include any outstanding claims. The final account must be fully documented and, in fact, the wording is 'all vouchers, documents and receipts as shall be necessary for computing the Final Contract Sum *or as may be required by the Architect*'. Any outstanding claim must be supported by the necessary vouchers, etc. and what is required is a moneyed-out claim, backed up by supporting evidence 'as may be required by the Architect'. No interest or finance charges element is allowable in respect of the period between the date of the contractor's failure to submit the clause 7.2 and 7.3 notice and estimate and the date of the final certificate.

The stage following failure to settle the claim will depend on which of the three versions of clause 25 is a contract term, and the ACA guidance indicates that the adjudication procedure is 'designed for use in larger and more complicated contracts'. Under the arbitration version of clause 25, the architect is to settle any disputes arising 'during the progress or after the completion or abandonment of the works' including, *inter alia*, those relating to 'any adjustment or alteration of the contract sum'. Consequently, he must first give written notice of his decision and must do so within 5 working days of being requested so to do by either party. Arbitration is the next stage. If the third version of clause 25 is in force, then any disputed claim must be settled by litigation in the ordinary courts.

Chapter 9

Sub-contract claims

INTRODUCTION

The principles involved in claims by sub-contractors or against sub-contractors are exactly the same as those involved in claims by main contractors, as discussed in previous chapters. Merely because a job proves unprofitable or costs more than was anticipated or allowed for does not give rise to any claim in law. As in the case of main contractor's claims against employers, we must distinguish between two types of claim, first, claims made under some express provision of the sub-contract (e.g. under clause 13 of NSC/4), and secondly, claims for damages at common law. This second type of claim is discussed in chapter 10.

This chapter discusses sub-contract claims arising under six forms of sub-contract, namely:

(1) The JCT Standard Form of Nominated Sub-Contract, NSC/4 and NSC/4a.
(2) The NFBTE/FASS/CASEC Domestic Sub-Contract Form DOM/1 and DOM/2.
(3) The NFBTE/FASS Sub-Contract Form (the 'Green Form').
(4) The NFBTE/FASS/CASEC Sub-Contract Form (the 'Blue Form').
(5) The JCT conditions of sub-contract for sub-contractors 'named' under IFC 84, NAM/SC.
(6) The ACA Form of Sub-Contract.

SUB-CONTRACT FORM NSC/4 AND NSC/4A

The Joint Contracts Tribunal issued the JCT Standard Form of (Nominated) Sub-Contract contemporaneously with JCT 1980 and it

257

exists in two versions. NSC/4 is for nominated sub-contractors 'who have tendered on Tender NSC/1 and executed Agreement NSC/2 and been nominated by Nomination NSC/3 under' clause 35.10.2, i.e. what the JCT terms the 'basic method'. NSC/4a is for use where the architect has adopted some other method of selecting a nominated sub-contractor and where Tender NSC/1 is not used. Readers are referred to *The Standard Form of Building Contract: JCT 80*, Second Edition, by Dr John Parris, chapter 5, for a discussion of nominated sub-contractors under JCT 1980. There is no difference in the 'claims' provisions of the two versions of the nominated sub-contract and the wording follows very closely the wording of the corresponding provisions in the main form JCT 1980, so that much of our commentary thereon in chapters 4 and 5 is equally applicable to NSC/4 and NSC/4a.

(a) Extensions of time under NSC/4 and NSC/4a

Extensions of sub-contract time are dealt with by clause 11.2, which (as amended by Amendment 4 issued in July 1987) provides as follows:

11.2 .1 .1 'If and whenever it becomes reasonably apparent that the commencement, progress or completion of the Sub-Contract Works or any part thereof is being or is likely to be delayed, the Sub-Contractor shall forthwith give written notice to the Contractor of the material circumstances including the cause or causes of the delay and identify in such notice any matter which in his opinion comes within clause 11.2.2.1. The Contractor shall forthwith inform the Architect of any written notice by the Sub-Contractor and submit to the Architect any written representations made to him by the Sub-Contractor as to such cause as aforesaid.

.1 .2 in respect of each and every matter which comes within clause 11.2.2.1, and identified in the notice given in accordance with clause 11.2.1.1, the Sub-Contractor shall, if practicable in such notice, or otherwise in writing as soon as possible after such notice:

.2 .1 give particulars of the expected effects thereof; and

.2 .2 estimate the extent, if any, of the expected delay in the completion of the Sub-Contract Works or any part thereof beyond the expiry of the period or periods stated in the Tender, Schedule 2, item 1C, or beyond the expiry of any extended period or periods previously fixed under clause 11 which results therefrom whether or not concurrently with delay resulting from any other matter which comes within clause 11.2.2.1; and

.1 .2 .3 the Sub-Contractor shall give such further written notices to the Contractor as may be reasonably necessary or as the Contractor may reasonably require for keeping up-to-date the particulars and estimate referred to in clause 11.2.1.2.1 and .2 including any material change in such particulars or estimate.

.1 .3 The Contractor shall submit to the Architect the particulars and estimate referred to in clause 11.2.1.2.1 and .2 and the further notices referred to in clause 11.2.1.2.3 to the extent that such particulars and estimate have not been included in the notice given in accordance with clause 11.2.1.1 and shall, if so requested by the Sub-Contractor, join with the Sub-Contractor in requesting the consent of the Architect under clause 35.14 of the Main Contract Conditions.

11.2 .2 If on receipt of any notice, particulars and estimate under clause 11.2.1 and of a request by the Contractor and the Sub-Contractor for his consent under clause 35.14 of the Main Contract Conditions the Architect is of the opinion that:

.2 .1 any of the matters which are stated by the Sub-Contractor to be the cause of the delay is an act, omission or default of the Contractor, his servants or agents or his sub-contractors, their servants or agents (other than the Sub-Contractor, his servants or agents) or the occurrence of the Relevant Event; and

.2 .2 the completion of the Sub-Contract Works or any part thereof is likely to be delayed thereby beyond the period or periods stated in the Tender, Schedule 2, item 1C, or any revised such period or periods

then the Contractor shall, with the written consent of the Architect, give an extension of time by fixing such revised or further revised period or periods for the Completion of the Sub-Contract Works or any part thereof as the Architect in his written consent then estimates to be fair and reasonable. The Contractor shall, in agreement with the Architect, when fixing such revised period or periods state:

.2 .3 which of the matters, including any of the Relevant Events, referred to in clause 11.2.2.1 they have taken into account; and

.2 .4 the extent, if any, to which the Architect, in giving his written consent, has had regard to any instructions under clause 13 of the Main Contract Conditions requiring the omission of any work or obligation or restriction since the previous fixing of any such revised period or periods for the completion of the Sub-Contract Works or any part thereof,

and shall, if reasonably practicable having regard to the sufficiency of the aforesaid notice, particulars and estimate, fix such revised period or periods not later than 12 weeks from the receipt by the Contractor of the notice and of reasonably sufficient particulars and estimates, or, where the time between receipt thereof and the expiry of the period or periods for the completion of the Sub-Contract Works or any part thereof is less than 12 weeks, not later than the expiry of the aforesaid period or periods. If, upon receipt of the aforesaid notice, particulars and estimate and request of the Contractor and the Sub-Contractor, the Architect is of the opinion that he is unable to give his written consent to any revision or further revision of the period or periods for completion of the Sub-Contract Works or any part thereof, the Architect shall so inform the Contractor who shall inform the Sub-Contractor of the opinion of the Architect not later than 12 weeks from the receipt by the Contractor of the aforesaid notice, particulars and estimate and request by the Sub-Contractor or, where the period of time between such receipt and the expiry of the period or periods for the completion of the Sub-Contract Works is less than 12 weeks, not later than the expiry of the aforesaid period or periods.

11.2 .3 After the first exercise by the Contractor of the duty under clause 11.2.2, the Contractor, with the written consent of the Architect, may fix a period or periods for completion of the Sub-Contract Works or any part thereof shorter than that previously fixed under clause 11.2.2 if, in the opinion of the Architect, the fixing of such shorter period or periods is fair and reasonable having regard to any instructions issued under clause 13 of the Main Contract Conditions requiring the omission of any work or obligation or restriction where such issue is after the last occasion on which the Contractor with the consent of the Architect made a revision of the aforesaid period or periods.

.4 If the expiry of the period when the Sub-Contract Works should have been completed in accordance with the agreed programme details in the (for NSC/4) Tender, Schedule 2, item 1C (for NSC/4a) Appendix, part 4, as revised by any operation of the provisions of clause 11, occurs before the date of practical completion of the Sub-Contract Works certified under clause 35.16 of the Main Contract Conditions the Contractor with the consent of the Architect, may

and

not later than the expiry of 12 weeks after the aforesaid date of practical completion of the Sub-Contract Works, the Contractor, with the consent of the Architect, shall
either:

.1 fix such a period or periods for completion of the Sub-Contract Works or any part thereof longer than that previously fixed under clause 11.2 as the Architect in his written consent considers to be fair and reasonable having regard to any of the matters referred to in clause 11.2.2.1 whether upon reviewing a previous decision or otherwise and whether or not the matters referred to in clause 11.2.2.1 have been specifically notified by the Sub-Contractor under clause 11.2.1; or

.4 .2 fix such a period or periods for completion of the Sub-Contract Works or any part thereof shorter than that previously fixed under clause 11.2 as the Architect in his written consent considers to be fair and reasonable having regard to any instruction issued under clause 13.2 of the Main Contract Conditions requiring as a Variation the omission of any work where such issue is after the last occasion on which the Contractor made a revision of the aforesaid period or periods; or

.3 confirm in writing to the Sub-Contractor the period or periods for the completion of the Sub-Contract Works previously fixed.

Provided always the Sub-Contractor shall use constantly his best endeavours to prevent delay in the progress of the Sub-Contract Works. Howsoever caused, and to prevent any such delay resulting in the completion of the Sub-Contract Works being delayed or further delayed beyond the period or periods for completion; and the Sub-Contractor shall do all that may reasonably be required to the satisfaction of the Architect and the Contractor to proceed with the Sub-Contract Works.

11.2 .5 The following are the Relevant Events referred to in clause 11.2.2.1:

.5 .1 *force majeure*;

.5 .2 exceptionally adverse weather conditions;

.5 .3 loss or damage occasioned by any one or more of the 'Clause 22 Perils';

.5 .4 civil commotion, local combination of workmen, strike or lock-out affecting any of the trades employed upon the Works or any of the trades engaged in the preparation, manufacture or transportation of any of the goods or materials required for the Works;

.5 .5 compliance by the Contractor and/or Sub-Contractor with the Architect's instructions:

.5 .5 .1 under clauses 2.3, 13.2, 13.3, 23.2, 34, 35 or 36 of the Main Contract Conditions, or

.5 .5 .2 in regard to the opening up for inspection of any work covered up or the testing of any of the work, materials or goods in accordance with clause 8.3 of the Main Contract Conditions (including making good in consequence of such opening up or testing) unless the inspection or test showed that the work, materials or goods were not in accordance with the Main Contract or the Sub-Contract as the case may be;

.5 .6 the Contractor, or the Sub-Contractor through the Contractor, not having received in due time necessary instructions, drawings, details or levels from the Architect for which the Contractor or the Sub-Contractor, through the Contractor, specifically applied in writing provided that such application was made on a date which having regard to the Completion Date or the period or periods for the completion of the Sub-Contract Works was neither unreasonably distant from nor unreasonably close to the date on which it was necessary for the Contractor or the Sub-Contractor to receive the same;

.5 .7 delay on the part of Nominated Sub-Contractors (other than the Sub-Contractor) or of Nominated Suppliers in respect of the Works which the Contractor has taken all practicable steps to avoid or reduce;

.5 .8 .1 the execution of work not forming part of the Main Contract by the Employer himself or by persons employed or otherwise engaged by the Employer as referred to in clause 29 of the Main Contract Conditions or the failure to execute such work;

.5 .8 .2 the supply by the Employer of materials and goods which the Employer has agreed to provide for the Works or the failure so to supply;

.5 .9 the exercise after the Base Date by the United Kingdom Government of any statutory power which directly affects the execution of the Works by restricting the availability or use of labour which is essential to the proper carrying out of the Works, or preventing the Contractor or Sub-Contractor from, or delaying the Contractor or Sub-Contractor in, securing such goods or materials or such fuel or energy as are essential to the proper carrying out of the Works;

.5 .10 .1 the Contractor's or Sub-Contractor's inability for reasons beyond his control and which he could not reasonably have foreseen at the Base Date for the purposes of the Main Contract or the Sub-Contract as the case may be to secure such labour as is essential to the proper carrying out of the Works; or

11.2 .5 .10 .2 the Contractor's or Sub-Contractor's inability for reasons beyond his control and which he could not reasonably have foreseen at the Base Date for the purposes of the Main Contract or the Sub-Contract as the case may be to secure such goods or materials as are essential to the proper carrying out of the Works;

.5 .11 the carrying out by a local authority or statutory undertaker of work in pursuance of its statutory obligations in relation to the Works, or the failure to carry out such work;

.5 .12 failure of the Employer to give in due time ingress to or egress from the site of the Works or any part thereof through or over any land, buildings, way or passage adjoining or connected with the site and in the possession and control of the Employer, in accordance with the Contract Bills and/or the Contract Drawings, after receipt by the Architect of such notice, if any, as the Contractor is required to give, or failure of the Employer to give such ingress or egress as otherwise agreed between the Architect and the Contractor;

.5 .13 the valid exercise by the Sub-Contractor of the right in clause 21.8 to suspend the further execution of the Sub-Contract Works.

.5 .14 where it is stated (for NSC/4) in the Tender, Schedule 1, item 10 (for NSC/4a) in the Appendix, part 2, Section B that clause 23.1.2 of the Main Contract Conditions applies to the Main Contract, any deferment by the Employer in giving possession of the site of the Works to the Contractor.'

The text should be compared and contrasted with clause 25 of JCT 80, which it parallels closely, and our comments in this chapter will be confined to the differences between claims under the two forms. Largely, these arise from the nature of the contractual relationship. The only parties to the sub-contract are the main contractor and the sub-contractor; there is no contractual relationship between sub-contractor and employer. This is a consequence of the doctrine of privity of contract, which means that only the parties to a contract can acquire rights and liabilities under it. The practical consequence for present purposes is that the sub-contractor makes claims against the main contractor who passes them up and down the contractual chain, assuming that the 'claim' is one which the employer accepts responsibility for in law.

The first sentence of clause 11.2.1.1 is akin to JCT 80, clause 25.2.1.1 and it is for the sub-contractor to give written notice of delay to the main contractor. He must do this 'forthwith' (i.e. immediately, without delay: see *Concise Oxford Dictionary*) *'if and whenever it becomes reasonably apparent that the commencement, progress or completion'* of the whole or part of the sub-contract works *'is being or is likely to be delayed'*. The notice must identify any matter which in his opinion comes within clause

11.2.2.1. Clause 11.2.2.1 refers to 'an act, omission or default of the Contractor, his servants or agents or his sub-contractors, their servants or agents ... or the occurrence of a Relevant Event'. The sub-contractor's notice to the contractor must therefore identify not only a relevant event, i.e. one of the grounds listed in clause 11.2.5, but also refer to any alleged act, default or omission of the main contractor or those for whom he is responsible in law, if the sub-contractor alleges that this is a cause of delay.

The contractor is to notify the architect forthwith of the sub-contractor's written notice; he is also to 'submit to the architect any written representations made to him by the sub-contractor' as to the causes of delay, which may include his own default, etc. The sub-contractor's notice is itself to state the 'material circumstances' including the cause or causes of the delay, and it must go into some detail as to how and why the delay is likely to occur.

The sub-contractor is under further obligations. *If practicable* in the notice itself, or otherwise as soon as possible after the notice, he must 'give particulars of the expected effects' of each delaying cause identified in the notice, and in our view each cause is to be considered in isolation. He must also give his own estimate of the expected delay in completion of the sub-contract works resulting from each and every delaying cause he has identified in his notice – again considered in isolation 'whether or not concurrently with delay resulting from any other matter which comes within clause 11.2.2.1', i.e. acts, omissions or defaults of the contractor or those for whom he is responsible in law and 'Relevant Events'.

The sub-contractor's duty does not even stop there; he must keep each notice of delay under review and revise his statement of particulars and estimates and/or give whatever further notices may reasonably be necessary to keep the contractor up to date with developments as they occur.

By clause 11.2.1.3 the contractor must submit the particulars, estimates, etc. to the architect, and undertakes 'if so requested by the Sub-Contractor' to join with the sub-contractor in requesting the architect's consent to an extension under JCT 80, clause 35.14.1.

When, and only when, he has received the notice, particulars, estimate, and request for his consent from the contractor, must the architect consider and decide (1) whether any of the causes of delay specified in the notice is a relevant event or default, etc. of the contractor and (2) whether completion of the sub-contract works or any part of them is, in fact, likely to be delayed thereby.

If his conclusions are positive, but only if it is reasonably practicable for him to do so having regard to the sufficiency of the information supplied, the architect must give his written consent to the contractor, granting an extension of time. It is the contractor who fixes the new completion date, but he can only do this with the architect's written consent, which must specify the extension that the architect 'then estimates to be fair and reasonable'.

It is stated that *in agreement with the architect* the contractor is to state in his extension (a) which matters they have taken into account, and (b) the extent, if any, to which the architect, in giving consent to the extension, has taken into account any omission instruction under clause 13.2 of JCT 80 'issued ... since the *revised* period or periods for the completion of the Sub-Contract works ...'. Thus, under NSC/4 and NSC/4a terms, *this cannot be done in the first extension of time*, in contrast to the situation under JCT 80, clause 25. There seems no reason for this difference between the two documents and we must assume it to be an error in drafting.

The contractor is given a time limit of 12 weeks from receipt of a notice of delay and of 'reasonably sufficient particulars and estimate' from the sub-contractor in which to grant an extension of time. If there are less than 12 weeks left between receipt of the notice, particulars and estimate and the currently fixed completion date, the architect must reach his decision, and give his written consent, and the contractor must grant any extension no later than that date.

As in JCT 80, an amendment made in July 1987 now requires the architect, if he does not consider any extension of time to be due, to inform the contractor of that decision, which must then be passed down to the sub-contractor not later than 12 weeks after receipt of the requisite notice, particulars or estimate or not later than the expiry of the sub-contract period or periods whichever is the earlier.

Clause 11.2.3 is the provision empowering the contractor (and the architect) to take into account any main contract omission instructions issued, omitting work, obligations or restrictions since the completion date was last fixed, so that the time necessary for completion has in their opinion been thereby reduced; there is no express provision equivalent to clause 25.3.6, JCT 80 but, in our view, on general principle the sub-contractor cannot be deprived of his original completion period without his own express consent.

There are three points to note. First, this can only be done after the first extension of time since, until then, the original completion date applies. Secondly, while extensions previously granted can be reduced, or even extinguished completely so as to return to the original date, no earlier date than that can be fixed by the contractor unilaterally no matter how much work is omitted. Thirdly, extensions previously granted can only be reduced on account of omissions of work instructed since an extension was last granted. Each extension is deemed to take into account omissions of work instructed up to the date of the extension.

Clause 11.2.4, in common with JCT 80 clause 25.3.3, was amended in July 1987 to make it clear that the architect in making his final decision on extensions of time, can take into account any events entitling the sub-contractor to an extension of time which occur between the expiry of the period or periods previously fixed for completion of the sub-contract works and actual practical completion.

As under clause 25.3.4 of JCT 80, clause 11.2.4 of NSC/4 and NSC/4a requires the sub-contractor to 'use constantly his best endeavours to prevent delay in the progress of the Sub-Contract Works, *howsoever caused*'. This is an important sub-contractual obligation. He is also required to use his best endeavours 'to prevent any such delay resulting in the completion of the Sub-Contract Works being delayed or further delayed'. The sub-contractor is also required to 'do all that may reasonably be required to the satisfaction of the Architect and the Contractor to proceed with the Sub-Contract Works'. The requirement is to *prevent* delay and, in our view, as under JCT 80, the requirements in this proviso do not require the sub-contractor actually to spend money (but see the discussion on the meaning of this phrase in Chapter 2).

The contractor is to review the completion date in light of any relevant events whether or not they have been notified by the sub-contractor. He must do this not more than 12 weeks after the issue of the certificate of practical completion issued under clause 35.16 of the main contract. The obligation is quite plain: the contractor is to review the extensions of time granted and make a final decision as to the sub-contractor completion date, which he must convey to the sub-contractor (with the architect's written consent) in writing. In doing this he must review all extensions previously granted and take into account any causes of delay of which he is aware and which he considers should fairly entitle the sub-contractor to an extension even though the sub-contractor has not notified him of them.

This final review is only to enable the contractor (and the architect) either to confirm the completion date previously fixed or to grant a further extension of time. The contractor may not reduce extensions previously granted unless, *since an extension was last granted*, the architect has issued an omission instruction under main contract clause 13.2, thereby reducing the time needed to complete what is left.

Relevant events

Clause 11.2.5 lists the relevant events, the occurrence of which, in principle, gives rise to an extension of time. Grounds 1 to 12 parallel those listed in JCT 80, clause 25.4, and reference should be made to our commentary thereon.

Clause 11.2.5.13 lists an additional ground: 'the valid exercise by the Sub-Contractor of the right in clause 21.8 to suspend the further execution of the Sub-Contract Works'.

Clause 21.8 confers on the sub-contractor a right to suspend the execution of the sub-contract works if (i) the main contractor has failed to discharge his obligation to make interim payments, and (ii) the employer has either not operated the direct payment provisions or has so operated them but – for some reason – has not paid the sub-contractor the whole of the amount due, within 35 days from the date of issue of the relevant interim certificate. Before the sub-contractor can claim an extension of time on this ground he must establish that he has validly exercised his clause 21.8 rights.

'An act, omission or default of the Contractor, his servants or agents or his sub-contractors, their servants or agents' is an additional ground for extension of time: see clause 11.2.2.1. This phrase is not, in our view, sufficient to extend to sub-sub-contractors (or 'tertiary contractors' as they are sometimes called): see *City of Manchester* v. *Fram Gerrard Ltd* (1977).

Finally, if the sub-contractor is aggrieved by the architect's failure to give his written consent (clause 11.2.2) to an extension in due time or at all and/or by the terms of that consent, e.g. the extension granted, he has a right to require the main contractor to join in arbitration proceedings, subject to safeguards as to costs: clause 11.3.

(b) Direct loss and/or expense claims under NSC/4 and NSC/4a
Clause 13 provides:

13 'Matters affecting regular progress – direct loss and/or expense – Contractor's and Sub-Contractor's rights

13.1 .1 If the Sub-Contractor makes written application to the Contractor stating that he has incurred or is likely to incur direct loss and/or expense in the execution of the Sub-Contract for which he would not be reimbursed by a payment under any other provision in the Sub-Contract due to deferment of giving to the Contractor possession of the site of the Works where it is stated (for NSC/4) in the Tender, Schedule 1 item 10 (for NSC/4a) in the Appendix, part 2, Section B that clause 23.1.2 of the Main Contract Conditions applies to the Main Contract or by reason of the regular progress of the Sub-Contract

Works or of any part thereof having been or being likely to be materially affected by any one or more of the matters referred to in clause 13.1.2 the Contractor shall require the Architect to operate clause 26.4 of the Main Contract Conditions so that the amount of that direct loss and/or expense, if any, may be ascertained. Provided always that:

.1 .1 the Sub-Contractor's application shall be made as soon as it has become, or should reasonably have become, apparent to him that the regular progress of the Sub-Contract Works or of any part thereof has been or was likely to be affected as aforesaid; and

.1 .2 the Sub-Contractor shall submit to the Contractor such information in support of his application as the Contractor is requested by the Architect to obtain from the Sub-Contractor in order reasonably to enable the Architect to operate clause 26.4 of the Main Contract Conditions; and

.1 .3 the Sub-Contractor shall submit to the Contractor such details of such loss and/or expense as the Contractor is requested by the Architect or the Quantity Surveyor to obtain from the Sub-Contractor in order reasonably to enable the ascertainment of that loss and/or expense under clause 26.4 of the Main Contract Conditions.

13.1 .2 The following are the matters referred to in clause 13.1.1:

.2 .1 the Contractor, or the Sub-Contractor through the Contractor, not having received in due time necessary instructions, drawings, details or levels from the Architect for which the Contractor, or the Sub-Contractor through the Contractor, specifically applied in writing provided that such application was made on a date which having regard to the Completion Date or the period or periods for completion of the Sub-Contract Works was neither unreasonably distant from nor unreasonably close to the date on which it was necessary for the Contractor or the Sub-Contractor to receive the same; or

.2 .2 the opening up for inspection of any work covered up or the testing of any of the work, materials or goods in accordance with clause 8.3 of the Main Contract Conditions (including making good in consequence of such opening up or testing), unless the inspection or test showed that the work, materials or goods were not in accordance with the Main Contract or the Sub-Contract as the case may be; or

.2 .3 any discrepancy in or divergence between the Contract Drawings and/or the Contract Bills and/or the Numbered Documents; or

.2 .4 the execution of work not forming part of the Main Contract by the Employer himself or by persons employed or otherwise engaged by the Employer as referred to in clause 29 of the Main Contract Conditions or the failure to execute such work or the supply by the Employer of materials and goods which the Employer has agreed to provide for the Works or the failure so to supply;

.2 .5 Architect's instructions issued in regard to the postponement of any work to be executed under the provisions of the Main Contract or the Sub-Contract; or

.2 .6 failure of the Employer to give in due time ingress to or egress from the site of the Works, or any part thereof through or over any land, buildings, way or passage adjoining or connected with the site and in the possession and control of the Employer, in accordance with the Contract Bills and/or the Contract Drawings, after receipt by the Architect of such notice, if any, as the Contractor is required to give or failure of the Employer to give such ingress or egress as otherwise agreed between the Architect and the Contractor; or

.2 .7 Architect's instructions issued under clause 13.2 of the Main Contract Conditions requiring a Variation or under clause 13.3 of the Main Contract Conditions in regard to the expenditure of provisional sums (other than work to which clause 13.4.2 of the Main Contract Conditions refers).

13.1 .3 Any amount from time to time ascertained as a result of the operation of clause 13.1.1 shall be added to the Sub-Contract Sum or included in the calculation of the Ascertained Final Sub-Contract Sum.

13.1 .4 The Sub-Contractor shall comply with all directions of the Contractor which are reasonably necessary to enable the ascertainment which results from the operation of clause 13.1.1 to be carried out.

13.2 If the regular progress of the Sub-Contract Works (including any part thereof which is sub-sub-contracted) is materially affected by any act, omission or default of the Contractor, his servants or agents, or any sub-contractor, his servants or agents or sub-sub-contractor (other than the Sub-Contractor, his servants or agents or sub-sub-contractors) employed by the Contractor on the Works, the Sub-Contractor shall within a reasonable time of such material effect becoming apparent give written notice thereof to the Contractor and the agreed amount of any direct loss and/or expense thereby caused to the Sub-Contractor shall be recoverable from the Contractor as a debt.

13.3 If the regular progress of the Works (including any part thereof of which is sub-contracted) is materially affected by any act, omission or default of the Sub-Contractor, his servants or agents, or any sub-sub-contractor employed by the Sub-Contractor on the Sub-Contract Works, the Contractor shall within a reasonable time of such material effect becoming apparent give written notice thereof to the Sub-Contractor and the agreed amount of any direct loss and/or expense thereby caused to the Contractor (whether suffered or incurred by the Contractor or by sub-contractors employed by the Contractor on the Main Contract Works from whom claims under similar provisions in the relevant sub-contracts have been agreed by the Contractor, sub-contractor and the Sub-Contractor) may be deducted from any monies due or to become due to the Sub-Contractor or may be recoverable from the Sub-Contractor as a debt.

13.4 The provisions of clause 13 are without prejudice to any other rights or remedies which the Contractor or Sub-Contractor may possess.

Clause 13 gives the sub-contractor a right to claim *through* the main contractor for direct loss and/or expense not covered 'by payment under any other provision in the Sub-Contract'. It parallels JCT 80, clause 26 and, so far as claims made *by* the sub-contractor are concerned, for the most part the situation is exactly the same as with claims by the contractor under JCT 80, clause 26, to which readers are referred: see chapter 5.

Specific comment is, however, required on the terms of clause 13.2, which is headed 'Disturbance of regular progress of Sub-Contract Works – Sub-Contractor's claims'. It deals with disturbance claims that arise as a result of the fault of the main contractor or those for whom he is responsible in law. For a claim under this head to be successful, the *regular progress* of the sub-contract works *including any part thereof which is sub-sub-contracted* must be *materially* affected by 'any act, omission or default of the Contractor, his servants or agents, or any sub-contractor his servants or agents or *sub-sub-contractor* ... employed by the contractor on the works ...'.

The onus is on the sub-contractor to give written notice of the claim to the main contractor. This he must do *within a reasonable time* of the material effect on progress becoming apparent.

The clause envisages that the amount of such a disturbance claim will be agreed between the parties by negotiation: '*the agreed amount* of any direct loss and/or expense thereby caused ... shall be recoverable from the Contractor as a debt'.

If the parties are unable to agree, then the dispute is referable to arbitration under Article 3.

Main contractor's claims

Clause 13.3 is a matching provision dealing with main contractor's claims that arise as a result of 'any act, omission or default of the Sub-Contractor, his servants or agents, or any sub-sub-contractor employed by the Sub-Contractor on the Sub-Contract Works', and the procedure is the same. It should be noted that such claims extend to claims by other sub-contractors of the main contractor, provided they are agreed between all three parties. When claims made under clause 13.3 are agreed, the main contractor may deduct the amount agreed from monies due or to become due to the sub-contractor or, if necessary, recover the sums due as a debt. In practice, the main contractor will rely on the express right of set-off conferred on him by clause 23.

Clause 13.4 preserves to both parties their other rights and remedies, i.e. claims at common law, as to which see chapter 10.

(c) Delayed completion by the sub-contractor

The main contractor's right to claim against a nominated sub-contractor for delay in completion of the sub-contract works is set out in clause 12 of Form NSC/4 and 4a as follows:

12.1 If the Sub-Contractor fails to complete the Sub-Contract Works (or any part thereof) within the period or periods specified for completion or any revised period or periods as provided in clause 11.2.2, the Contractor shall so notify the Architect and give the Sub-Contractor a copy of such notification.

12.2 The Sub-Contractor shall pay or allow to the Contractor a sum equivalent to any loss or damage suffered or incurred by the Contractor and caused by the failure of the Sub-Contractor as aforesaid. Provided that the Contractor shall not be entitled to so claim unless the Architect in accordance with clause 35.15 of the Main Contract Conditions shall have issued to the Contractor (with a copy to the Sub-Contractor) a certificate in writing certifying any failure notified under clause 12.1.

Clause 35.15 of the Main Contract Conditions runs as follows:

35.15.1 If any Nominated Sub-Contractor fails to complete the Sub-Contract Works (or where the Sub-Contract Works are to be completed in parts any part thereof) within the period specified in the Sub-Contract or within any extended time granted by the Contractor with the written consent of the Architect, and the Contractor so notifies the Architect with a copy to the Nominated Sub-Contractor, then, provided that the Architect is satisfied that clause 35.14 has been properly applied, the Architect shall so certify in writing to the Contractor. Immediately upon the issue of such a certificate the Architect shall send a duplicate copy thereof to the Nominated Sub-Contractor.

35.15.2 The certificate of the Architect under clause 35.15.1 shall be issued not later than 2 months from the date of notification to the Architect that the Nominated Sub-Contractor has failed to complete the Sub-Contract Works or any part thereof.

The main contractor's right to claim for delayed completion of the sub-contract works is therefore dealt with on a different basis from his right to claim for the effect of any act, omission or default of the sub-contractor upon regular progress of the main contract works (see discussion of clause 13.3 of NSC/4 and 4a above). It is a condition precedent to the contractor's right to claim that he should have the architect's certificate issuable under main contract clause 35.15.1. That certificate, as with the non-completion certificate under the main contract clause 24.1 – see chapter 2 page 33 – is to be a simple statement of the fact that the sub-contractor has not completed within the specified period or any extended period yet granted. There is, however, the important proviso that the architect is only to issue the certificate if he is satisfied that the provisions of clause 35.14 of the main contract (also embodied in clause 11 of the sub-contract) regarding extensions of time have been properly applied, and the architect is therefore given a period of 2 months before he may become obliged to issue the certificate. The architect is thus clearly placed under an obligation to make proper investigation to ensure that the main contractor has passed to him all notices and applications from the sub-contractor regarding delays to the sub-contract works (including those alleging delay caused by the main contractor's own default) and that all extensions of time for which he has given permission have been properly granted. For the contrasting position under the old 'Green Form' sub-contract see page 285.

The importance of the issue of the architect's certificate under clause 35.15.1 of JCT 80 as a condition precedent to the main contractor's right to claim against the sub-contractor was emphasised by the case of *Tubeworkers Ltd* v. *Tilbury Construction Ltd* (1985). The case was under the old 'Green Form' of sub-contract under JCT 1963, but the principles are the same.

The main contractor applied to the architect for a certificate stating that the nominated sub-contractor was in delay. The architect purported to issue such a certificate on 14 July 1983, but it was generally agreed that it was defective and the main contractor did not at that time take any steps to rely upon it. On 13 September 1983 the architect issued an interim certificate for payment under the main contract including a direction for the payment of a substantial sum to the sub-contractor. On 31 October 1983 the main contractor asked the architect to issue a new, proper, certificate of delay and this was issued by the architect on 9 November 1983. On 16 November 1983, having withheld payment to the sub-contractor under the interim certificate in the meantime, the main contractor put forward a counterclaim to the sub-contractor for a considerably larger sum as a purported 'set-off' under clause 13A of the 'Green Form' (equivalent to clause 23 of NSC/4 and 4a). The Official Referee held that the main contractor, under the terms of the sub-contract relating to 'set-off' (which are identical to those in NSC/4 and 4a), was not entitled to withhold payment since, at the time that payment became due, he did not have a valid architect's certificate of delay, and this was not cured by the subsequent issue of a valid certificate of delay. However, the Official Referee granted a stay of execution of his order for summary judgment in favour for the sub-contractor under RSC Order 14 to enable the main contractor's counterclaim to be prosecuted. The Court of Appeal refused to uphold the stay of execution since, in the words of Lord Justice Kerr, 'such a stay contradicts the terms of the sub-contract and substitutes the exercise of the court's powers for those of the adjudicator on which the [main contractor] *ex hypothesi* is not in a position to rely'.

While it might be argued that the absence of the word 'direct' would give rise to a wider entitlement, we do not believe that in practice there is any real distinction between the 'loss or damage suffered or incurred' which the main contractor can recover under this clause and the 'direct loss and/or expense' which he can recover under clause 13.3, although it is possible that he can claim consequential loss under this provision. The main contractor's right to deduct the amount of any 'loss or damage' from payments certified as due to the sub-contractor will be subject to the conditions governing 'set-off' set out in clause 23 and 24 of Form NSC/ 4 and 4a.

DOMESTIC SUB-CONTRACT FORM DOM/1

Domestic sub-contractors are work and material sub-contractors who are not nominated by the architect under clause 35 of JCT 80. The full title of this document, which is issued jointly by NFBTE, FASS and CASEC, is 'The Standard Form of Sub-Contract for Domestic Sub-Contractors for use where the main contract is in one of the JCT Local Authorities/Private Editions either with or without quantities' and, unlike the former 'Blue' sub-contract form, which it has superseded, it is intended for use only with the JCT main form. The 'Blue Form' – commented on later in this chapter – could be used in conjunction with other standard form contracts, such as GC/Works/1. Those interested in the detailed provisions of the 'Blue Form' should refer to Dr V. Powell-Smith's *The Standard (Non-Nominated) Form of Building Sub-Contract* (IPC Building & Contract Journals Ltd, 1980). DOM/1 was published in 1980.

There is also a version (DOM/2) provided for use in conjunction with the JCT Standard Form 'with Contractor's Design'.

(a) Extensions of time under DOM/1
Extensions of time are dealt with by clause 11, which reads as follows:

11. 'SUB-CONTRACTOR'S OBLIGATION – CARRYING OUT AND COMPLE-
TION OF SUB-CONTRACT WORKS – EXTENSION OF SUB-CONTRACT
TIME

11.1 The Sub-Contractor shall carry out and complete the Sub-Contract Works in accordance with the details in the Appendix, part 4, and reasonably in accordance with the progress of the Works but subject to receipt of the notice to commence work on site as stated in Appendix, part 4, and to the operation of clause 11.

11.2 .1 If and whenever it becomes reasonably apparent that the commencement, progress or completion of the Sub-Contract Works or any part thereof is being or is likely to be delayed, the Sub-Contractor shall forthwith give written notice to the Contractor of the material circumstances including, insofar as the Sub-Contractor is able, the cause or causes of the delay and identify in such notice any matter which in his opinion comes within clause 11.3.1.

.2 In respect of each and every matter which comes within clause 11.3.1, and identified in the notice given in accordance with clause 11.2.1, the Sub-Contractor shall, if practicable in such notice, or otherwise in writing as soon as possible after such notice:

.2 .1 give particulars of the expected effects thereof; and

.2 .2 estimate the extent, if any, of the expected delay in the completion of the Sub-Contract Works or any part thereof beyond the expiry of the period or periods stated in the Appendix, part 4, or beyond the expiry of any extended period or periods previously fixed under clause 11 which results therefrom whether or not concurrently with delay resulting from any other matter which comes within clause 11.3.1; and

.2 .3 the Sub-Contractor shall give such further written notices to the Contractor as may be reasonably necessary or as the Contractor may reasonably require for keeping up to date the particulars and estimate referred to in clause 11.2.2.1 and .2 including any material change in such particulars or estimate.

11.3 If on receipt of any notice, particulars and estimate under clause 11.2 the Contractor properly considers that:

.1 any of the causes of the delay is an act, omission or default of the Contractor, his servants or agents or his sub-contractors, their servants or agents (other than the Sub-Contractor, his servants or agents) or is the occurrence of a Relevant Event; and

.2 the completion of the Sub-Contract Works is likely to be delayed thereby beyond the period or periods stated in the Appendix, part 4, or any revised such period or periods.

then the Contractor shall, in writing, give an extension of time to the Sub-Contractor by fixing such revised or further revised period or periods for the completion of the Sub-Contract Works as the Contractor then estimates to be reasonable.

11.4 When fixing such revised period or periods, the Contractor shall, if reasonably practicable having regard to the sufficiency of the notice, particulars and estimate, fix such revised period or periods within the following time limit:

.1 not later than 16 weeks from the receipt by the Contractor of the notice and of reasonably sufficient particulars and estimates; or

.2 where the time between receipt thereof and the expiry of the period or periods for the completion of the Sub-Contract Works is less than 16 weeks, not later than the expiry of the aforesaid period or periods.

11.5 The Contractor, when fixing such revised period or periods, shall state:

.1 which of the matters, including any of the Relevant Events, referred to in clause 11.3.1 he has taken into account; and

.2 the extent, if any, to which the Contractor has has regard to any direction requiring as a Variation the omission of any work issued since the previous fixing of any such revised period or periods for the completion of the Sub-Contract Works.

11.6 After the first exercise by the Contractor of the duty under clause 11.3, the Contractor may fix a period or periods for completion of the Sub-Contract Works shorter than that previously fixed under clause 11.3 if, in the opinion of the Contractor, the fixing of such shorter period or periods is fair and reasonable having regard to any direction issued requiring as a Variation the omission of any work where such issue is after the last occasion on which the Contractor made a revision of the aforesaid period or periods.

11.7 Not later than the expiry of 16 weeks from the date of practical completion of the Sub-Contract Works, or from the date of Practical Completion of the Works, whichever first occurs, the Contractor shall, in writing, either:

.1 fix such a period or periods for completion of the Sub-Contract Works longer than that previously fixed under clause 11 as the Contractor properly considers to be fair and reasonable having regard to any of the matters referred to in clause 11.3.1 whether upon reviewing a previous decision or otherwise and whether or not the matters referred to in clause 11.3.1 have been specifically notified by the Sub-Contractor under clause 11.2; or

.2 fix such a period or periods for completion of the Sub-Contract Works shorter than that previously fixed under clause 11 as the Contractor properly considers to be fair and reasonable having regard to any direction issued requiring as a Variation the omission of any work where such issue is after the last occasion on which the Contractor made a revision of the aforesaid period or periods; or

.3 confirm to the Sub-Contractor the period or periods for the completion of the Sub-Contract Works previously fixed.

11.8 The operation of clause 11 shall be subject to the proviso that the Sub-Contractor shall use constantly his best endeavours to prevent delay in the progress of the Sub-Contract Works or any part thereof, however caused, and to prevent any such delay resulting in the completion of the Sub-Contract Works being delayed or further delayed beyond the period or periods for completion, and the Sub-Contractor shall do all that may reasonably be required to the satisfaction of the Architect and the Contractor to proceed with the Sub-Contract Works.

11.9 No decision of the Contractor under clauses 11.2 to .7 inclusive shall fix a period or periods for completion of the Sub-Contract Works which will be shorter than the period or periods stated in the Appendix, part 4.

11.10 The following are the Relevant Events referred to in clause 11.3.1:

.1 *force majeure;*

.2 exceptionally adverse weather conditions;

.3 loss or damage occasioned by any one or more of the 'Clause 22 Perils';

.4 civil commotion, local combination of workmen, strike or lockout affecting any of the trades employed upon the Works or any of the trades engaged in the preparation, manufacture or transportation of any of the goods or materials required for the Works;

.5 compliance by the Contractor with the Architect's instructions (which shall be deemed to include compliance by the Sub-Contractor with the Contractor's directions which pass on such instructions):

.5 .1 under clauses 2.3, 13.2, 13.3, 23.2, 34, 35 or 36 of the Main Contract Conditions, or

.5 .2 in regard to the opening up for inspection of any work covered up or the testing of any of the work, materials or goods in accordance with clause 8.3 of the Main Contract Conditions (including making good in consequence of such opening up or testing) unless the inspection or test showed that the work, materials or goods were not in accordance with the Main Contract or the Sub-Contract as the case may be:

.6 the Contractor, or the Sub-Contractor through the Contractor, not having received in due time necessary instructions, drawings, details or levels from the Architect for which the Contractor or the Sub-Contractor, through the Contractor, specifically applied in writing provided that such application was made on a date which having regard to the Completion Date or the period or periods for the completion of the Sub-Contract Works was neither unreasonably distant from nor unreasonably close to the date on which it was necessary for the Contractor or the Sub-Contractor to receive the same;

.7 delay on the part of Nominated Sub-Contractors or of Nominated Suppliers in respect of the Works which the Contractor has taken all practicable steps to avoid or reduce;

.8 .1 the execution of work not forming part of the Main Contract by the Employer himself or by persons employed or otherwise engaged by the Employer as referred to in clause 29 of the Main Contract Conditions or the failure to execute such work;

.8 .2 the supply by the Employer of materials and goods which the Employer has agreed to provide for the Works or the failure so to supply;

.9 the exercise after the Date of Tender by the United Kingdom Government of any statutory power which directly affects the execution of the Works by restricting the availability or use of labour which is essential to the proper carrying out of the Works, or preventing the Contractor or Sub-Contractor from, or delaying the Contractor or Sub-Contractor in, securing such goods or materials or such fuel or energy as are essential to the proper carrying out of the Works;

.10 .1 the Contractor's or Sub-Contractor's inability for reasons beyond his control and which he could not reasonably have foreseen at the Date of Tender for the purposes of the Main Contract or the Sub-Contract as the case may be to secure such labour as is essential to the proper carrying out of the Works;

.10 .2 the Contractor's or Sub-Contractor's inability for reasons beyond his control and which he could not reasonably have foreseen at the Date of Tender for the purposes of the Main Contract or the Sub-Contract as the case may be to secure such goods or materials as are essential to the proper carrying out of the Works;

.11 the carrying out by a local authority or statutory undertaker of work in pursuance of its statutory obligations in relation to the Works, or the failure to carry out such work;

.12 failure of the Employer to give in due time ingress to or egress from the site of the Works or any part thereof through or over any land, buildings, way or passage adjoining or connected with the site and in the possession and control of the Employer, in accordance with the Contract Bills and/or the Contract Drawings, after receipt by the Architect of such notice, if any, as the Contractor is required to give, or failure of the Employer to give such ingress or egress as otherwise agreed between the Architect and the Contractor;

.13 the valid exercise by the Sub-Contractor of the right in clause 21.6 to suspend the further execution of the Sub-Contract Works.'

To all intents and purposes this parallels the provisions of NSC/4 and NSC/4a, clause 11, so that our commentary thereon is relevant. However, the wording is not in every instance identical, and the following points should be noted:

(1) In clause 11.2.1 the sub-contractor's obligation to give notice of the material circumstances is a qualified one. The material circumstances are to include the cause or causes of the delay, *insofar as the sub-contractor* is able to identify them. In practice, we feel that this qualification will make little difference.

(2) The architect is not involved at all in granting extensions of time. The duty is the contractor's alone. This apart, the procedure is the same as is the case under NSC/4 and NSC/4a, clause 11.

(3) The time limit is 16 weeks, as opposed to 12 weeks; this time limit runs from receipt of what the contractor considers to be 'reasonably sufficient' notice, particulars and estimate.

(4) Omission directions given by the contractor can be taken into account.

(5) The period for the contractor's review is 16 weeks from the date of practical completion of the sub-contract works, or from the date of practical completion of the main contract works, whichever first occurs.

(6) In clause 11.8, the operation of the extension of time provisions is made subject to the proviso that the sub-contractor shall 'use constantly his best endeavours to prevent delay ... and the Sub-

Contractor shall do all that may reasonably be required to the satisfaction of the *Architect and the Contractor to proceed with* the Sub-Contract Works'. Why the architect should have been introduced at this point is not clear; but the dual obligation is of no practical significance.

(7) Clause 11.9 is vital; it parallels clause 25.3.6 of JCT 80, and means that, no matter how much work is omitted, the sub-contractor is always entitled to his original sub-contract completion date: 'No decision of the Contractor ... shall fix a period or periods for completion ... which will be shorter than the period or periods stated in the Appendix....'

This apart, the provision is identical in its operation to the corresponding clause in NSC/4 and NSC/4a.

Clause 11 of DOM/2 is the corresponding provision under that sub-contract form and follows the wording of Clause 11, DOM/1. with the necessary drafting changes to take account of the differing circumstances in which it is used.

(b) Direct loss and/or expense claims under DOM/1
This matter is dealt with in clause 13, and is the matching provision to NSC/4 and NSC/4a clause 13. The text reads as follows:

13 'MATTERS AFFECTING REGULAR PROGRESS – DIRECT LOSS AND/OR EXPENSE – CONTRACTOR'S AND SUB-CONTRACTOR'S RIGHTS

13.1 If the regular progress of the Sub-Contract Works is materially affected by any act, omission or default of the Contractor, his servants or agents, or any sub-contractor, his servants or agents (other than the Sub-Contractor, his servants or agents), or is materially affected by any one or more of the Relevant Matters referred to in clause 13.3 and if the Sub-Contractor shall within a reasonable time of such material effect becoming apparent make written application to the Contractor, the agreed amount of any direct loss and/or expense thereby caused to the Sub-Contractor shall be recoverable from the Contractor as a debt. Provided always that:

　.1 the Sub-Contractor's application shall be made as soon as it has become, or should reasonably have become, apparent to him that the regular progress of the Sub-Contract Works or of any part thereof has been or is likely to be affected as aforesaid; and

　.2 the Sub-Contractor shall submit to the Contractor such information in support of his application as is reasonably necessary to show that the regular progress of the Sub-Contract Works or any part thereof has been or is likely to be affected as aforesaid; and

.3 the Sub-Contractor shall submit to the Contractor such details of such loss and/or expense as the Contractor requests in order reasonably to enable that direct loss and/or expense as aforesaid to be agreed.

13.2 If, and to the extent that, it is necessary for the agreement of any direct loss and/or expense applied for under clause 13.1, the Contractor shall state in writing to the Sub-Contractor what extension of time, if any, has been made under clause 11 in respect of the Relevant Events referred to in clause 11.10.5.1 (so far as that clause refers to clauses 2.3, 13.2, 13.3 and 23.2 of the Main Contract Conditions) and in clauses 11.10.5.2, 11.10.6, 11.10.8 and 11.10.12.

13.3 The following are the Relevant Matters referred to in clause 13.1:

.1 the Contractor, or the Sub-Contractor through the Contractor, not having received in due time necessary instructions, drawings, details or levels from the Architect for which the Contractor or the Sub-Contractor through the Contractor specifically applied in writing provided that such application was made on a date which having regard to the Completion Date or the period or periods for completion of the Sub-Contract Works was neither unreasonably distant from nor unreasonably close to the date on which it was necessary for the Contractor or the Sub-Contractor to receive the same;

.2 the opening up for inspection of any work covered up or the testing of any work, materials or goods in accordance with clause 8.3 of the Main Contract Conditions (including making good in consequence of such opening up or testing), unless the inspection or test showed that the work, materials or goods were not in accordance with the Main Contract or the Sub-Contract as the case may be:

.3 any discrepancy in or divergence between the Contract Drawings and/or the Contract Bills under the provisions of the Main Contract;

.4 the execution of work not forming part of the Main Contract by the Employer himself or by persons employed or otherwise engaged by the Employer as referred to in clause 29 of the Main Contract Conditions or the failure to execute such work or the supply by the Employer of materials and goods which the Employer has agreed to provide for the Works or the failure so to supply;

.5 Architect's instructions issued in regard to the postponement of any work to be executed under the provisions of the Main Contract or the Sub-Contract, which shall be deemed to include Contractor's directions issued under clause 4 in respect of such matters;

.6 failure of the Employer to give in due time ingress to or egress from the site of the Works, or any part thereof through or over any land, buildings, way or passage adjoining or connected with the site and in the possession and control of the Employer, in accordance with the Contract Bills and/or the Contract drawings, after receipt by the Architect of such notice, if any, as the Contractor is required to give or failure of the Employer to give such ingress or egress as otherwise agreed between the Architect and the Contractor;

.7 Architect's instructions issued under clause 13.2 of the Main Contract Conditions requiring a Variation or under clause 13.3 of the Main Contract

Conditions in regard to the expenditure of provisional sums (other than work to which clause 13.4.2 of the Main Contract Conditions refers), which shall be deemed to include Contractor's directions issued under clause 4 which pass on such instructions.

13.4 If the regular progress of the Works is materially affected by any act, omission or default of the Sub-Contractor, his servants or agents, and if the Contractor shall within a reasonable time of such material effect becoming apparent make written application to the Sub-Contractor, the agreed amount of any direct loss and/or expense thereby caused to the Contractor may be deducted from any monies due or to become due to the Sub-Contractor or may be recoverable from the Sub-Contractor as a debt. Provided always that:

.1 the Contractor's application shall be made as soon as it has become, or should reasonably have become, apparent to him that the regular progress of the Works or of any part thereof has been or is likely to be affected as aforesaid; and

.2 the Contractor shall submit to the Sub-Contractor such information in support of his application as is reasonably necessary to show that the regular progress of the Works or of any part thereof has been or is likely to be affected as aforesaid; and

.3 the Contractor shall submit to the Sub-Contractor such details of such loss and/or expense as the Sub-Contractor requests in order reasonably to enable the ascertainment and agreement of that direct loss and/or expense as aforesaid.

13.5 The provisions of clause 13 are without prejudice to any other rights or remedies which the Contractor or Sub-Contractor may possess.'

Again, our commentary on NSC/4 and NSC/4a clause 13 is relevant, as is our discussion of the position under clause 26 of JCT 80: see pages 268 and 163, respectively.

Here, however, the draftsman has not slavishly followed the wording of the similar clauses in other forms, although it seems to have the same effect.

The text should be compared and contrasted with NSC/4 and NSC/4a, clause 13, and the following points should be noted:

(1) Clause 13.1: The wording indicates that compliance with the provisions as to written notice is a condition precedent. The sub-contractor must make written application to the main contractor 'within a reasonable time' of the material effect on progress becoming *apparent* (*not* reasonably apparent), although this is qualified by proviso .1, which introduces the word 'reasonably'.

(2) The sub-contractor's obligation is to 'submit ... such information

in support of his application as is reasonably necessary to show that ... regular progress ... has been or is likely to be affected ...'.

(3) He is also to submit 'such details of such loss and/or expense as the Contractor requests in order reasonably to enable that direct loss and/or expense ... to be agreed', i.e. moneyed-out claims backed up by supporting evidence.

(4) Clause 13.2, like JCT 80, clause 26.3, appears to link extensions of time to direct loss and/or expense claims: see our commentary on clause 26.3, page 182, and the list of relevant events should be noted.

(5) Clause 13.1 refers to 'Relevant Matters', i.e. grounds giving rise to a potential claim. Apart from acts, omissions, or defaults of the main contractor or those for whom he is responsible in law, the 'Relevant Matters' are listed in clause 13.3.

Main contractor's claims

Clause 13.4 deals with claims by the main contractor against the sub-contractor in respect of 'disturbance of regular progress' of the main contract works. Unlike the corresponding provision in NSC/4 and NSC/4a (clause 13.2) there is no reference to sub-sub-contractors; and the contractor is required to make written application to the sub-contractor (and not merely to give written notice): the main contractor's right to claim is subject to the same three conditions as is the sub-contractor's right to claim against him.

Clause 13.5 preserves the common law rights of both contractor and sub-contractor.

The contractor's right to set-off is dealt with by clause 23, and the adjudication provision is in clause 24.

THE STANDARD FORM OF NOMINATED SUB-CONTRACT, 1963 EDITION – the 'GREEN FORM'

Claims between main contractor and sub-contractor

Clause 8 of the 'Green Form' runs as follows:

8 (a) The Sub-Contractor shall commence the Sub-Contract Works within an agreed time or if none is agreed, then within a reasonable time after the receipt by him of an order in writing under this Sub-Contract from the Contractor to that effect and shall proceed with the same with due expedition.

The Sub-Contractor shall complete the Sub-Contract Works and each section thereof within the period specified in Part II of the Appendix to this Sub-

Contract or within such extended period or periods as may be granted pursuant to the provisions hereinafter contained.

If the Sub-Contractor fails to complete the Sub-Contract Works or any section thereof within the period specified or any extended period or periods as herein after provided, he shall pay or allow to the Contractor a sum equivalent to any loss or damage suffered or incurred by the Contractor and caused by the failure of the Sub-Contractor as aforesaid. The Contractor shall at the earliest opportunity give reasonable notice to the Sub-Contractor that loss or damage as aforesaid is being or has been suffered or incurred.

PROVIDED that the Contractor shall not be entitled to claim any loss or damage under this clause unless the Architect shall have issued to the Contractor (with a duplicate copy to the Sub-Contractor) a certificate in writing stating that in his opinion the Sub-Contract Works or the relevant section thereof ought reasonably to have been completed within the specified period or within any extended period or periods as the case may be.

(b) Upon it becoming reasonably apparent that the progress of the Sub-Contract Works is delayed, the Sub-Contractor shall forthwith give written notice of the cause of the delay in the progress or completion of the Sub-Contract Works or any section thereof to the Contractor, who shall inform the Architect thereof and of any representations made to him by the Sub-Contractor as to such cause as aforesaid.

If on receipt of such information and representations as aforesaid the Architect is of the opinion that the completion of the Sub-Contract Works is likely to be or has been delayed beyond the periods or period stated in Part II of the Appendix hereto or beyond any extended periods previously fixed under this Clause,

(i) by reason of any of the matters specified in Clause 7(1) of this Sub-Contract or by any act or omission of the Contractor, his sub-contractors his or their respective servants or agents; or

(ii) for any reason (except delay on the part of the Sub-Contractor) for which the Contractor could obtain an extension of time for completion under the Main Contract

then the Contractor shall, but not without the written consent of the Architect, grant a fair and reasonable extension of the said period or periods for completion of the Sub-Contract Works or each section thereof (as the case may require) and such extended period or periods shall be the period or periods for completion of the same respectively and this clause shall be read and construed accordingly.

PROVIDED always that if the Sub-Contractor shall feel aggrieved by a failure of the Architect to give his written consent to the Contractor granting an extension of the said period or periods for completion of the Sub-Contract Works, then, subject to the Sub-Contractor giving to the Contractor such indemnity and security as the Contractor may reasonably require, the Contractor shall allow the Sub-Contractor to use the Contractor's name and if necessary will join with the Sub-Contractor as plaintiff in any arbitration proceedings by the Sub-Contractor in respect of the said complaint of the Sub-Contractor.

(c) (i) The Contractor shall subject to Clause 12 of this Sub-Contract enforce and make available to the Sub-Contractor the benefit of any right under the Main Contract to claim for loss and expense caused by disturbance to regular progress of the Main Contract Works and the Sub-Contractor shall comply with all requirements reasonably necessary to enable the Contractor to obtain the aforesaid benefit.

(ii) If the regular progress of the Sub-Contract Works is materially affected by any act, omission or default of the Contractor, his servants or agents, or any sub-contractor employed on the Works the Sub-Contractor shall as soon as such material effect becomes apparent give written notice thereof to the Contractor and the agreed amount of any direct loss or expense thereby caused to the Sub-Contractor shall be added to the Sub-Contract Sum and regarded as a debt due to the Sub-Contractor.

(iii) If the regular progress of the Main Contract Works (including any part thereof which is sub-contracted) is materially affected by any act, omission or default of the Sub-Contractor, his servants or agents, or any sub-contractor employed by him on the Sub-Contract Works, the Contractor shall as soon as such material effect becomes apparent give written notice thereof to the Sub-Contractor and the agreed amount of any direct loss or expense thereby caused to the Contractor (whether suffered or incurred by the Contractor or by sub-contractors employed by the Contractor on the Main Contract Works from whom claims under similar provisions in the relevant sub-contracts have been agreed by the Contractor, sub-contractor and the Sub-Contractor named in these conditions) shall be regarded as a debt due to the Contractor and deducted from the Sub-Contract Sum.

As regards claims by nominated sub-contractors against the main contractor, the provisions of the 'Green Form' are not markedly different from those set out in Form NSC/4 or 4a. Clause 8(b)(i) gives the sub-contractor a right to an extension of time if he is delayed 'by any act or omission of the Contractor, his sub-contractors his or their respective servants or agents' – wording similar to, if less precise than, that of clause 11.2.2.1 of NSC/4 and 4a. The sub-contractor is required to give written notice of the cause of any such delay to the main contractor 'who shall inform the Architect thereof and of any representations made to him by the Sub-Contractor as to such cause as aforesaid'. If 'the Architect is of the opinion that the completion of the Sub-Contract Works is likely to be or has been delayed ... then the Contractor shall, but not without the written consent of the Architect, grant a fair and reasonable extension' of the period or periods for completion of the Works.

The wording is, of course, far less precise than that of NSC/4 and 4a – for instance it is not so clearly established that the contractor must grant to the sub-contractor the same extension of time as the architect has given his consent to – but the overall effect is much the same.

As to the recovery of money, clause 8(c)(ii) of the 'Green Form' runs as follows:

'If the regular progress of the Sub-Contract Works is materially affected by any act, omission or default of the Contractor, his servants or his agents, or any sub-contractor employed on the Works the Sub-Contractor shall as soon as such material effect becomes apparent give written notice thereof to the Contractor and the agreed amount of any direct loss or expense thereby caused to the Sub-Contractor shall be added to the Sub-Contract Sum and regarded as a debt due to the Sub-Contractor.'

There are various slight differences between this wording and that of NSC/4 and 4a, clause 13.2. There is no specific reference to work sub-sub-let or to other sub-sub-contractors. More importantly, in place of the stark statement in NSC/4 and 4a that the amount of any loss or expense 'shall be recoverable from the Contractor as a debt', there is the requirement that any such sum 'shall be added to the Sub-Contract Sum ... '. This has caused considerable difficulties under clause 30(5)(c) of the main contract 1963 Edition, which refers to 'the amounts paid or payable under the appropriate contracts by the Contractor to nominated sub-contractors ...' as being included in the final adjustment of the contract sum. These words have been held by some to mean that the total payable by the contractor, including amounts of loss or expense payable as a result of his own default, should be included in the amount to be paid to him under the main contract. This clearly cannot have been the intention of the Joint Contracts Tribunal, but it certainly appears to be what clause 30(5)(c)says – although it has been widely and properly ignored in practice.

As regards claims by main contractor against sub-contractor, the main contractor, as in NSC/4 and 4a, can claim against the sub-contractor on two grounds: for the effect of acts, omissions or defaults of the sub-contractor upon regular progress of the main contract works, or for delay in completion of the sub-contract works.

Clause 8(c)(iii) of the 'Green Form' runs as follows:

'If the regular progress of the Main Contract Works (including any part thereof which is sub-contracted) is materially affected by any act, omission or default of the Sub-Contractor, his servants or agents, or any sub-contractor employed by him on the Sub-Contract Works, the Contractor shall as soon as such material effect becomes apparent give written notice thereof to the Sub-Contractor and the agreed amount of any direct loss or expense thereby caused by the Contractor (whether suffered or incurred by the Contractor or by sub-contractors employed by the Contractor on the Main Contract Works from whom claims under similar provisions in the relevant sub-contracts have been agreed by the Contractor, sub-contractor and the Sub-Contractor named in these conditions) shall be regarded as a debt due to the Contractor and deducted from the Sub-Contract Sum.'

This wording is almost identical, with minor drafting changes, to that of clause 13.3 of NSC/4 and 4a. The contractor's notice is to be given 'as soon as' the effect on progress becomes apparent instead of 'within a reasonable time'. There is no specific reference to the contractor's right to deduct agreed amounts from payments to the sub-contractor, but in view of the terms of clause 13A(1) regarding 'set-off' this is probably of little significance. The reference to deduction of any such amount from the sub-contract sum is open to the same objection in view of the terms of clause 30(5)(c) of the main contract 1963 Edition, but to the contrary effect – i.e. it could be said that, as the loss or expense is to be deducted from the sub-contract sum, it is not an amount 'paid or payable ... by the Contractor' and should therefore not be paid by the employer to the contractor. Again this is clearly not intended by the Tribunal, who must have intended the contractor to have the benefit of any such claims against the sub-contractor, and it is generally and rightly ignored in practice.

The rights of the main contractor with regard to delay in completion of the sub-contract works are set out in clause 8(a), after definition of the sub-contractor's obligations with regard to completion, as follows:

'If the Sub-Contractor fails to complete the Sub-Contract Works or any section thereof within the period specified or any extended period or periods as hereinafter provided, he shall pay or allow the Contractor a sum equivalent to any loss or damage suffered or incurred by the Contractor and caused by the failure of the Sub-Contractor as aforesaid. The Contractor shall at the earliest opportunity give reasonable notice to the Sub-Contractor that loss or damage as aforesaid is being or has been suffered or incurred.

PROVIDED that the Contractor shall not be entitled to claim any loss or damage under this clause unless the Architect shall have issued to the Contractor (with a duplicate copy to the Sub-Contractor) a certificate in writing stating that in his opinion the Sub-Contract Works or the relevant section thereof ought reasonably to have been completed within the specified period or within any extended period or periods as the case may be.'

The obligation of the architect with regard to the certificate mentioned in the proviso is set out in clause 27(d)(ii) of the main contract 1963 Edition as follows:

'If any nominated sub-contractor fails to complete the sub-contract works or (where the sub-contract Works are to be completed in sections) any section thereof within the period specified in the sub-contract or within any extended time granted by the Contractor with the written consent of the Architect, then if the same ought reasonably so to have been completed the Architect shall certify in writing accordingly; immediately upon issue the Architect shall send a duplicate copy of any such certificate to the nominated sub-contractor.'

It will be seen that, as with the equivalent provisions of NSC/4 and 4a, clause 12 and the main contract 1980 Edition, clause 35.15, the main contractor has no right to claim against the sub-contractor for failure to complete the works in time without a certificate from the architect. However, the nature of that certificate is significantly different in the two Editions. In the 1980 Edition the certificate is to be simply a statement of the fact that the sub-contractor has not completed within the specified period or periods; in the 1963 Edition it is to be a statement of opinion – that the sub-contractor 'ought reasonably' to have so completed.

In our experience the nature of the architect's certificate under the 1963 Editions of the main contract and sub-contract – widely known as a '27(d)(ii) certificate' – has been generally misunderstood. It should simply consist of a statement of the architect's opinion that the sub-contractor ought reasonably to have completed his work or the relevant section within whatever period was stated in the sub-contract or is now applicable following the grant of any extensions of time. It should not actually state what that period is, nor should it in any circumstances state the date by which, in the architect's view, the work should have been completed. Since the architect's control over nominated sub-contractors and their sub-contracts is minimal under the 1963 Editions of the main contract and sub-contract (in marked contrast to his very considerable control over the terms and operation of the sub-contract under the 1980 Editions) he is unlikely to be in possession of all the relevant facts and any periods or dates that he specifies are, in our experience, unlikely to coincide with the actual periods or dates required by the sub-contract. All the architect is required to say is that, in his opinion, there is nothing which ought reasonably to have prevented the sub-contractor from meeting his contractual obligations as regards time.

On the other hand, the issue of the certificate is clearly a judicial act. Its issue gives the main contractor monetary rights against the sub-contractor which he would not otherwise possess. In our view the architect clearly owes a duty of care to both main contractor and sub-contractor in issuing, or refusing to issue, such a certificate and that duty includes a duty to act judicially. His position is almost that of arbitrator between main contractor and sub-contractor. This has, indeed, been emphasised by the case of *Brightside Kilpatrick Engineering Services* v. *Mitchell Construction (1973) Ltd* (1975), where the court decided that the refusal of the architect to grant a 27(d)(ii) certificate could not be a matter to be arbitrated upon in an arbitration under the sub-contract, since neither the main contractor nor the sub-contractor had any responsibility for the architect's decisions (it should be noted also that the arbitration clause 24 in the 'Green Form' does not give the arbitrator any express power to open up or review any certificate of the architect). It presumably follows that the issue, as opposed to the refusal to issue, of the certificate would also not be open to arbitration under the sub-contract.

In our opinion, therefore, an architect would be failing in his duty to a sub-contractor, and may even be liable to him in damages, if he issues a 27(d)(ii) certificate simply at the request of the contractor and without making proper investigation and enquiry, including seeking the views of the sub-contractor, in order to satisfy himself that he is in possession of sufficient facts to form a proper opinion. It may be, for instance, that a simple enquiry to the sub-contractor will reveal that the main contractor has failed to pass on notices of delay sent to him by the sub-contractor, perhaps because they allege that the delays are due to the main contractor's default. On the other hand the architect would be failing in his duty to the main contractor if he flatly refused to issue a 27(d)(ii) certificate; it is up to the architect to make the proper enquiries and, if he is satisfied following such enquiries that there is no legitimate reason for the sub-contractor's failure to complete the work within the period established under the sub-contract, to issue a certificate to that effect so that the contractor may claim his proper entitlement against the sub-contractor.

It is ironic that the 1980 Edition of the main contract, in clause 33.15, in relation to the more factual and less judicial certificate of the architect thereby required, places a specific obligation upon the architect to satisfy himself that the extension of time provisions in the sub-contract have been properly operated before issuing that certificate and gives him 2 months in which to make the necessary enquiries. Such a specific provision in the 1963 Edition would have avoided many acrimonious and time- and money-wasting disputes.

(See also the discussion of the importance of the issue of the architect's certificate of delay as instanced by the case of *Tubeworkers Ltd* v. *Tilbury Construction Ltd* (1985) on page 271.)

The provisions of the 'Green Form' as regards the right of the main contractor to set-off claims against payments certified as due to the sub-contractor as set out in clauses 13A and 13B (as amended in February 1976) are identical to those set out in clauses 23 and 24 of NSC/4 and 4a.

Claims by sub-contractor against employer

As regards time, clause 8(b) of the 'Green Form', in addition to giving the sub-contractor the right to an extension of time if delayed by 'any act or omission of the Contractor, his sub-contractors his or their respective servants or agents', also entitles him to extension of time if he is delayed 'by reason of any of the matters specified in Clause 7(1)'. Although headed 'variations etc.' clause 7(1) in fact refers to the sub-contractor's obligation to comply with *any* instructions of the architect passed on to him by the contractor in writing and 'for any reason (except delay on the part of the Sub-Contractor) for which the Contractor could obtain an extension of time for completion under the Main Contract'. We find it difficult to understand the specific reference to clause 7(1) of the sub-contract, which would appear to give the sub-contractor the right to an extension of time if delayed by *any* instruction of the architect – including, say, instructions for the removal of defective work or materials, which we cannot believe to be the intention. It would seem, in any case, to be redundant, since the right to an extension of time if delayed 'for any reason ... for which the Contractor could obtain an extension of time for completion under the Main Contract' would in any case entitle the sub-contractor to an extension if delayed by specific architect's instructions as listed in clause 23(e) of the main contract, 1963 Edition. This is unfortunately, typical of what can only be described as the slipshod drafting of many of the provisions of this Form – no doubt the result of haste in getting out the Form to meet the requirements of the 1963 Edition of the main contract.

We have referred earlier to the requirements as to notice of delay from the sub-contractor and the obligations of main contractor and architect following such notice.

The 'Green Form' therefore lacks the detailed provisions regarding extensions of time set out in clause 11 of NSC/4 and 4a. This has led to many problems in practice – particularly the lack, already referred to, of any specific obligation to grant the sub-contractor the same period of extension for which the architect has given his consent.

As regards monetary claims by the sub-contractor against the employer, again the 'Green Form' lacks any detailed clause such as clause 13.1 of NSC/4 and 4a. The only clause that appears to give the sub-contractor the right to make claims against the employer is clause 8(c)(i), which runs as follows:

'The Contractor shall subject to Clause 12 of this Sub-Contract enforce and make available to the Sub-Contractor the benefit of any right under the Main Contract to claim for loss and expense caused by disturbance to regular progress of the Main Contract Works and the Sub-Contractor shall comply with all requirements reasonably necessary to enable the Contractor to obtain the aforesaid benefit.'

Clause 12 runs:

'The Contractor will so far as he lawfully can at the request and cost of the Sub-Contractor obtain for him any right or benefits of the Main Contract so far as the same are applicable to the Sub-Contract Works but not further or otherwise.'

This is identical (save for the lack of the works 'if any' after 'cost') to clause 22 of NSC/4 and 4a.

Clause 8(c)(i) might be said to have the effect of incorporating the relevant clauses 11(6), 24(1) and 34(3) of the main contract, 1963 Edition into the sub-contract. However, it makes the sub-contractor entirely dependent upon the main contractor for pursuance of his claims, and the lack of any specific requirements as to the giving of notices, etc. by the sub-contractor can lead, and often has, led to problems. Effectively it means that the sub-contractor's claims become a part of the main contractor's claims under the relevant provisions of the main contract, to be pursued by the main contractor on the sub-contractor's behalf.

THE STANDARD FORM OF DOMESTIC SUB-CONTRACT, 1963 EDITION – the 'BLUE FORM'

Just as the 1980 Domestic Sub-Contract Form DOM/1 is essentially an adaptation of the Nominated Sub-Contract Form NSC/4 and 4a, so the 'Blue Form' is essentially an adaptation of the 'Green Form' – although in many respects the 'Blue Form' is, in respect of its wording, a considerable improvement on the 'Green Form'.

Most of the comments and comparisons of the 'Green Form' with NSC/4 and 4a therefore apply, *mutatis mutandis*, to a comparison of the 'Blue Form' with DOM/1 – save, of course, to the lack of any requirements for the involvement of, and certification by, the architect. The extension of time clause 9(3), for instance, again gives the sub-contractor an entitlement to an extension of time for any reason for which the main contractor is so entitled under the main contract, plus 'any act, default or omission of the Contractor or any other sub-contractor employed by the Contractor on or in connection with the Main Contract Works'. The improvement in wording over the equivalent clause 8(b)(i) of the 'Green Form' can be seen. The granting of an appropriate extension is then, of course, entirely between the main contractor and sub-contractor. There is no separate entitlement of the main contractor to claim against the sub-contractor for delay in completion of the sub-contract works, however; the contractor's entitlement is simply in respect of the effect of 'any act, omission or default of the Sub-Contractor, his servants or agents or any sub-contractor employed by him on the Sub-Contract Works' upon 'regular progress' of the main contract works – which would presumably include the effect of delayed completion. Otherwise the rights of sub-contractor and main contractor to claim against each other are as they are under the 'Green Form'.

The right of the sub-contractor to claim against the employer through the main contractor is, as in the 'Green Form', dependent upon the clause [10(1)], which requires the main contractor to enforce and make available to the sub-contractor the benefit of his own right to claim under the main contract.

SUB-CONTRACT CONDITIONS FOR SUB-CONTRACTORS NAMED UNDER THE INTERMEDIATE FORM OF BUILDING CONTRACT (NAM/SC)

The provisions for extensions of time and claims for and against sub-contractors 'named' under clause 3.3 of the JCT Intermediate Form (IFC 84) are contained in clause 12 and 14 of Form NAM/SC and run as follows:

12 **Sub-Contractor's obligation – carrying out and completion of Sub-Contract Works – extension of Sub-Contract period**

12.1 The Sub-Contractor shall carry out and complete the Sub-Contract Works in accordance with NAM/T, Section I, item 15, and Section II, item 1, and reasonably in accordance with the progress of the Works subject to receipt of the notice to commence work on site as stated in NAM/T, Section II, item 1, and to the operation of clause 12.

12.2 Upon it becoming reasonably apparent that the commencement, progress or completion of the Sub-Contract Works is being or is likely to be delayed, the Sub-Contractor shall forthwith give written notice of the delay, specifying the cause in so far as he is able, to the Contractor, and if the completion of the Sub-Contract Works is likely to be or has been delayed beyond the period or periods referred to in NAM/T, Section II, item 1, or any extended period or periods previously fixed under this clause, by:

> any act, omission or default of the Contractor, his servants or agents or his sub-contractors, their servants or agents (other than the Sub-Contractor, his servants or agents), or

> by any of the events in clause 12.4,

then the Contractor shall so soon as he is able to estimate the length of delay beyond that period or periods make in writing a fair and reasonable extension of the period or periods for completion of the Sub-Contract Works.

12.3 If any act, omission or default as referred to in clause 12.2.1 or an event referred to in 12.7.5 to 12.7.8, 12.7.11 or 12.7.13 occurs after the expiry of the period or periods stated in NAM/T, Section II, item 1, (or after the expiry of any extended period or periods previously fixed under this clause) but before practical completion of the Sub-Contract Works is achieved the Contractor shall so soon as he is able to estimate the length of the resulting delay, if any, beyond that period or periods make in writing a fair and reasonable extension of the period or periods for completion of the Sub-Contract Works.

12.4 At any time the Contractor may make an extension of the period or periods for completion of the Sub-Contract Works in accordance with the provisions of clause 12.2 or 12.3, whether upon reviewing a previous decision or otherwise, whether or not the Sub-Contractor has given notice as referred to in clause 12.2. Such an extension of time shall not reduce any previously made.

12.5 Provided always that the Sub-Contractor shall use constantly his best endeavours to prevent delay and shall do all that may be reasonably required to the satisfaction of the Contractor to proceed with the Sub-Contract Works.

12.6 The Sub-Contractor shall provide such information required by the Contractor as is reasonably necessary for the purposes of clauses 12.2, 12.3 and 12.4.

12.7 The following are the events referred to in clause 12.2:

12.7 .1 *force majeure*;

12.7 .2 exceptionally adverse weather conditions;

12.7 .3 loss or damage caused by any one or more of the 'Clause 6.3 Perils';

12.7 .4 civil commotion, local combination of workmen, strike or lock-out affecting any of the trades employed upon the Works or any trade engaged in the preparation, manufacture or transportation of any of the goods or materials required for the Works;

12.7 .5 compliance by the Contractor with the Architect's/the Supervising Officer's instructions (which shall be deemed to include compliance by the Sub-Contractor with the Contractor's directions which pass on such instructions):

.5 .1 under clause 1.4, 3.3.1, 3.3.3, 3.6, 3.8 or 3.15 of the Main Contract Conditions; or

.5 .2 in regard to the opening up or the testing of any of the work, materials or goods in accordance with clause 3.12 or 3.13.1 of the Main Contract Conditions (including making good in consequence of such opening up or testing) unless the inspection or test showed that the work, materials or goods were not in accordance with this Contract;

12.7 .6 the Contractor, or the Sub-Contractor through the Contractor, not having received in due time necessary instructions, drawings, details or levels from the Architect/the Supervising Officer for which the Contractor or the Sub-Contractor through the Contractor specifically applied in writing provided that such application was made on a date which having regard to the period or periods for the completion of the Sub-Contract Works or any extension thereof then fixed was neither unreasonably distant from nor unreasonably close to the date on which it was necessary for the Contractor or the Sub-Contractor to receive the same;

12.7 .7 the execution of work not forming part of the Main Contract by the Employer himself or by persons employed or otherwise engaged by the Employer as referred to in clause 3.11 of the Main Contract Conditions or the failure to execute such work;

12.7 .8 the supply by the Employer of materials and goods which the Employer has agreed to provide for the Works or the failure so to supply;

12.7 .9 where it is stated in NAM/T, Section I, item 6 that clause 2.3.10 of the Main Contract Conditions applies, the Contractor's or the Sub-Contractor's inability for reasons beyond his control and which he could not reasonably have foreseen at the Date of Tender to secure such labour as is essential to the proper carrying out of the Works;

12.7 .10 where it is stated in NAM/T, Section 1, item 6 that clause 2.3.11 of the Main Contract Conditions applies, the Contractor's or the Sub-Contractor's inability for reasons beyond his control and which he could not reasonably have foreseen at the Date of Tender to secure such goods or materials as are essential to the proper carrying out of the Works;

12.7 .11 failure of the Employer to give in due time ingress to or egress from the site of the Works or any part thereof through or over any land, buildings, way or passage adjoining or connected with the site and in the possession and control of the Employer, in accordance with the Contract Documents, after receipt by the Architect/the Supervising Officer of such notice, if any, as the Contractor is required to give, or failure of the Employer to give such ingress or egress as otherwise agreed between the Architect/the Supervising Officer and the Contractor;

12.7 .12 the carrying out by a local authority or statutory undertaker of work in pursuance of its statutory obligations in relation to the Works, or the failure to carry out such work;

12.7 .13 the deferment of the Employer giving posession of the site under clause 2.2 of the Main Contract Conditions;

12.7 .14 the valid exercise by the Sub-Contractor of the right in clause 19.6 to suspend the further execution of the Sub-Contract Works.

12.8 In clauses 12 and 13 any references to delay, notice or extension of period or periods include further delay, further notice or further extension of period or periods as appropriate.

14 Disturbance of regular progress

14.1 If the Sub-Contractor shall make written application to the Contractor within a reasonably time of it becoming apparent that the Sub-Contractor has incurred or is likely to incur direct loss and/or expense, for which he would not be reimbursed under any other provision of this Contract, due to the commencement or regular progress of the Sub-Contract Works or any part thereof having been materially affected by any act, omission or default of the Contractor, his servants or agents, or any sub-contractor, his servants or agents (other than the Sub-Contractor, his servants or agents) or is materially affected by any one or more of the matters referred to in clause 14.2, the agreed amount of any direct [loss] and/or expense thereby caused to the Sub-Contractor shall be added to the Sub-Contract Sum; provided that the Sub-Contractor shall in support of his application submit such information required by the Contractor as is reasonably necessary for the purposes of this clause.

14.2 The following are matters referred to in clause 14.1:

14.2 .1 the Contractor or the Sub-Contractor through the Contractor, not having received in due time necessary instructions, drawings, details or levels from the Architect/the Supervising Officer for which the Contractor or the Sub-Contractor through the Contractor specifically applied in writing provided that such application was made on a date which having regard to the period or periods for completion of the Sub-Contract Works was neither unreasonably distant from nor unreasonably close to the date on which it was necessary for the Contractor or the Sub-Contractor to receive the same;

14.2 .2 the opening up for inspection of any work covered up or the testing of any work, materials or goods in accordance with clause 3.12 or the Main Contract Conditions (including making good in consequence of such opening up or testing), unless the inspection or test showed that the work, materials or goods were not in accordance with the Main Contract or the Sub-Contract as the case may be;

14.2 .3 the execution of work not forming part of the Main Contract by the Employer himself or by persons employed or otherwise engaged by the Employer as referred to in clause 3.11 of the Main Contract Conditions or the failure to execute such work;

14.2 .4 the supply by the Employer of materials and goods which the Employer has agreed to provide for the Works or the failure so to supply;

14.2 .5 failure of the Employer to give in due time ingress to or egress from the site of the Works, or any part thereof through or over any land, buildings, way or passage adjoining or connected with the site and in the possession and control of the Employer in accordance with the Contract Documents after receipt by the Architect/the Supervising Officer of such notice, if any, as the Contractor is required to give or failure of the Employer to give such ingress or egress as otherwise agreed between the Architect/the Supervising Officer and the Contractor;

14.2 .6 the Architect's/the Supervising Officer's instructions issued under clause 1.4, 3.3.1, 3.3.3, 3.6, 3.8 or 3.15 of the Main Contract Conditions and the Contractor's directions consequent thereon issued under clause 5;

14.2 .7 the deferment of the Employer giving possession of the site under clause 2.2 of Main Contract Conditions:

14.2 .8 the valid exercise by the Sub-Contractor of the right in clause 19.6 to suspend the further execution of the Sub-Contract Works.

14.3 If the regular progress of the Works is materially affected by any act, omission or default of the Sub-Contractor, his servants or agents, and if the Contractor shall within a reasonable time of such material effect becoming apparent make written application to the Sub-Contractor, the agreed amount of any direct loss and/or expense thereby caused to the Contractor may be deducted from any monies due or to become due to the Sub-Contractor or may be recoverable from the Sub-Contractor as a debt; provided that the Contractor shall, in support of his application submit such information required by the Sub-Contractor as is reasonably necessary for the purposes of this clause.

14.4 The provisions of clause 14 are without prejudice to any other rights or remedies which the Contractor or Sub-Contractor may possess.

(In the Form as currently printed clause 12.7.6 to .9 have been inadvertently repeated.)

The references to NAM/T are to the Form of Tender and Agreement which constitute the sub-contract as actually executed by the main contractor and the sub-contractor, Form NAM/SC containing the conditions of sub-contract being issued separately and incorporated by reference into the agreement.

Clauses 12 and 14 of NAM/SC are essentially simplified versions of the equivalent clauses 11 and 13 of the domestic sub-contract Form DOM/1 produced for use with JCT 80. This reflects the position of 'named' sub-contractors under IFC 84. In contrast to nominated sub-contractors under JCT 80, for instance, the architect is not required to certify amounts for payment to the sub-contractor, there is no provision for direct payment by the employer if the main contractor defaults on payment and the architect is not required separately to certify practical completion of the sub-contractor's work. The architect will only be involved if either the sub-contractor or the main contractor is so seriously in default under the sub-contractor that either becomes entitled to determine the employment of the other, when the architect is required to step in to deal with the situation that then arises.

The simplification in comparison with DOM/1 is similar in nature to the simplification that has taken place in the extension of time and 'claim' provisions in IFC 84 as compared with JCT 80; see the discussion on pages 188–194. There are only two changes to which attention should be drawn:

- In parallel with clause 2.3 of IFC 84 (see page 60) clause 12.3 makes specific provision for delaying events occuring after the sub-contract works ought to have been completed and before actual practical completion.
- Clause 12.4 empowers the contractor to grant an extension of time of his own volition and without notice from the sub-contractor at any time during the progress or after completion of the sub-contract works; in DOM/1 (clause 11.7) this power can only be exercised within the period of 16 weeks after practical completion of either the sub-contract or main contract works, whichever is the earlier. It would appear that, under NAM/SC, this power could be exercised by the main contractor at any time up to the issue of the Final Certificate under the main contract.

The clauses are well covered in outline in *Sub-Contracts under the JCT*

Intermediate Form by Peter R Hibberd, Chapter 10.

The equivalent clauses 12 and 14 in Domestic Sub-Contract Form IN/ SC produced by the Building Employers' Confederation and the sub-contractors' organisations for use with IFC 84 are identical to those in Form NAM/SC and therefore do not require separate consideration.

THE ACA FORM OF SUB-CONTRACT 1982

This form of sub-contract was issued unilaterally by the Association of Consultant Architects in October 1982 and is designed for use with the ACA Form of Building Agreement, which is discussed in chapter 8.

The use of the sub-contract form is not obligatory under the main contract but its drafting follows very closely the main contract provisions and, in our view, it can only be used in conjunction with that form. Claims under the sub-contract form (as under the ACA contract itself) are limited; and this applies to claims both for extensions of time and for money.

(a) Extensions of time
The sub-contract provisions for extensions of time are contained in clause 7, which (as amended in the Second Edition 1984) reads as follows:

7. **COMMENCEMENT, COMPLETION AND DELAYS IN THE EXECUTION OF THE SUB-CONTRACT WORKS**

7.1 The Sub-Contractor shall commence the execution of the Sub-Contract Works within ☐ 10 ☐ working days of receipt of the Contractor's written instruction so to do. The Sub-Contractor shall proceed with the same regularly and diligently and in accordance with the Sub-Contract Time Schedule and shall complete the same on or before the date or dates for completion stated in the Sub-Contract Time Schedule, subject as hereinafter provided in this Clause 7.

7.2 No extension of time shall be granted to the Sub-Contractor except in the case of:

    (a) any circumstance entitling the Contractor to an extension of time for completion of the Works or (if appropriate) of any Section in which the Sub-Contract Works are comprised; or

    (b) any act, instruction, default or omission of the Contractor, whether authorised by or in breach of this Sub-Contract which the Sub-Contractor shall prove to the satisfaction of the Contractor has prevented the completion of the Sub-Contract Works by the date or dates for completion stated in the Sub-Contract Time Schedule; or

    (c) any instruction to postpone given in accordance with Clause 7.5;

In any such event the Contractor shall grant to the Sub-Contractor such extension of time to the date or dates for completion of the Sub-Contract Works as he then estimates to be fair and reasonable. Provided that no account shall be taken of any of the circumstances referred to in Clause 7.2(a) unless the Sub-Contractor shall have given written notice and full and detailed particulars to the Contractor at the time and in the manner in which notice and particulars are required to be given by the Contractor to the Architect or the Supervising Officer, as the case may be, under the Agreement.

7.3 If the Sub-Contract Works or any part of them are not completed in accordance with the provisions of Clause 7.1, the Contractor shall give to the Sub-Contractor written notice to that effect.

7.4 In considering any extension of time the Contractor shall be entitled to take into account at any time before the Taking-Over of the Works or of the last Section (if appropriate) in which the Sub-Contract Works are comprised, the effects of any omission from the Sub-Contract Works. Where the Architect reviews all or any of his previous decisions under Clause 11.7 of the Agreement and fixes a date for the Taking-Over of the Works or of any Section later than that previously stated, adjusted or fixed, the Contractor shall review the extensions of time (if any) previously granted by him under Clause 7.2 of this Sub-Contract in respect of the circumstances referred to in Clause 7.2(a) accordingly.

The first matter which should be noted – for it is highly relevant to claims – is that the sub-contractor's obligation in clause 7.1 is to 'commence the execution of the sub-contract works ... proceed with the same regularly and diligently and in accordance with the ... Time Schedule and ... complete the same *on or before* the date or dates for completion ...'. We think that the views expressed by Mr Justice Megarry in *Hounslow Borough Council* v. *Twickenham Garden Developments Ltd* (1970) are equally applicable to sub-contractor's claims under this clause. If the sub-contractor 'is well ahead with his works and is then delayed [by something giving him a claim for extension of time], the [contractor] may nevertheless reach the conclusion that completion of the works is not likely to be delayed beyond the date for completion'. Whether the sub-contractor has proceeded 'regularly and diligently' with the works is a question of fact; and as Mr Justice Megarry said in the same case:

'These are elusive words on which the dictionaries help little. The words convey a sense of activity, of orderly progress, and of industry and perseverance; but such language provides little help on the question of how much activity, progress and so on is to be expected. They are words used in a standard form of building contract and in those circumstances it may be that there is evidence that could be given, whether of usage among architects, builders, and building owners or otherwise, that could be helpful in construing those words. At present, all that I can say is that I remain somewhat uncertain as to the concept enshrined in those words.'

Extensions of time as such are dealt with by clause 7.2, the wording of which makes it clear that the sub-contract is entitled to extensions of time only on the grounds stated in the clause. These grounds fall into three groups:

(1) 'Any circumstance entitling the Contractor to an extension of time' under the main contract.
(2) 'Any act, instruction, default or omission of the Contractor, whether authorised by or in breach of this Sub-Contract *which the sub-contractor shall prove* to the satisfaction of the contractor has prevented completion of the sub-contract works...'.
(3) 'Any instruction to postpone given in accordance with Clause 7.5.'

These provisions are very restrictive.

(1) Grounds under main contract

Assuming that the ACA sub-contract is used in conjunction with the ACA main form, there are two possibilities, since the main form contains alternative versions of clause 11.5 – Extensions of time. Alternative 1 is the narrow version, since it entitles the main contractor (and hence the sub-contractor) to an extension of time in respect of delay or disturbance caused by 'any act, instruction, default, or omission of the employer, or of the architect on his behalf, whether authorised by or in breach of this Agreement', and this is apt to extend to breaches, etc., of the express and implied terms of the contract or sub-contract as appropriate.

Alternative 2 lists five specific causes; and in both cases our commentary on the ACA main contract terms should be referred to: see pages 247–255.

(2) Main contractor's defaults, etc.

This ground is self-explanatory; and reference should be made to our discussion on pages 232–233, which emphasises that there need not necessarily be a legal wrong involved.

(3) Postponement instructions

Clause 7.5 empowers the contractor, *inter alia*, to postpone the completion of all or any part of the sub-contract works and obliges the sub-contractor 'immediately [to] take such measures as are necessary to comply with such instruction...'.

The giving of written notice to the contractor by the sub-contractor is clearly a condition precedent to the operation of the extension of time provisions, as is made clear by the final sentence in clause 7.2 beginning 'Provided that no account shall be taken...'. This effectively incorporates the procedural provisions of the main contract: as to which see our commentary on ACA main contract extensions of time provisions: pages 244–255. Written notice by the sub-contractor is not required in respect of the grounds listed in paragraphs (b) and (c) of clause 7.2.

The sub-contractor's entitlement is to such an extension of time as the contractor '*then* estimates to be fair and reasonable'. Clause 7.4 states that, in considering any extension of time, the contractor is entitled to have regard to any omission of work from the sub-contract – the contract wording is 'take into account –' and also that where, under clause 11.7 of the main contract, the architect reviews his previous decisions on extensions of time and fixes a *later* date than that previously set, the contractor must (in the first edition of the Form the word was 'may') review any extensions of time which he has granted previously to the sub-contractor, *but only in respect of* the matters referred to in clause 7.2(a), i.e. grounds under the main contract.

(b) Money claims under ACA Sub-Contract

This important matter is covered by clause 9 of the sub-contract, which parallels clause 7 of the ACA main contract, discussed in chapter 8, pages 230–237 and effectively incorporates the procedural and allied provisions of the main contract form in the sub-contract.

Clause 9 reads as follows:

9. DAMAGE, LOSS AND/OR EXPENSE

9.1 The Sub-Contractor shall give to the Contractor any notices, particulars, estimates or other information which the Contractor is required to give to the Architect or to the Supervising Officer, as the case may be, under the provisions of the Agreement in sufficient time to enable the Contractor to claim any adjustment to the Contract Sum or any damage, loss and/or expense to which he is entitled under the provisions of the Agreement.

9.2 If the regular progress of the Sub-Contract Works is disrupted or delayed by any circumstance other than Architect's or Supervising Officer's instructions (to which the provisions of Clause 5 shall apply) entitling the Contractor to claim from the Employer damage, loss or expense under clause 7 of the Agreement, the

Contractor shall at the request of the Sub-Contractor recover for the Sub-Contractor any damage, loss or expense suffered or incurred by the Sub-Contractor by reason of such disruption or delay to the Sub-Contract Works: Provided always that the Sub-Contractor shall comply with his obligations under clause 9.1.

9.3 If, pursuant to the provisions of Clause 9.2 of this Sub-Contract, the Contractor recovers any damage, loss and/or expense in respect of any circumstance which has affected the execution of the Sub-Contract Works, the Contractor shall in turn pay to the Sub-Contractor such proportion of it (if any) as may, in the Contractor's opinion, be fair and reasonable and such proportion shall be added to the Sub-Contract Sum.

9.4 Save in the case of Contractor's instructions (to which the provisions of clause 5 shall apply), if any act, omission, default or negligence of the Contractor or his employees, agents or Sub-Contractors disrupts the regular progress of the Sub-Contract Works or delays the execution of them in accordance with the dates stated in the Sub-Contract Time Schedule and, in consequence of such disruption or delay, the Sub-Contractor suffers or incurs damage, loss and/or expense, he shall be entitled to recover the same from the Contractor as a debt.

Clause 9.1 obliges the sub-contractor to give to the contractor 'any notices, estimates or other information which the Contractor is obliged to give to the Architect' under the main form. He must do this 'in sufficient time to enable the Contractor to claim any adjustment to the Contract Sum or any damage, loss and/or expense' on his own or the sub-contractor's behalf. Once again, this is an example of contractual claims being passed up the contract chain.

Claims under clause 9 are of two types , dealt with separately in clauses 9.2 and 9.4, respectively.

Clause 9.2 is concerned with 'Claims against the Employer', i.e. those claims for which the employer accepts responsibility. It is quite plain from the wording that such claims extend to both 'disturbance' and 'prolongation': the sub-clause refers to work being 'disrupted or delayed': and all that is required is that the *regular progress* of the sub-contract works should be disrupted or delayed by 'any circumstance other than Architect's instructions ... entitling the Contractor to claim from the Employer' under the terms of clause 7 of the main contract'. (Architect's instructions are dealt with separately by main contract clause 8: see our commentary thereon at pages 237–241.) This clause obliges the contractor to 'recover for the sub-contractor' any 'damage, loss or expense suffered or incurred' by the latter 'by reason of such disruption or delay to the Sub-Contract Works', i.e. the main contractor must pass on the sub-contractor's claims. This is subject to the overall proviso (which is a condition precedent) that the sub-contractor shall have given the main contractor the requisite notices, etc. under clause 9.1. In simple terms, the sub-contractor provides details of his claim to the main contractor who then passes them on to the employer under the main contract terms.

Clause 9.3 deals with settlement of claims, and the vague wording is to be deprecated. In short, the contractor is to pay over to the sub-contractor 'such proprotion (if any)' of any monies which he recovers under the Main Contract claims provisions 'as may, in the Contractor's opinion, be fair and reasonable'; the contractor's opinion would be something which could be challenged in arbitration if the optional arbitration provision (clause 15) applies; and similarly in the case of the alternative litigation provision.

Clause 9.4 deals with claims by the sub-contractor against the main contractor and is concerned with claims which the main contractor cannot pass on to the employer. Contractor's instructions are dealt with separately in clause 5, which is in almost identical terms to the corresponding main contract provision, clause 8; and reference should be made to our commentary thereon: see pages 237–241. Contractor's instructions apart, clause 9.4 is merely declaratory of what would be the position at common law in any case. It says that the sub-contractor is entitled to recover, as against the main contractor, any 'damage, loss and/ or expense' that he suffers or incurs as a result of 'any act, omission, default or negligence of the Contractor or his employees, agents or Sub-Contractors' which *disrupts* the regular progress of the sub-contract works, 'or delays the execution of them in accordance with the dates stated in the Sub-Contract Time Schedule'. This provision is wholly unsatisfactory since it provides no express machinery for the recovery of such claims; and it is an extraordinary provision to find in what is clearly a carefully-drafted contractual document. At the very least one would have expected to find provisions equivalent to those in the JCT sub-contract forms discussed earlier in this chapter; as it is, it would seem that sub-contractor's claims under clause 9.4 must be pursued in arbitration or litigation, as appropriate. In practice, we both think and hope that main contractors and sub-contractors will be able to agree such claims. Presumably, the sums so agreed would be included in the interim payments under clause 10.2.(b).

In our view the ACA provisions are very unsatisfactory from the point of view of both contractors and sub-contractors and it may well be that sub-contractors operating under this Form may be better advised to sue at common law.

Chapter 10

Common law claims

INTRODUCTION

The claims discussed in other chapters are those that arise under specific clauses in the contract and, in general, this specific right to claim, for example for 'direct loss and/or expense' under JCT 80, clause 26, is in addition to any right to damages that the contractor possesses at common law for breach of contract or, for example, under the law of tort. Indeed, JCT 80, clause 26.6 makes this clear:

'The provisions of Clause 26 are without prejudice to any other rights or remedies which the Contractor may possess.'

(The last sentence of clause 4.11 of IFC 1984 is to the same effect.)

The practical effect of this is that JCT 80 and 63 (and, indeed, all other current standard forms) allow additional or alternative claims for damages based on the same facts, so that the contractor may pursue his remedy under the express contract term without prejudicing his right to claim at common law. It was held by Mr Justice Vinelott in *London Borough of Merton* v. *Stanley Hugh Leach Ltd* (1985) that the contractor is not obliged to make a claim under such a clause in respect of those grounds specified in the clause which are also breaches of contract, such as the architect's failure to provide information in response to the contractor's application. He may prefer to wait until completion and join the claim for damages with other claims for damages for breaches of other obligations under the contract. Common law claims are generally based on implied terms in the contract. Of course, the contractor can only recover his loss once but a common law claim may avoid any restrictions imposed upon the contractual claim by the terms of the contract itself.

There is an important distinction between contractual and common

301

law claims. Where the contractor makes a claim under a specific contract provision, such as clause 26, JCT 80, he is asking that the machinery provided for by the contract be operated in his favour. Accordingly, he must observe the procedural provisions in the contract relating to the giving of notices and so on. The wording of the particular provision relied upon may also circumscribe his remedy – and this it usually does by limiting the amount of his claim by excluding what is usually called 'consequential loss': see *Saintline Ltd* v. *Richardson, Westgarth & Co* (1940).

Under the JCT Forms it is only claims that arise under specific contract clauses that can be ascertained and certified by the architect and paid for under the normal contract provisions for payment. The architect has no power – express or implied – to make payments in respect of common law claims. Such claims are governed by the general law. Once the arbitration procedure is invoked, however, the arbitrator has power to deal with common law claims, but such claims must be expressly pleaded in the points of claim submitted by the claimant. Under JCT terms of contract, in our view and that of most other commentators it is plain that the arbitrator may decide a claim based on tort alone (as well as breach of contract) and the limitation is that the tort must arise out of the transaction which is the subject-matter of the contract: see *Re Polemis and Furness, Withy & Co.* (1921).

In *Ashville Investments Ltd* v. *Elmer Contractors Ltd* (1987) the Court of Appeal held that, on the true interpretation of clause 35 of JCT 63 that the arbitrator has power to award damages for misrepresentation and mistake as well as power to order rectification of the contract. Lord Justice May said:

> 'I have no doubt that a dispute between the parties based upon alleged mistake at the time this contract was entered into, and upon an alleged misrepresentation or negligent mis-statement are ones "arising in connection" with that contract and thus within the scope of the arbitration clause ... there is ... nothing in that clause which would preclude an arbitrator from granting rectification or awarding damages if he finds such allegations made out.'

Under the ACA terms (see chapter 8) it is clear that the architect has power to assess common law claims as well: clause 7.1 of the ACA Contract refers specifically to claims resulting from 'any act, omission, default or negligence of the Employer or of the Architect'; and the contractor is 'entitled to recover the same in accordance with the provisions of this clause'. The provisions of clauses 7.2, 7.3 and 7.4 must be observed if the architect is to deal with such claims. Clause 7.5, in our view, makes it clear that failure to comply with those procedural provisions is not fatal to the contractor's claim; it merely delays the time of settlement. Consequently, we feel that the contractor's common law rights are unaffected by the express provisions of the clause.

Finally, as regards common law claims, these will only be subject to the Limitation Act 1980; and the contractor may pursue such common law claims at any time within the period of limitation, i.e. six years for actions based on simple contract or tort or 12 years if the contract is under seal. Recent developments in negligence law effectively prevent a party to a contract also having a claim in tort against the other party arising out of the same facts, and in any case contract provisions relating to the 'finality' of a final certificate under the contract do not apply to common law claims under any of the standard forms in current use.

However, recent case law points to a narrowing of negligence liability, as indicated by *Department of the Environment* v. *Thomas Bates & Sons Ltd* (1987), which emphasises that the contractor's duty in tort is one to use reasonable care and skill in the construction of a building so that it does not, within a reasonable time, give rise to imminent danger to the health or safety of people on the premises or cause physical damage to the premises.

IMPLIED TERMS IN BUILDING CONTRACTS

The question of implied terms is fully dealt with in all the standard texts on general contract law and, in the context of building contracts, the matter is amply discussed by Dr John Parris in *The Standard Form of Building Contract: JCT 1980,* 2nd edition; Sections 2.06 Types of implied terms and 4.03–4.05 Implied terms in construction contracts, design and build contracts and sub-contracts and in JCT 80. In practice, in the context of building contract claims, the concern is with those terms which will be implied into the contract by the courts, in order to make the contract commercially effective; *The Moorcock* (1889).

Where the express terms of the contract are clear and unambiguous, the courts will not imply a term simply to extricate a party from difficulties. In *Trollope & Colls Ltd* v. *North West Metropolitan Regional Hospital Board* (1973) Lord Pearson put the matter clearly:

'An unexpressed term can be implied if and only if the court finds that the parties must have intended that term to form part of their contract: it is not enough for the court to find that such a term would have been adopted by the parties as reasonable men if it had been suggested to them: it must have been a term that went without saying, a term *necessary* to give business efficacy to the contract, a term which, although tacit, formed part of the contract which the parties made for themselves'.

In the recent case of *London Borough of Merton* v. *Stanley Hugh Leach Ltd* (1985) one of the many points at issue concerned the implication of certain implied terms. Mr Justice Vinelott considered the general approach to be adopted as to the implication of terms in a contract in JCT 63 form, referring to the cases in which the courts have considered whether a term should be implied into a contract and which cover a wide variety of situations.

Most common law claims arising under building contracts are based on implied terms relating to the employer failing to co-operate with the contractor or interfering with the contractor's progress. In *London Borough of Merton* v. *Stanley Hugh Leach Ltd*, the contractor sought that a number of terms be implied into a JCT contract. The first two of these were:

(i) The employer would not hinder or prevent the contractor from carrying out its obligations in accordance with the terms of the contract and from executing the works in a regular and orderly manner.

(ii) The employer would take all steps reasonably necessary to enable the contractor so to discharge its obligations and to execute the works in a regular and orderly manner.

Mr Justice Vinelott unhesitatingly held that the first term ought to be implied:

'The implied undertaking not to do anything to hinder the other party from performing his part of the contract may, of course, be qualified by a term express or to be implied from the contract and the surrounding circumstances. But the general duty remains so far as qualified ... It is difficult to conceive of a case in which this duty could be wholly excluded'.

As regards the second term – the employer's duty to do all that is reasonably necessary to bring the contract to completion – Mr Justice Vinelott was equally emphatic. He accepted that it is well settled law that the courts will imply a duty to do whatever is necessary to enable the other party to perform his obligations under the contract: *Mackay* v. *Dick* (1881). He noted that there are limitations on the principle, and referred with approval to the views expressed by Mr Justice Devlin in *Mona Oil Equipment Co.* v. *Rhodesia Railway Co.* (1949):

'I can think of no term that can properly be implied other than one based on the necessity for co-operation. It is, no doubt, true that every business contract depends for its smooth working on co-operation, but in the ordinary business contract, and apart, of course, from express terms, the law can enforce co-operation only in a limited degree – to the extent that it is necessary to make the contract workable. For any higher degree of co-operation the parties must rely on the desire that both of them usually have that the business should be done'.

Any building contract requires close co-operation between the contractor and the architect. The JCT contracts contain many examples of the co-operation which the architect is required to give to the contractor. For example, by issuing instructions during the progress of the works and by providing further drawings to explain or amplify the contract drawings. Without that co-operation the contract cannot be completed expeditiously and efficiently. However, the exact parameters of the duty of co-operation are unclear, but, in the words of Mr Justice Vinelott, this second implied term

'extends to those things which the architect must do to enable the contractor to carry out the work and that the building owner is liable for any breach of this duty on the part of the architect'.

Another case in which a similar implied term was conceded is *Holland Hannen & Cubitts* v. *WHTSO* (1981) where the contract was also in JCT 1963 form. The term there was to the effect that 'the employer would do all things necessary to enable the contractor to carry out and complete the works expeditiously, economically and in accordance with the contract'. The important point is that the employer will only be liable for breach in respect of those functions performed by the architect acting as the employer's agent and not when he is acting as certifier because in the latter case the employer is not vicariously liable.

In *Leach*, Mr Justice Vinelott summarised the position under a JCT contract in this way:

'Under the standard conditions, the architect acts as the servant or agent of the building owner in supplying the contractor with the necessary drawings, instructions, levels and the like and in supervising the progress of the work and ensuring that it is properly carried out ... To the extent that the architect performs these duties the building owner contracts with the contractor that the architect will perform them with reasonable diligence and with reasonable skill and care. The contract also confers on the architect discretionary powers which he must exercise with due regard to the interests of the contractor and the building owner. The building owner does not undertake that the architect will exercise his discretionary powers reasonably; he undertakes that although the architect may be engaged or employed by him, he will leave him free to exercise his discretion fairly and without improper interference by him ... It is now clear that insofar as the architect exercises discretionary powers and the exercise of his discretion can be reviewed by the arbitrator, the arbitrator stands in the shoes of the architect and does not exercise a purely arbitral role ... But to the extent that the architect acts as agent or servant of the building owner by the contract his acts are not subject to review by the arbitrator – though they may found a claim for damages for breach of contract the extent of which will fall to be determined by the arbitrator'.

Apart from the two foregoing implied terms, it is an implied term of every building contract that the employer will give possession of the site to the contractor in sufficient time to enable him to complete the works by the due date: *Freeman & Son* v. *Hensler* (1900). All the standard form building contracts in common use contain express terms providing for the giving of possession of the site. In that case, of course, the employer's failure to give possession as provided in the contract is a breach for which the contractor will be entitled to damages in respect of any resultant loss.

None of the standard form contracts in current use displaces the first two implied terms mentioned, and thus the employer is liable at common law for breach of them. This can have important practical implications, and consideration must be given to one of the most common grounds of common law claim arising under JCT 63 and JCT 80 prior to its amendment in July 1987.

Late possession of site

As we have seen in every building contract it is an implied term that the employer will give possession of the site to the contractor within a reasonable time, i.e. in sufficient time to enable the contractor to complete the works by the contractual date: *Freeman* v. *Hensler* (1900).

Under JCT terms, there is specific provision for the contractor to be given possession on the date specified in the Appendix.

JCT 63, clause 21(1) provides:

'On the Date for Possession stated in the Appendix to these Conditions possession of the site *shall* be given to the Contractor who shall thereupon begin the Works...'.

In its original form, JCT 80, clause 23.1 provided:

'On the Date of Possession, possession of the site *shall* be given to the Contractor who shall thereupon begin the Works...'.

Any failure by the employer to give possession on the date named is a breach of contract and, indeed, it is a breach of a major term ('condition') of the contract. It is a breach not only of the express terms of the JCT contracts but also a breach of the term that is implied at common law. Since default in giving possession is a breach of a major term of the contract ('condition'), failure so to do, and acceptance by the contractor of the employer's breach, entitle the contractor to repudiate the contract and to sue for damages for breach, and these would include the loss of the profit that he would otherwise have earned: see *Wraight Ltd* v. *P.H. & T. Holdings Ltd* (1968). Few contractors would wish to take such a drastic course, and accordingly may elect to treat the breach as a breach of warranty only and to claim damages at common law for any loss actually incurred. In other words, at the very least, the contractor is entitled to damages for breach: *Hounslow Borough Council* v. *Twickenham Garden Developments Ltd* (1970).

The right to possession of the site on the date given in the Appendix is an absolute one. In *Hounslow Borough Council* v. *Twickenham Garden Developments Ltd* (1970), Mr Justice Megarry said this:

'The contract necessarily requires the building owner to give the contractor such possession, occupation and use as is necessary to enable him to perform the contract, but whether in a given case the contractor in law has possession must, I think, depend at least as much on what is done as on what the contract provides ...'.

Whether or not, therefore, the contractor has been given sufficient possession is a matter of fact. In *The Rapid Building Group Ltd* v. *Ealing Family Housing Association Ltd* (1984), which arose under a contract in JCT 63 form, at the time when, by clause 21, the defendants were bound to give the plaintiffs possession of the site, they were unable to do so because its north east corner (an area of some size) was occupied by squatters. The defendants took eviction proceedings, but it was at least 19 days before the site was cleared of squatters so as to enable the contractors to take possession of the whole of the site. The Court of Appeal (affirming the decision of Judge John Newey QC, a very experienced Official Referee) held that the defendants were in clear breach of clause 21 because of their failure, for whatever reason, to remove the squatters until an appreciable time after they were bound to give the plaintiffs possession. Although the contractors entered on the site, the trial judge found that they were unable to clear it and so the breach caused appreciable delay and disruption, which entitled the contractors to damages. This case should be contrasted with *Porter* v. *Tottenham Urban District Council* (1915), another decision of the Court of Appeal, where the contractor was wrongfully excluded from the site by a third party for whom the employer was not responsible in law and over whom he had no control. There was no clause 21, and the court held that there was no implied warranty by the council against wrongful interference by a third party – an adjoining owner – with the only access to the site. Equally, *The Rapid Building* case is distinguishable from *LRE Engineering Services Ltd* v. *Otto Simon Carves Ltd* (1981), where the point at issue was whether main contractors were in breach of a sub-contract term requiring that 'access ... shall be afforded', and this was denied to the sub-contractors because of unlawful picketing during a steel strike.

There are comparatively few reported English cases dealing with interferences with the contractor's possession of the site, but under the JCT forms the position seems to be that the employer must ensure that the contractor has uninterrupted possession of the whole of the site during the period of the contract, unless there is interference by third parties over whom the employer has no control. The position of employer's licensees, such as other direct contractors, is expressly covered by the contracts, e.g. JCT 80, clause 25.4.8. In the Canadian case of *The Queen in Right of Canada* v. *Walter Cabott Construction Ltd* (1975), the Federal Court of Appeal held that it was an implied term of a building contract that 'it is fundamental to a building contract that work space should be provided unimpeded by others' (*per* Mr Justice Urie), and this is also the case under English law unless the contract provides to the contrary.

Under JCT terms (both in 1963 and 1980 Editions, before the 1987 amendment) there was no power in the architect to postpone the giving of possession of the site. It is sometimes argued that JCT 63, clause 21(2) and JCT 80, clause 23.2 conferred on the architect a power to postpone the giving of possession. For example, Donald Keating, in *Building Contracts*, 4th Edition, page 343, states:

> 'The architect can, it is submitted, give an instruction (Clause 21(2)) postponing commencement of work ... and can extend time for completion under Clause 23(e).'

In fact, in our view, this is erroneous, because clause 21(2) of JCT 1963 and clause 23 of JCT 80 referred only to the architect's power to 'issue instructions in regard to the postponement of *any work* to be executed'; nowhere in those JCT contracts was any power given to the architect to postpone the giving of possession. Under JCT 80 terms, indeed, there is a distinction between 'the Works' and 'work'. 'The Works' means either the work contracted for, as in Article 1, or the site, as in clause 8.5. In contract, 'work' means 'work carried out under the contract', as in clause 13.1.1. A power to postpone 'any work to be executed' is not the same as a power to postpone or defer the giving of possession of the site. As Dr John Parris rightly observes:

> '...a great deal more is involved in giving the contractor possession of the site than just allowing him to execute work and JCT 80 clause 23.2 is not wide enough to cover failure to do so: *Roberts* v. *Bury Commisioners* (1880); *London Borough of Hounslow* v. *Twickenham Gardens* (1970)': [*The Standard Form of Building Contract: JCT 80,* 2nd Edition, Section 7.04 Employer's failure to give possession of site.]

The employer's failure to give possession of the site, as indicated by Mr Justice Megarry, is a breach of contract, and such breach gives rise to a common law claim for damages. The sensible and practical answer, of course, is for the parties (i.e. employer and contractor) to vary the contract by agreement between them, always bearing in mind that the architect has no power, express or implied, that will enable him to vary the contract on the employer's behalf.

These sort of problems do not arise under a JCT 80 contract incorporating Amendment 4 (July 1987) because clause 23.1 has been amended and a new sub-clause has been introduced which provides:

23.1.2 'Where clause 23.1.2 is stated in the Appendix to apply the Employer may defer
the giving of possession for a period not exceeding six weeks or such lesser period
stated in the Appendix calculated from the Date of Possession'.

There is an appropriate Appendix entry and consequential amendments have been made to clauses 25 (extensions of time) and 26 (loss and expense caused by matters affecting regular progress of the Works).

A similar provision appears in the JCT Intermediate Form, 1984 edition, (clauses 2.2, 2.4.14, 4.11(a) and the Appendix). If it applies, it enables the employer to defer giving the contractor possession of the site for a period not exceeding 6 weeks or such shorter period as he has inserted in the Appendix. Under the Intermediate Form, the employer has the right to defer possession for a period actually stated in the Appendix which cannot exceed 6 weeks unless, of course, clause 2.2 of IFC 84 is appropriately amended.

The consequential amendments to the 1980 edition allow an extension of time to be fixed under clause 25 and direct loss and/or expense to be claimed in respect of any deferment of possession by the employer. There are corresponding provisions in the Intermediate Form 1984 in clauses 2.4.1 and 2.4.11(a).

The position is also straightforward under the terms of the ACA Contract, both in its 1982 and 1984 editions, since clause 11.1 thereof provides:

> '... the Employer shall give to the Contractor possession of the Site, or such part or parts of it as may be specified, on the date or dates stated in the Time Schedule ...'.

Failure to so give possession is, of course, a breach of contract on the employer's part, but it seems to us that the architect's powers under that contract are sufficiently wide to enable him to postpone the giving of possession. Moreover, under ACA terms, the architect can give the contractor an extension of time under clause 11.5 (in either of its alternatives) in respect of

> 'any act, instruction, default or omission of the Employer, or of the Architect on his behalf, whether authorised by or in breach of this Agreement'.

That wording is sufficiently wide to cover failure to give possession in accordance with clause 11.1 and disturbance to regular progress and loss and expense involved can be dealt with under clause 7.1, which again refers to 'any act, omission, default or negligence of the Employer or of the Architect' disrupting 'the regular progress of the works or of any section' or delays the execution of them in accordance with the time schedule, or in the case of an architect's instruction, by valuation under clause 17.

The position appears to be the same under GC/Works/1: see clauses 6 and 28(2)(c) thereof and our discussion of claims arising under GC/Works/1 in chapter 7.

Site conditions

Claims in respect of site conditions may arise in two principal ways, first, where the contractor is given misinformation by the employer about site conditions, and secondly in relation to the particular provisions of JCT 80, clause 2.2.2.1 of which requires that the bills have been prepared in accordance with the Standard Method of Measurement, 6th (now 7th) Edition.

The contractor's claim for negligent misrepresentation and/or breach of warranty and/or under the Misrepresentation Act 1967, as amended, may arise for misrepresentations made by or on behalf of the employer. As a result of the Misrepresentation Act 1967, the remedies which were formerly restricted to cases of fraud or recklessness apply to all misrepresentations unless the party who made the representation can prove 'that he had reasonable ground to believe and did believe up to the time the contract was made that the facts represented were true'. In our view, liability for misrepresentation is unaffected by the general common law rule that the employer does not warrant that the site is fit for the works or that the contractor will be able to construct on the site: *Appleby* v. *Myers* (1867). Architects are personally liable at common law for any fraudulent or negligent misstatement or representation (*Hedley Byrne & Co.* v. *Heller and Partners Ltd* (1963)) and also under the 1967 Act. The substituted section 3 of that Act restricts the employer's power to exclude liability for misrepresentation.

There is no doubt that, in an appropriate case, the contractor may have a claim against the employer for misrepresentations about site and allied conditions made during pre-contractual negotiations. For example, in the Australian case of *Morrison-Knudsen International Co. Inc.* v. *Commonwealth of Australia* (1972), the contractor claimed that basic information provided to him at pre-tender stage 'as to the soil and its contents at the site ... was false, inaccurate and misleading ... the clays at the site, contrary to the information, contained large quantities of cobbles'. On a preliminary issue (since the effect of the documents could not be finally determined until all the relevant facts were established), Lord Barwick CJ concluded:

'The basic information in the site document appears to have been the result of much technical effort on the part of a department of the defendant. It was information which the plaintiffs had neither the time nor the opportunity to obtain for themselves. It might even be doubted whether they could be expected to obtain it by their own efforts as a ... tenderer. But it was indispensable information if a judgment were to be formed as to the extent of the work to be done ...'.

Similarly, in *Holland Hannen & Cubitts (Northern) Ltd* v. *Welsh Health Technical Organisation* (1981) – a case which ended in a settlement in favour of the contractors – one of the claims made by the contractors against the employers was for 'damages for negligent misrepresentations and/or breach of warranty and/or pursuant to the Misrepresentation Act 1967 arising out of representations made or warranties given by or on behalf of' the employer. These related, *inter alia*, to statements in the preliminaries section of the Bills about the sequence of operations, letters from the architects, and statements made at pre-contractual meetings. In an appropriate case, therefore, an action would lie in respect of misleading statements about site conditions.

A factual misrepresentation made during pre-contractual negotiations by or on behalf of the employer and relied on by the contractor may give rise to an action under the 1967 Act. The possibilities are illustrated by the decision of the Court of Appeal in *Howard Marine & Dredging Co. Ltd* v. *A. Ogden & Sons (Excavations) Ltd* (1978) where barge-owners were held liable to dredging contractors who had hired a barge for dredging works on the faith of a misrepresentation of the dead weight of the barge. The defendant's marine manager had stated that the barge's payload was 1600 tonnes, whereas in fact it was only 1055 tonnes. His misstatement was based on his recollection of an incorrect figure given in Lloyd's Register. See also *Cremdean Properties Ltd* v. *Nash* (1977).

The second possibility is suggested by Dr John Parris in *The Standard Form of Building Contract: JCT 80*, 2nd Edition Section 10.09 Claims for site conditions, in relation to contracts in JCT 80 Form. Clause 2.2.2.1 provides that 'the Contract Bills ... are to have been prepared in accordance with SMM6' which, amongst other things, provides as follows:

'The Standard Method of Measurement provides a uniform basis for measuring building works and embodies the essentials of good practice but more detailed information than is required by this document shall be given where necessary in order to define the precise nature and extent of the required work.'

We agree with Dr Parris that this seems to obligate the employer to provide the contractor with information in his possession about potentially difficult site conditions. Other provisions require the employer to provide specific information, an in particular SMM 6th Edition D.3.2 provides:

'If the above information is not available a description of the ground and strata *which is to be assumed* shall be stated.'

In such circumstances, we agree with Dr Parris that the contractor will have a claim against the employer, should site conditions *not* be as assumed. Support for this view is to be found in *C. Bryant & Son Ltd* v. *Birmingham Hospital Saturday Fund* (1938), where Bryant contracted to erect a convalescent home in the RIBA form of contract, 1931 edition, but incorporating the 1909 edition as well, clause 11 of which provided:

'The quality and quantity of the work included in the contract sum shall be deemed to be that which is set out in the bills of quantities, which bills, unless otherwise stated, shall be deemed to have been prepared in accordance with the standard method of measurement of building works last before issued by the Chartered Surveyors' Institution. Any error in description or in quantity in, or omission of items from, the bills ... shall not vitiate this contract, and shall be rectified and treated as an extra or omission [and valued accordingly]'.

The relevant SMM provided that 'Where practicable the nature of the soil shall be described and attention shall be drawn to any existing trial holes. Excavation in rock shall be given separately'. Excavation in rock was not shown separately, although the contractor was required by the bills to satisfy himself as to site conditions and so on. On a case stated, Mr Justice Lewis agreed with the arbitrator that Bryant was entitled to the extra cost of excavating the rock, the existence of which was known to the architect, although not shown in any of the contract documents.

COLLATERAL WARRANTIES AND IMPLIED TERMS

Bacal Construction (Midlands) Ltd v. *Northampton Development Corporation* (1975) provides an object-lesson as to the dangers involved in altering a standard form of contract. It also shows the possibility of the contractor suing at common law for breach of a collateral warranty or an implied term that the ground conditions are as described in the tender documents. The tender documents in that case for the design and construction of some 518 dwellings and ancillary buildings included a statement that the site was a mixture of Northamptonshire sand and upper lias clay, but tufa was discovered subsequently. The employers had told the contractors in writing at the time of the tender that their design was to assume the soil conditions disclosed at the boreholes, which gave no warning of the presence of tufa. The contractors recovered damages for breach of an implied term or collateral warranty that the ground conditions would accord with the hypotheses on which they were instructed to design. The contract was an amended form of JCT 63, and *inter alia* the Court of Appeal held that the necessary re-designing of the foundations and the additional work occasioned by the discovery of the tufa did not rank as variations for the purposes of the contract. Lord Justice Buckley said:

'Bacal have submitted that there are strong commercial reasons for implying such a term or warranty in the contract as they have suggested. First, before designing the foundations of any building, it is essential to know the nature of the site conditions. Secondly, where the contract is for a comprehensive development of the kind here in question, the contractor must know the soil conditions at the site of each projected block in order to be able to plan his timetable and estimate his requirements for materials. These are matters which relate directly to the contract price. Thirdly, if the work is interrupted or delayed by unforeseen complications, the contractor is unlikely to be able to complete his contract in time.'

The Court of Appeal, affirming Mr Justice O'Connor, accepted this analysis.

GENERAL

We have not explored all the possibilities of common law claims in detail because, as indicated, under JCT terms at least, such claims must be pursued by way of litigation or arbitration, unless the architect obtains the employer's express authority to negotiate and settle such claims. Contractors who believe that they have such common law (or 'ex-contractual' claims, as they are sometimes called) should therefore consult their lawyers. But our discussion serves to emphasise that no standard form contract is a self-sufficient document; it must be read

Chapter 11

Preparation and negotiation of claims

INTRODUCTION

'Claim' is a dirty word in the employer section of the industry. Why this should be so we do not know since the JCT contracts specifically entitle the contractor to 'claim' reimbursement of 'direct loss and/or expense', which he incurs as a result of certain events specified in the contract, all of which are within the direct control of the employer or of those for whom he must bear the responsibility in law. This may be taken to be a somewhat stark pro-contractor view since undoubtedly there are situations in which the employer will find himself paying substantial sums because of circumstances which are completely beyond his control – or, indeed, that of his architect or other advisers – e.g. major re-design of foundations resulting from unexpected ground conditions that normal surveys could not have revealed, which are subject to the sort of implied term found to exist in *Bacal Construction (Midlands) Ltd* v. *Northampton Development Corporation* (1975), where it was held at common law 'that the ground conditions would accord with the hypotheses upon which' the contractors were instructed to work, and in fact they did not. Indeed, the JCT and other standard forms of building contract and sub-contract assume that 'claims' are likely to be made as the contract proceeds.

In fact, contract claims for both time and money are a feature of any construction project. Claims are very simple to originate, but are not always easy to substantiate, and therein lies the employer's protection. He is only bound to meet claims that are based on some express or implied provision of the contract and it is for the contractor to prove his claim. Where the claim is based on some express contract term, the contractor must also show that he has followed the administrative machinery provided by the contract itself. Above all, contract claims must be

315

founded on facts and these facts must be substantiated by the contractor.

Contractors must appreciate that merely because they are losing money on a particular contract does not mean that they are entitled to look to the employer for reimbursement. They must be able to establish that the loss results directly from some act or default of the employer or those for whom he is responsible in law, or else is referable to some express term of the contract entitling them to reimbursement.

THE 'GLOBAL' APPROACH

In general, it is necessary for the contractor to establish each and every head of claim, by means of supporting documentation and other evidence. In some circumstances, however, a 'global' apportionment of the claim may be admissible and in our view this applies to claims for extensions of time as well as claims for money. This 'global' approach was recognised by Mr Justice Donaldson (as he then was) in *J. Crosby & Sons Ltd* v. *Portland UDC* (1967) which was decided under the ICE Conditions of Contract (4th Edition).

One of the points at issue was that the contractors had made a general claim for delay and disorganisation. Completion had been delayed by 46 weeks by a combination of matters, some of which entitled the contractors to additional time and/or money and some of which did not. Mr Justice Donaldson upheld the arbitrator's view that the contractor was entitled to compensation on a global basis in respect of 31 weeks of the overall delay and rejected the employer's argument that the arbitrator must necessarily build up the sum by finding amounts due under each of the individual heads of claim upon which the contractor relied in support of his overall claim for delay and disruption.

The parameters of this approach are closely confined. The 'global' approach is only justified where a claim depends 'on an extremely complex interaction in the consequences of various denials, suspensions and variations' and where 'it may well be difficult or even impossible to make an accurate apportionment of the total extra cost between the several causative events'. Mr Justice Donaldson felt that in those limited circumstances there is no reason why an architect, engineer or arbitrator 'should not recognise the realities of the situation and make individual awards in respect of those parts of individual items of the claim which can be dealt with in isolation and a supplementary award in respect of the remainder of those claims as a composite whole'.

This does not, of course, relieve the contractor of producing substantiating evidence and proving each head of claim. What it does is to enable the architect, etc. to adopt a commonsense method of measuring certain complex claims where it is impossible or totally impracticable to prove each individual item. The general and limiting qualification under JCT forms is well expressed by the Editors of *Building Law Reports* (Vol. 5, p. 123):

'The events which are the subject of the claim must be complex and interact so that it is difficult if not impossible to make an accurate apportionment. It is very tempting to take the easy course and to lump all the delaying events together in order to justify the total overrun or total financial shortfall. That argument is justifiable only if the alternative course is shown to be impracticable.'

In other words, the *J. Crosby & Sons Ltd* approach is very much a long-stop and cannot be relied upon in the vast majority of cases. It cannot be invoked where in reality a contractor cannot establish a valid claim but can merely show a financial shortfall and the dangers of this approach are illustrated by the American case of *Bruno Law* v. *US* (1971), where a contractor claimed over $US 1 million extra on a contract, apparently on the theory that it was sufficient to take the overrun between the original and actual completion dates, point to a number of individual delays for which the employer was allegedly responsible, and which contributed to the overall delay, and then arrive at the conclusion that the entire overrun time was attributable to the employer. The trial commissioner pointed out that, upon the evidence,

'Many of the incidents relied on by plaintiff were isolated and non-sequential and therefore could not possibly have caused any significant delay in the overall progress of the contract. Furthermore, with respect to the great bulk of such incidents, plaintiff has failed to prove, or indeed even to attempt to prove, the crucial factors of the specific extent of the alleged wrongful delay to the project operations caused thereby'.

The court upheld the trial commissioner's award of approximately one-fifth of the amount claimed by the contractor on the basis of approximately one-tenth of the alleged specific items of delay.

The point was made again in the case, already much-quoted in this book, of *London Borough of Merton* v. *Stanley Hugh Leach Ltd* (1985). The type of calculation put forward by Leach as a claim under the contract was well described by the arbitrator in a passage from his Interim Award quoted by Mr Justice Vinelott in his judgment as follows:

'The calculation commences with the 'direct site costs', which I can only interpret as being the total expenditure incurred by [Leach] on all labour, plant and materials involved in the construction works. From the very limited information available to me I can interpret the word 'direct' as indicating that the costs relate to [Leach's] own expenditure and that of his direct sub-contractors to the exclusion of expenditure through nominated sub-contractors and suppliers.

From this total site cost, [Leach] deduct the assessment for fluctuations which under clause 31A of the conditions are to be adjusted on a net basis. A percentage for profit and overheads is then added to the total site costs excluding fluctuations and finally the net fluctuations are added back to arrive at the alleged remunerable total cost to the contractor of £3,721,970.

If one could imagine a building contract which proceeded to completion without any hitch, delay or variation whatsoever this calculation would provide [Leach] at line (5) with a direct comparison with his tender figure. However as that ideal situation is rarely, if ever, met and certainly was not met in the instant contract, the figures in line (1) (and so those in lines (4) and (7)) must include the costs to [Leach] of all the 'hitches' of whatever nature that occurred on the site.'

Mr Justice Vinelott went on:

'I find it impossible to see how [this calculation] can be treated as even an approximation for a claim, whether or not rolled up (as in *Crosby*), under clause 11(6) or 24(1) [of JCT 63]. As the arbitrator points out in the passage I have cited, the calculation in effect relieves Leach from the burden of additional costs resulting from delays in respect of which Leach is not entitled to any extension of the completion date'

or he might have added, to any recovery of 'direct loss and/or expense'.

And yet claims such as that submitted by Leach (a claim in that case for a sum well into seven figures and contained on one side of a sheet of A4 paper albeit backed up with a vast mass of other material) are very commonly submitted by contractors to those charged with the duty of making some realistic ascertainment of the actual loss and/or expense suffered as a result of specific events. They do not help.

SUBSTANTIATED CLAIMS

Many contractors seem to approach contract claims in the same way as the claimants in *Bruno Law* v. *US* and in *Merton* v. *Leach*, and many a potentially valid claim founders because of lack of proper substantiating evidence and the contractor's inability to (a) establish the direct link between cause and effect with regard to delays, and (b) provide sufficient particulars of the resulting loss and/or expense. Moreover, as Donald Keating rightly says (*Building Contracts*, 4th Edition, page 262):

> 'General words intended to arouse sympathy or other emotion favourable to the contractor's interest should be used sparingly lest they excite the suspicion that the contractor really thinks his claim is founded in mercy and not in law. Further, it is rarely useful to say that the contractor has suffered loss due to causes outside his control or which he did not reasonably anticipate. It is elementary law ... that such factors are not grounds in law for extra payment unless, which is rare, they are expressly so made. If put forward as the sole grounds of a claim the reader may well assume that there are no other grounds.'

In fact, emotion of this kind is out of place in a claims situation, and so is emotive language. What the claimant must do is to state the facts giving rise to his alleged entitlement, point to the contract term under which the claim originates, establish that he has satisfied any conditions precedent to his claim, and set out the financial basis of his claim. In relation to this last requirement, clause 26.1.3 of JCT 80 requires the contractor to submit, upon request, such details of the loss and/or expense incurred as are reasonably necessary to enable the architect or quantity surveyor to carry out the ascertainment. We would suggest that this should best take the form of a fully moneyed-out statement of what the contractor considers to be his entitlement supported by appropriate evidence. Similarly, in clauses 11(6), 24(1) and 34(3) of JCT 63 (and indeed under clause 34.3 of JCT 80), although there is no specific requirement of the contractor to provide even the details called for in clause 26.1.3 of JCT 80, the contractor should submit moneyed-out claims in the same way.

If the contractor is to provide substantiating evidence he must have adequate records. His obligation if he is to sustain his claim is to provide the architect and/or quantity surveyor with *all* the information necessary for them to ascertain the direct loss and/or expense. This information will include cost records, charts showing actual progress measured against programme, original tendering calculations showing level of anticipated profit, possibly even profit-and-loss accounts and balance sheets (particularly when head-office overheads are to be examined).

It is clear that a heavy burden is placed upon the contractor, but unless detail of this kind is provided no proper ascertainment can be made. In *Peak Construction (Liverpool) Ltd* v. *McKinney Foundations Ltd* (1970), when dealing with the sort of evidence required to substantiate a head-office-overheads and loss-of-profit claim, Lord Justice Salmon was of the view that not only was the evidence of the contractor's auditor as to profitability relevant, but also 'some evidence as to what the site organisation consisted of, what part of the head-office staff is being referred to, and what they were doing at the material times ...'. He also suggested that it would be useful to have an analysis of the contractor's yearly turnover for a period of some seven years in order to establish the level of profitability and the effect upon it of the particular contract disruption and overrun.

Contractors will readily appreciate that it is in their interests to keep detailed records of all cost factors related to individual contracts, and be prepared to abstract these for the purpose of substantiating any contract claim.

Application of principles

The foregoing is best illustrated by an example. Where there is a claim for direct loss and/or expense arising under JCT 80, clause 26.2.7, in respect of a variation, the contractor's claim must establish the following:

(1) that an instruction amounting to a variation has been validly issued and acted upon;
(2) the date of issue and receipt of the variation instruction;
(3) the nature of the variation;
(4) the time at which it was *necessary* to carry out the work pursuant to the instruction;
(5) that the carrying out of the variation instruction *necessarily* affected regular progress of the works;
(6) the extent to which the work was affected as a direct result of the carrying out of the variation;
(7) that the contractor made a proper and timely application to the architect in respect of direct loss and/or expense;
(8) sufficient particulars of the direct loss and/or expense suffered or incurred.

Item (1) may seem straightforward, but the difficulty which even this can involve for the contractor is illustrated by *M. Harrison & Co. (Leeds) Ltd* v. *Leeds City Council* (1980), where an architect issued a document headed 'Variation Order No. 1', which read as follows:

> 'You are hereby authorised to execute the following work involving a variation on your Contract, in accordance with the terms thereof, namely ...
> *Omit* Item A page 159 The PC Sum for Structural Steel work £77,000.
> *Add* Place an order with [XYZ Ltd] for the supply and erection of structural steelwork at the above in accordance with the fixed price quotation enclosed ... in the sum of £98,084 1s 6d.'

Despite this apparently clear wording, it was held that this instruction did not amount to a variation within the meaning of clause 11 of JCT 63 (now clause 13, JCT 80) for, as Lord Justice Megaw remarked in his judgment, 'the definition in that clause is narrow'.

Item (2) is necessary because the period of notice of the variation will have a bearing upon the contractor's ability to accommodate it by reasonable adjustment of his programme.

Item (3) is self-explanatory: the variation should be described.

The emphasis under item (4) must be on the word *necessary* since the contractor must demonstrate that he executed the variation at a time that reasonably mitigated the amount of any direct loss and/or expense incurred. If the timing of the execution of the work was forced upon the contractor, say by the timing of the issue of the instruction itself, then the contractor should give particulars.

As to item (5) the emphasis is on the word *necessarily*. The contractor must establish that the effect upon regular progress was unavoidable by any reasonable means. If, for example, the contractor has chosen to carry out the work at the time most convenient to him and as a result greater disruption than was necessary has ensued, he should recover only the direct loss and/or expense which should have resulted had his own convenience not been to the forefront.

It is obviously essential to show how and to what extent regular progress was affected by the variation (item (6)).

Item (7) is of great importance since the contractor's entitlement to reimbursement under the contract provisions depends upon his having satisfied the administrative requirements.

Under JCT 80, clause 26.1.3, the contractor is not obliged to supply particulars of his loss and/or expense (item (8)) until asked for them, but in our view it is clearly in his interests to provide them, whether requested or not and, as previously indicated, a fully moneyed-out statement (backed by supporting evidence) is desirable.

It is not necessary to prepare the claim in any particular form, but every claim should be prepared with the possibility of eventual arbitration or litigation in mind. It is therefore advisable that it should be in such a form that it can be readily used for the purpose of formal pleadings.

NATURE OF SUPPORTING EVIDENCE

Many claims submitted by contractors are deficient in the matter of supporting evidence. Some consist merely of broad and sweeping assertions of incompetence on the part of the design team or generalised allegations of disruption and loss without any hard foundation. Others, while marginally more detailed and substantiated, on examination fail to meet the criteria we have set out since, although superficially they link particular disruption and cost to particular causes of delay, they totally fail to establish that the extent of the disruption and cost inevitably and directly arose from the cause alleged and is not avoidable.

The nature of the back-up evidence will obviously depend on the type of claim, but in almost every case detailed cost records and comparative programme/progress schedules will be necessary, together with references to correspondence, records of site meetings, site diaries and the like.

(a) Cost records

Ideally cost records should be capable of pin-pointing the precise cost effects of particular events, but this is a counsel of perfection, which we have never seen fulfilled. None the less this is the ideal to be aimed for and the increasing use of computers, adequately programmed, should make this task very much easier. Despite this development, it will still remain the fact that the adequacy and accuracy of cost records will always ultimately depend upon the keeping of detailed time-sheets by workpeople and particularly by site supervisory staff. Currently, time-sheets for manual workers are of a general nature, and care should be taken to ensure that they are in such a form that relevant information to support a particular claim can be readily abstracted. In the case of a claim arising from a variation, for example, supervisory staff should take care to direct workpeople actually carrying out the work involved to record separately the time actually spent on the variation work. This applies similarly to those executing work not itself varied, but nevertheless affected, by the introduction of the variation.

Similar considerations apply to records of plant time while records of materials should present no particular problem. The essential point is that the cost records relied upon should be clearly referable to the particular disruption or other event.

(b) Programme/progress schedules
Clause 5.3.1.2 of JCT 80 requires the contractor 'within fourteen days of any decision by the Architect' with regard to the completion date under the contract to provide the architect with two copies of any amendments and revisions to the master programme to take account of that decision. While useful for general monitoring purposes, neither the original nor amended master programme is likely to be sufficient to substantiate a monetary claim arising from any particular cause of delay or disruption. It is certainly some evidence and should be referred to.

What is needed to substantiate a money claim is a schedule or chart showing the progress that could have been achieved had the particular cause of delay or disruption not arisen, compared with actual achievement. As much annotation as possible should be provided to demonstrate precisely the manner in which progress was affected.

(c) Correspondence
Copies of any letters, memoranda, etc. relevant to the claim should be annexed, including, of course, copies of the relevant applications, etc. required by the terms of the contract. Particular paragraphs in the correspondence can be referenced by numbers and referred to in the claim document and cross-referenced to cost records, progress schedules and so on.

(d) Records of site meetings
These are often misleadingly referred to as 'site minutes' and can provide useful supporting evidence. Usually, such records are prepared by one party without reference to the other. On receipt of a copy, the other party should check it carefully and challenge any alleged inaccuracies, ambiguities or misrepresentations at that time and ensure that the relevant corrections are recorded both in correspondence and in the record of the next meeting. If such inaccuracies are not challenged contemporaneously, with the passage of time it will become increasingly difficult (though not impossible) to establish that they are not an accurate record of what actually happened.

(e) Site diaries
Site diaries are useful background but are of limited probative value, and

sometimes contain entries that may be embarrassing to the person putting them forward. Diaries kept by each side, e.g. by the contractor and the clerk of works, may well differ in their recording of the same events. The court's attitude in such cases is shown by the approach of Judge Sir William Stabb in *Oldschool* v. *Gleeson (Construction) Ltd* (1976), where there was a conflict between the diaries kept by a consulting engineer and the site agent. The judge said:

> 'I found [the agent's] diary entries unsatisfactory, in the sense that they do not record warnings and complaints when, as I believe, these were given. I cannot believe that the district surveyor could have written in these terms on 21 March if [his assistant] had not in fact given the same warning, and yet not a hint of it appears in [the agent's] diary; which, together with other instances, leads me to think that he was not anxious to record criticisms or complaints when they were made, and where such appear in [the engineer's] diary and not in the diary of [the agent], I am bound to say that I have no hesitation in accepting [the engineer's] contemporaneous record as being the accurate one.'

Site diaries are, however, often useful as substantiating evidence as to progress, etc.

'SCOTT' OR OFFICIAL REFEREE'S SCHEDULE

A 'Scott' or Official Referee's Schedule is a formal document used in litigation and arbitration, setting out the issues in dispute in tabular form, with space for the contentions of the opposing parties to be set out against each other for easy reference. While it is inappropriate to submit a claim in such a form initially, the claim should be prepared so that the factual information in it can, if necessary, easily be transferred to such a schedule.

There is no standard form for a Scott Schedule, but various examples are to be found set out in Emden's *Building Contracts and Practice*, 8th Edition, vol. 1, pages 556–7 and Keating's *Building Contracts*, 4th Edition, pages 262–7. The following is an example of such a schedule relating to a contractor's claim resulting from variations arising under clause 13 of JCT 80:

Ref no.	Nature of Variation	A.I. no.	Claimant's		Respondent's		Arbitrator's Comments
			Details	Amount Claimed	Comments	Amount conceded	

PRACTICAL EXAMPLES

The principles set out in this chapter are best illustrated by comparing and contrasting three examples. The first two examples set out below are illustrations of two claims that are superficially attractive but, on detailed examination, are defective in many important particulars. They should not be used as models and in fact are examples of how not to prepare a claim.

The third example is set out in the Appendix (pp. 347–354) and is the build-up of a contractor's entitlement to reimbursement of direct loss and/or expense under JCT 80, clause 26.

Document A

This is a claim arising under clause 24 of JCT 63. The basis of the claim is that as a result of late architect's instructions (clause 24(1)(a)) the contract overran by 38 weeks and the contractor has made a written application for an extension of time under clause 23(f). This application has in fact been made after the contract has been completed, and no extension of time has apparently yet been granted.

The original tender figure was £186,654 and the final account figure, at the time of the claim, is alleged by the contractor to be £192,486, though the bill of variations has not yet been completed by the quantity surveyor. The original period was 62 weeks, commencing in June 1978.

DOCUMENT A

Kestrel Builders Limited
40 Optimist Street
Anytown
Blankshire

Sparrow & Hawk
Chartered Architects
21 Sceptical Street
Anytown
Blankshire

10 September 1980

Dear Sirs,

Refurbishment of Thirty Properties: Ydegdart, North Wales

Claim for reimbursement of loss and expense in accordance with our claim for extension of time of thirty-eight weeks dated 10 September 1980. We detail below our assessment of the claim for reimbursement of loss and expense.

The main causes of the extensions of time claimed are due to late delivery of Architect's Instructions.

The direct loss and expense suffered is detailed and quantified hereunder:

1. *Time related overheads and profit*

The views used to ascertain these costs are those set out in the work 'Hudson's Building and Engineering Contracts', edited by I.N. Duncan Wallace MA, QC.

Confirmation of these views can be found in the fourth edition of 'Building Contracts' published in March 1978 by D. Keating QC. This can be found on pages 152 and 153 of that work.

The above views are similarly legally established by the judgment in the case of: *Peak Construction (Liverpool) Limited* v. *McKinney Foundations Limited*, 1 July 1970. In accordance with the ruling in that case we enclose as evidence of the prevention of our company from earning profits and overhead contributions elsewhere the following correspondence.

A. Three tenders, which have all been accepted, but very little work has been able to be executed due to the situation on the Ydegdart contract.
B. Letter dated 15 August 1980 showing effect on our loss of work and goodwill.

The margin to be recovered is based on the average margin recovered over the last two years being 20% as shown in our auditor's certificate attached.

Recovery as anticipated on tender sum of £186,654 is:

$$20\% \times \frac{186,654}{62} = £602.11 \text{ per week}$$

Actual recovery based on our Final Account figure is:

$$20\% \times \frac{192,486}{100} = £384.97 \text{ per week}$$

Shortfall of recovery is:

602.11 − 384.97 × 100 weeks	£21,714.00

2. *Reimbursement of site supervision costs*

J. Bloggs – Foreman	38 weeks' wages and expenses	£3952.87
A. Smith – Chargehand	38 weeks' wages and expenses	2786.06
	Total	£6738.93

3. Increased costs

The index figures used are based on the Firm Price Index of the BCIS cost of new building and are indicative of the way costs have risen. The index figures obtained show June 1978 = 164; August 1979 = 195. The figure for June 1980 not being available a provisional assessed figure of 220 has been used.

Contract situation

	June 1978	August 1979
Index	164	195

Difference 31
Expressed as a percentage:

$$\frac{31}{164} \times 100 = 18.90\%$$

Based on the Final Account of £192,486 the theoretical provision for increased costs is:

$$\frac{192,486 \times 18.90\%}{2} = £18,189.93$$

Extended contract situation

	June 1978	June 1980
Index	164	220

Difference 56
Expressed as a percentage:

$$\frac{56}{164} \times 100 = 34.15\%$$

Based on the Final Account the theoretical cost of increased costs incurred is:

$$\frac{192,486 \times 34.15\%}{2} = £32,866.98$$

Therefore loss incurred:

	£32,866.98
less	18,189.93
	£14,677.05

Loss of productivity on labour

Disruption caused to productivity is assessed at 20%
Labour recovery in Final Account is:

	£192,486.00	
Less 20%	38,497.20	
Net cost	£153,988.80	
Labour 60%	92,393.28	
Disruption at 20%		£18,478.66

Summary

Loss of Overheads and Profit	£21,714.00
Site Supervision Costs	6,738.93
Increased Costs	14,677.05
Loss of Productivity	18,478.66
Total claim For Thirty-eight Week Extension	£61,608.64

Commentary

This claim is not untypical and clearly does not meet the requirements of a valid claim. It relates the direct loss and/or expense incurred solely to the delay in completion, with the exception of the loss of productivity claim, which is unsubstantiated. Although reference is made to the separate claim for extension of time, which may give some substantiation of the period of delay alleged by the contractor, this claim by itself establishes no causal link at all between the alleged late delivery of instructions and the amount claimed. In any case, it is clearly not a valid application under clause 24(1), JCT 63, since it makes no reference to regular progress of the works having been materially affected.

The claimant refers to the views expressed by Mr Keating but conveniently overlooks the passage on page 261 of his *Building Contracts*, 4th Edition, where, in considering an example of a 'direct loss and/or expense claim' under clause 24(1)(a), he emphasises that in such a case it is necessary to state five things:

(i) The date when the contractor specifically applied in writing for the information.
(ii) The due time when he should have received it.
(iii) The date when he actually received it.
(iv) The written application for direct loss and/or expense.
(v) *Sufficient* particulars of that loss or expense.

Document A fails under each of these heads.

Our detailed comments on this claim are as follows. Paragraph 1 of the contractor's letter relates the money claim solely to the claim for extension of time. There is, of course, no necessary connection between the two. The paragraph ought to have stated in terms that the letter constituted an application under clause 24(1), that it related to the effect on regular progress of the works of the alleged late delivery of instructions, and that it was an application for reimbursement under the clause. The word 'assessment', which is used by the contractor, in itself shows that the letter does not constitute any serious attempt to set out the actual facts or to provide real substantiation of the amount claimed.

The second paragraph is also wholly inadequate in that it gives no particulars of the default complained of. It ought to have set out items (i) to (iii) of Mr Keating's list (above).

The contractor's claim for time-related overheads and profit is based on one of the formula methods which we have discussed in chapter 4 and in fact the reference to Keating's *Building Contracts* does not appear to support the method adopted by the contractor. The method adopted does not even correspond to the formula set out in *Hudson's Building Contracts*, 10th Edition, page 599, and at no point has the contractor established that he has suffered any actual loss or expense under this head. His claim in fact consists of totally unsupported statements and while it may be true that his recovery of overheads during the original contract period, on a weekly basis, may have been less than anticipated, the sum will in fact have been made up during the period of overrun during which the contract will have been earning an overhead recovery not previously anticipated. Certainly, this claim does not establish that the contractor's overhead commitment and expenditure have in any way increased or that any monetary loss has been suffered on the contract as a whole.

Additional site supervision costs would clearly be a recoverable head of claim but a direct causal relationship would have to be established between the alleged late delivery of information and the necessity to employ supervisory staff for the additional period. The figures would, in any event, require substantiation by way of wages sheets, etc.

Assuming that the contract was on a firm-price basis, a claim for increased costs would be permissible, but the method adopted is in our view wholly unsatisfactory. The contract was one for *refurbishment* of thirty properties; it is therefore inappropriate to use an index relating to the cost of *new* building. Indeed, over the period in question, this could well work to the contractor's disadvantage since refurbishing contracts are labour intensive to a gerater degree than are contracts for new building. Even had the correct index been used, an *assessed* figure is not acceptable. The indices have in any case been incorrectly quoted and are shown on a monthly basis, whereas they are in fact published on a quarterly basis. The contract situation as stated by the contractor is purely hypothetical. The contractor also applies indices to the total final account figure, which will include elements of overhead and profit.

The calculations are in any case incorrect, as the contractor applies the percentage increases deduced from the indices to the total final account figure. The correct calculation for the contract situation ought to be:

$$£192,486 \times \frac{100}{109.45} \times 9.45\% = £16,619.39$$

This calculation extracts from the gross figure of £192,486 the amount theoretically included in respect of increases in costs over the original contract period.

The equivalent calculation for the extended contract situation would be

$$£192,486 \times \frac{100}{109.45} \times 17.075\% = £30,029.22$$

Again, the calculation extracts from the gross figure of £192,486 the amount theoretically included in respect of increases in costs over the *original* contract period and then applies to that the 'actual' increase over the extended period. The net difference is therefore £13,409.83. This is of course on the assumption that a calculation based upon published indexed figures of this kind is in itself correct.

The ideal system of calculating this head of claim is, of course, to base it upon actual costs compared with a factual calculation of what increased costs would have been incurred on the same basic resources of labour, materials and plant employed over the original period.

Loss of productivity or uneconomic working is a possible head of claim, and is particularly difficult to assess as regards labour. We have given some indication earlier in this chapter as to how labour records could be best kept, and it is certainly not permissible (as has been done by this contractor) to add an arbitrary percentage to the allegedly anticipated labour costs. It is evident that the loss will vary according to the circumstances of the case.

A method that is commonly used is to compare the actual labour costs with those contemplated at the time of tender. This will necessitate abstracting the labour element from the contract price and the actual labour costs from the contractor's records. The gross difference between these two figures must be further adjusted to take account of any actual labour costs expended as a result of unclaimable circumstances, such as contemporaneous delay and disruption arising from *force majeure* or from the contractor's own inefficiency. Even this approach, however, falls short of the ideal in that it relates facts in the form of the ascertained actual costs to an estimate of what the costs otherwise would have been. The difference between the two, of course, is itself an estimate and not a fact.

Finally, even where the percentages used in the calculation could be substantiated, the calculation itself is obviously wrong. The correct calculation would be

$$£192,486 \times 60\% \times 20\% = £23,098.32$$

It is difficult to understand why the initial deduction of 20% has been made at all in the contractor's calculation; it seems to demonstrate a lack of ability to think through a calculation in a logical manner.

Note: Document A is based upon a number of claims which the authors have actually seen submitted by contractors in practice.

Document B

This claim arises under a contract for the erection of seventy-five dwelling units. The contract is in JCT Standard Form (1963 Edition). It is not clear from the claim (which is again based upon actual claims that the authors have seen in practice) whether it is being submitted under clause 11(6), 24(1) or 34(3), or any combination of those three. The original contract period was 52 weeks and 1 day (or 1 year) and the architect granted a 14-week extension of time.

The total extension time granted was made up as follows:

Clause 23(b) – Exceptionally inclement weather	2 weeks
Clause 23(e) – Variations	5 weeks
Clause 23(f) – Late instructions	2 weeks
Clause 23(g) – Nominated sub-contractor's delay	5 weeks
	14 weeks

The grounds for extension of time set out in clauses 23(e) and (f) are also, separately and independently, grounds for reimbursement of direct loss and/or expense under clauses 11(6) and 24(1)(a) respectively.

At this stage, although it would appear that a period of nearly 21 months has elapsed since the actual completion of the contract works, a final account has apparently still not been agreed. This is – unfortunately

– a not uncommon situation. The contractor's estimated final account figure is £1,046,272.75.

DOCUMENT B

Kestrel Builders Limited
40 Optimist Street
Anytown
Blankshire

1st April 1982

Sparrow & Hawk
Chartered Architects
21 Sceptical Street
Anytown
Blankshire

Dear Sirs,

Paradise Estate – Rehabilitation of 180 Units

Claim for loss and expense incurred, in accordance with the extension of the original contract period of 4th April 1979 to 4th April 1980; the contract overran from 4th April 1980 to 14th July 1980, a period of 14 weeks.

(a) Recovery of overheads and profit
We consider the disruption caused on this major contract affected our results for the year ending September 1980. As this contract was negotiated on a basis of a contract carried out and included in our accounts period ending September 1979, we consider if the disruption had not occurred, the results for September 1980 would have been more in line with those of September 1979.

For the recovery of overheads and profit we are, therefore, using an average percentage based on these two accounting periods. Copies of these two accounts are attached and these show:-

12 Month period ending 30th September, 1979

Turnover	£951,625.97 –	
Overheads	92,946.26 –	9.7671%
Profit	196,585.94 –	20.6579%
Overheads and profit		30.4250%

12 Month period ending 30th September, 1980

Turnover	£2,349,768.70	–	
Overheads	149,010.58	–	6.3415%
Profit	363,412.87	–	15.4659%
Overheads and profit			21.8074%

The average recovery of overheads and profit over this period is, therefore the average of 30.4250% and 21.8074% = 26.1162%

We are adopting the Hudson Formula for the recovery of overheads and profit and have, therefore, reduced the contract sum of £957,642 by 26.1162%

Calculation of recovery

$$\frac{26.1162}{100} \times \frac{707,542}{52} \times 14 = £49,749.29$$

(b) Increased costs of Labour (including Guaranteed Minimum Bonus)
Increased 30th June, 1980.
Craftsmen £60.20 (including Joint Board Supplement) to £80.40
Labourers £52.00 (including Joint Board Supplement) to £68.60

Sheet Number	Tradesmen	Labourers	Boys
	(details not reproduced)		
(5 weeks)–	69	37	15

Summary

69 No.	Tradesmen weeks	20.20 –	1393.80
37 No.	Labourers weeks	16.60 –	614.20
15 No.	Apprentices weeks	8.30 –	124.50
			£2132.50

Copy time sheets are enclosed, No. 1 – 39, but five sheets are missing. We therefore consider that if we average the labour for these weeks to the lesser adjacent areas average, it should be acceptable. The Clerk of Works reports will no doubt substantiate that these numbers were on site during these weeks.

Consequential increases in National Insurance Contributions payable by Employers (non-contracted-out) – 13.5% of £2,132.50 = £287.89.

(c) Site Supervision Staff
(i) General Foreman

April	1980	–	Gross	–	£542.64	–	100%	–	542.64
May	1980	–	Gross	–	£537.42	–	100%	–	537.42
June	1980	–	Gross	–	£584.26	–	100%	–	584.26
July	1980	–	Gross	–	£535.57	–	25%	–	133.89

Total . . £1798.21

The above can be substantiated by our accountants, who prepare all our wages and salaries, details attached.

(ii) Site Supervision Trades Hourly Paid
(a) Foreman Joiner and Completion Foreman –
100% Supervision
(b) Foreman Plumber – 75% Supervision
(c) Ganger – Supervision of labourers and plasterers –
100% Supervision.

Sheet Number Foreman Joiner Foreman Plumber Ganger Total

(details not reproduced)

Sheets 26 – 39

Total . . £5467.89

Note (i) As sheet 36 is missing, we have included the lesser adjacent total.
(ii) The Foreman Plumber has been charged at 75%, the Foreman Joiner and Ganger at 100%.
(iii) The gross totals have been calculated and are shown on the copy time sheets 26 – 39 inclusive and details attached.

(d) Increased Costs of Materials
Based on:
(a) Current estimates of Final Account – £1,046,272.75
(b) The difference between valuations – 11 taken 13.3.80
12 taken 11.4.80

Valuation No. 11 – Gross	912,376.00
less M.O.S.	45,328.63
	867,047.37

Valuation No. 12 – Gross	954,282.00
less M.O.S.	38,657.42
	915,624.58

The difference between
the two valuations

	915,624.58
	867,047.37
	48,577.21

÷ 2 =	24,288.61
add	867,047.37

Work carried out to 31.3.80   891,335.98

Therefore works to be
completed ...   £154,936.77

Less: Works carried out by
Nominated Sub-contractors
and Statutory Authorities.

Total	38,257.00
Less certified in Valuation No. 12	35,142.63

£3,114.37

Therefore, £151,822.40 of works to
be completed by Kestrel Builders Ltd
To establish a material content we would
refer to our accounts for the period ending
30.9.80 and you will find the material content consumed in that period as a percentage
of turnover is 38.956%
Therefore, on work to be completed of
£151,822.40 the material content using this
average content is ...   £59,143.93

Less stock on hand at 31.3.80 taken in conjunction with our 6 monthly accounting
period ...   £52,286.00

Materials purchased after 31.3.80 ...   £ 6,857.93

We consider the percentage to be adopted
is as the sheet attached, between the
1st and 2nd quarters of 1980, i.e. $\dfrac{216 - 205}{205} = 5.3659\%$

Therefore, on purchases of 6,857.93 the
increased cost would be ...   £ 367.99

(e) Amounts already certified and paid to
Nominated Sub-Contractor in excess of his
Final Account, i.e. Certified Val 22 – 37,563.37

Final Account – 36,948.52......   £ 614.85

(f) Cost of preparing this claim
Paid claims consultant's fees   £3,500

Summary

(a) Overheads & profit	49,749.29
(b) Labour Increase	2,132.50
National Insurance	287.89
(c) Site Supervision Staff	1,798.21
Others	5,467.89
(d) Materials	367.99
(e) Nominated Sub-Contractor	614.85
(f) Costs of preparing this claim	3,500.00
Total claim ...	£63,918.62

Yours faithfully,
Kestrel Builders Limited

Commentary

This claim is also technically defective in that the contractor nowhere establishes any causal connection between the disruptive events relied on and the alleged loss and/or expense. Similarly, the claim does not refer to specific clauses in the contract, nor is it formally expressed as an application under either clause 11(6) or clause 24(1). The claim is expressed under six heads, two of which are not permissible in any event as a matter of law.

Although it is not specifically stated in the claim, this must have been a firm price contract, with no fluctuations provision, because otherwise labour and material cost increases would already have been recovered to a large extent. However, we have seen cases in practice where such claims have been duplicated.

The claim relates to the whole of the 14-week period of extension, although as indicated above only 7 of these 14 weeks were on grounds that would entitle the contractor to reimbursement. This does not, of course, necessarily mean that 7 weeks is the period to be used for the calculation of the reimbursement, since the actual period of delay resulting from these causes may have been more or less than that estimated by the architect in granting his extension.

Each head of the claim will be considered in turn.

(a) Overheads and profit. The contractor's generalised statement of opinion in the first sentence is of no weight whatever. As to the actual figures quoted, although it would appear that the company's profitability has reduced in the second year, there is no evidence whatever that this was due solely to the factors on this particular contract; it could be more readily explained as a reflection of the very sharp increase in turnover and the strains of accommodating such an increase within the contractor's organisation.

Even if the contractor could establish that his monthly turnover was reduced – which is by no means the case here – thereby affecting the trading potential of his capital, this would not be reimbursable under the contract unless the contractor could show that there was an opportunity to employ his capital resources elsewhere, lost as a direct result of claimable disruption under this contract, and also could provide some evidence of the anticipated return on the alternative use of his capital resources: see *Peak Construction (Liverpool) Ltd* v. *McKinney Foundations Ltd* (1970) discussed on page 138.

There are two flaws in the contractor's next statement. The fact that 'this contract was negotiated on a basis of a contract carried out and included' in the previous accounting period is not relevant. In general pre-contractual negotiations are of no effect once a contract has been entered into. Equally, since the contract commenced on 4 April 1979, i.e. half-way through the first accounting year, it must be assumed not only that some of the turnover is reflected in the accounts for that first year, but also that the negotiations took place or could well have taken place at a much earlier stage. A monthly analysis of the turnover for the two accounting years might be of some assistance, though even then the relevance of this information would be highly questionable.

Although the contractor uses the formula set out in *Hudson's Building Contracts*, 10th Edition, page 599, and has indeed made an attempt to correct one of that formula's logical faults, the calculation is still incorrect. First, it ought to be based upon the final account figure rather than upon the contract sum. Secondly, the calculation to reduce the gross figure to a net figure is incorrect in the same way as is the similar calculation in document A. Thirdly, a deduction ought to be made for the overhead and profit recovery included in the pricing of additional work in the final account.

(b) Increased cost of labour. The operative date for wage increases promulgated by the authority of the National Joint Council for the Building Industry was 30 June. In principle, this calculation is preferable to that adopted in document A since at least it has some factual basis, and appears to be supported by some kind of documentary evidence, however incomplete. The application of this method is, we think, unfair to the contractor as it confines his recovery solely to the effect of an increase that took place very late in the contract. The correct comparison would be over the entire original and extended contract periods, relating hours worked over the contract as a whole to wage and other increases during the two periods.

Where, as in this case, a comparatively small proportion of substantiating documents are missing, it would seem to us reasonable to permit the claimant to average out these figures as the contractor has done.

The contractor appears to have based his claim for increases in social security and allied contributions on alternative bases, i.e. from the operative date of 1 October 1979 or only during the overrun period. There appears to be no justification whatever for taking the first approach in a claim for reimbursement of additional direct loss and/or expense, and the second approach would be justified only if this were fully a firm-price contract. If, as is usual, fluctuations in social security payments are recoverable by the inclusion of clause 31B, these increases would already be recoverable by the contractor under that clause.

(c) Site supervision staff. Additional site supervisory costs are an additional head of claim, and the claim under this head is *prima facie* valid subject to the reservations that we have already expressed above regarding the period of delay to be taken into account, and subject to proof.

(d) Increased material costs. The basis of this head of claim is difficult to understand. There is no evidence put forward that any actual increased cost was incurred in this respect. The whole calculation is theoretical and illogical, and the method used by the contractor to establish material content (by reference to the audited accounts) is nonsensical. Those accounts must relate to the whole range of the contractor's activities; whereas this claim should be concerned with the factual situation under this particular contract.

(e) Nominated sub-contractor. The basis of this claim appears to be that the architect has at some point over-certified payment due to a particular

nominated sub-contractor and that the contractor has paid this sum over. Even if this is so, it is for the contractor to recover the overpayment direct from the nominated sub-contractor. It does not form an additional head of claim under any clause of the JCT contract.

(f) Costs of claim. The contractor is not entitled to reimbursement for any costs that he has incurred in preparing the claim, and this head is not allowable at law. The only circumstances in which a contractor can recover costs is where a claim proceeds to arbitration or litigation and the arbitrator's award or judgment of the court condemns the employer in costs. On one view, under JCT 63 the contractor's involvement was restricted to giving notices under clauses 11(6) and 24(1) and to providing the necessary cost information to enable the loss to be ascertained; presumably this involvement is held to be more than covered under the heading of head-office overheads. If the contractor chooses to seek outside advice, this is his own concern, and is not in law part of the 'direct' loss and/or expense. In our view the position is unchanged under JCT 80: but see the *Tate & Lyle* case on page 131.

Both documents A and B appear to omit permissible items of claim. For instance, while both include claims in respect of the extended period of supervision on site, neither includes any other element of extended site costs such as plant, temporary huts, telephones, etc. Document B also does not contain any claim in respect of loss of productivity, which one would have expected to see. Equally, today one would expect to find a claim for reimbursement of interest or 'financing charges' following the decision in *F. G. Minter Ltd* v. *Welsh Health Technical Services Organisation* (1980).

Chapter 12

The quantity surveyor's approach to claims

The only major function ascribed solely to the quantity surveyor under the JCT Forms of Contract is the valuation of variations, including any necessary measurement for this purpose (clause 13, JCT 80; clause 11, JCT 63; clause 3.7 IFC 84) – see chapter 3. In JCT 80 the quantity surveyor is also expressly charged with the production of what is called (in clause 30.6.1.2) 'a statement of all the final Valuations under clause 13 including those relating to the work of Nominated Sub-Contractors' – in other words the final variation account; even that function was not expressly ascribed to him in the 1963 Edition (in relation to what is there called the 'Bill of Variations', clause 30(5)(a)).

Under the JCT Forms the ascertainment of the amount of 'direct loss and/or expense' incurred by and reimbursable to the contractor is primarily the responsibility of the architect. The quantity surveyor will only carry out that function if expressly so instructed by the architect (since the quantity surveyor will normally be engaged directly by the employer, any such instruction will presumably be issued by the architect in his capacity as agent for the employer). In practice, on the vast majority of contracts it is the quantity surveyor who ascertains the amount reimbursable to the contractor, since his training and experience best fit him for the task; and since any 'claim' put forward by the contractor as the basis of ascertainment will almost invariably have been produced by quantity surveyors in the contractor's own office, negotiations will obviously best be conducted from the employer's side by a member of the same profession, speaking the same language and thinking along the same lines. (See also chapter 5, page 173, for a discussion of the relative positions of architect and quantity surveyor where the latter carries out the ascertainment.)

Like that of the architect, the quantity surveyor's position is a strange and sometimes difficult one. He will have been retained directly by the employer (though sometimes through the architect) and, particularly where the employer is a local authority, may even be a member of the employer's own staff. His primary and contractual duty is therefore to the employer. Certainly, in all pre-contract functions, such as the preparation of cost estimates, cost planning, the preparation of the bills of quantities, and the arithmetical and technical checking of the priced bills submitted by the lowest tenderer, etc., his duty is wholly and exclusively to the employer – while, of course, always maintaining proper professional standards of integrity.

Once a contractor is appointed and the contract is let, however, the quantity surveyor, like the architect, assumes a dual function and a dual responsibility. His contractual relationship, whether under a consultancy agreement or under a direct contract of employment, will still be solely with the employer; but one of the duties assigned to him under that contract will be that of carrying out the functions ascribed to him under the building contract in accordance with the terms of the contract, so that the proper carrying out of those functions in strict compliance with the building contract terms in itself becomes an important part of his contractual duty to the employer. But he will also now have a duty to the contractor. In part that duty arises through the insertion of his name in the appropriate space in the articles of agreement to the building contract where, in effect, employer and contractor together agree that the person so named shall carry out the duties assigned to the quantity surveyor under the contract, so that he becomes a part of the intricate chain of relationships in which everyone involved with the building process, from the employer to the contractor's tea-boy on site, is entwined. The quantity surveyor is *not* a party to the contract, no more than is the architect. However, by inserting a name in that space the employer has, in effect, agreed with the contractor that the person so named will carry out the functions ascribed to the quantity surveyor in strict compliance with the terms of the contract governing those functions so that, if the quantity surveyor fails to carry out those functions in accordance with those terms, the employer will be liable to the contractor for that failure as a breach of a contractual undertaking – he will have 'failed to procure his Quantity Surveyor' to carry out those functions properly.

In addition to these contractual duties, the quantity surveyor will also owe a duty of care, in the exercise of his professional skills, to anyone who may be damaged by his failure to exercise those skills with reasonable care – that is, not only the main contractor, but also nominated sub-contractors and anyone else who may be so damaged. For instance, where it is a part of the quantity surveyor's duties to value work executed for the purpose of interim payment, a contractor who suffers damage through negligent under-valuation will clearly be as entitled to take legal action against the quantity surveyor as would an employer damaged by negligent over-valuation.

The quantity surveyor's duty then is to carry out the functions ascribed to him under the building contract in strict accordance with the terms of that contract, and he owes that duty both to the employer and to the contractor. Under clause 26 of JCT 80 for instance, it is the quantity surveyor's duty, if so instructed by the architect, to 'ascertain' the amount of 'direct loss and/or expense which has been or is being incurred by the Contractor' as a result of 'regular progress of the Works or any part thereof' having been 'materially affected' by one or more of the factors listed in clause 26.2 – the architect having already formed the opinion that regular progress of the works has been or is likely to be so affected. It is therefore his duty to find out the actual amount of loss and/or expense incurred by the contractor as a direct result of the effect upon regular progress. It is certainly his duty to ensure that the employer pays no more than the actual amount of loss and/or expense directly and properly incurred by the contractor; but it is equally his duty to ensure that the contractor recovers no less. It is most emphatically *not* his duty to deprive the contractor of amounts properly recoverable under the contract, nor can it ever be interpreted as part of his contractual or professional duty to the employer so to do.

On the other hand, as has already been made abundantly clear elsewhere in this book, there is a great deal of scope for interpretation of those words 'direct loss and/or expense' and in what may be said to arise as a direct result of 'regular progress of the Works' having been 'materially affected'. Some items of expense, such as the retention on site of supervisory staff, huts, etc. where a prolongation of the contract period is involved, will be immediately obvious, directly traceable to the primary cause of disruption and easily quantifiable. Other items of loss or expense will be far less easy to identify and quantify without question – items such as the loss of productive use of plant and labour. It may be difficult to trace with accuracy the precise effects of disruption and delay when, almost inevitably, loss and expense arising from causes for which the contractor can recover are inextricably mixed up with those arising from other causes such as *force majeure* and the contractor's own inefficiency.

In the vast majority of cases, therefore, large elements of the 'ascertainment' will in fact involve negotiation – the contractor putting forward his view of his entitlement for examination by the quantity surveyor appointed under the contract. Where those elements are involved we believe it is no longer appropriate for the quantity surveyor to adopt a severely impartial stance. The 'claim' being put forward by the contractor will have been prepared by his own quantity-surveying staff, and will inevitably, and properly, be biased in his favour. Contractors' quantity surveyors are under no obligation to be impartial; their duty is solely to their employer, and provided they keep within the bounds of professional propriety it is part of that duty to put forward the best possible case. If the quantity surveyor under the contract adopts a strictly impartial stance, there will be no one to argue the employer's case in negotiations over the 'claim' put forward by the contractor's quantity surveyors in those areas (of which there are many) where there are two perfectly proper and sustainable cases to be argued, one favouring the contractor and the other the employer. We believe that it is then the quantity surveyor's duty to put forward that view which favours the employer and to seek to convince his opposite number from the contractor's staff to the rightness of that view. When all negotiations are concluded, however, and agreement has not been reached, the quantity surveyor must then endeavour to stand back from the arguments, cease to see the matter solely from the employer's viewpoint, and make an unbiased recommendation to the architect as to the sum of money which, in his honest professional opinion, should be certified as due to the contractor. A quantity surveyor who, having failed to convince the contractor of the rightness of his arguments biased in favour of the employer, then continues to put forward that biased view without further thought is doing no favour to the employer. The end result may well be to involve the employer in quite unnecessary arbitration or litigation which he cannot ultimately win.

Clearly, in carrying out the duty of ascertainment the quantity surveyor will have little of the relevant detail within his own knowledge, and he will be largely dependent upon information provided by the contractor. In chapter 11 we have already given some indication of the kind of back-up material a contractor should provide in order for the ascertainment to take place. However, many smaller contractors will not have cost records in the kind of detail that we have suggested, and in those circumstances it is the quantity surveyor's duty to make the best assessment he can in the light of his own knowledge and experience; he should not refuse to make any recommendation at all simply because detailed substantiation of the precise amount is not available, but he should remember that the contract 'does not in any instance give him authority to determine any liability, or liability to make any payment or allowance': Mr Justice Webster in

County & District Properties Ltd v. *John Laing Construction Ltd* (1982).

For the sake of completeness we append, in tabular form, the situation regarding the quantity surveyor's duties under JCT 80 and the supporting Form of Sub-Contract (NSC/4 or NSC/4a).

Duties of the quantity surveyor under JCT 80

	Clause
Not to divulge or use, except for the purposes of the contract, any of the rates or prices in the contract bills	(5.7)
To value all variations, and instructions as to the expenditure of provisional sums	(13.4.1)
To give the contractor an opportunity to be present at time of measurement of variation valuations	(13.6)
If instructed by the architect, to ascertain the amount of direct loss and/or expense incurred by the contractor and resulting from the regular progress of the works being materially affected by one or more of the matters referred to in clause 26.2	(26.1)
If instructed by the architect, to ascertain the amount of direct loss and/or expense incurred by a nominated sub-contractor and resulting from the regular progress of the sub-contract works being materially affected by one or more of the matters referred to in clause 13.2 of NSC/4 or NSC/4a	(26.4.1)
To make interim valuations for every interim certificate if fluctuations clause 40 (price adjustment formulae) applies, and if that clause does not apply to make interim valuations whenever the architect considers them to be necessary for the purpose of an interim certificate, and	(30.1.2)
If the architect so instructs, to prepare a statement specifying the contractor's retention and the nominated sub-contract retention for each nominated sub-contractor	(30.5.2.1)
To prepare a statement of all the final valuations under clause 13 (valuation of variations and provisional sum work) including those relating to the work of nominated sub-contractors, and	(30.6.1.2)

If instructed by the architect, to ascertain the amount of direct loss and/or expense incurred by the contractor as a result of finding antiquities, etc.   (34.3.1)

JCT 80 also provides that, if the fluctuations clause 38 (contribution, levy and tax fluctuations), or clause 39 (labour and materials cost and tax fluctuations) applies, the quantity surveyor and the contractor may agree the net amount of the adjustment in respect of any of the events referred to in the clause. [(38.4.3), and (39.5.3).]

As regards this provision, Mr Justice Webster held, in *County and District Properties Ltd* v. *John Laing Construction Ltd* (1982), that this power covers quantum only and not liability.

Clause 40 (Use of Price Adjustment Formulae) also empowers the quantity surveyor to agree with the contractor 'any alteration to the methods and procedure for ascertaining the amount of formula adjustment to be made' provided that the amount 'will be the same or approximately the same as that ascertained in accordance with ... the Formula Rules' – though how that is to be checked without actually applying the Formula Rules is not explained!

Duties of the Quantity Surveyor under Sub-Contracts NSC/4 and NSC/4a

	Clause
If the sub-contractor quoted a sub-contract sum, to value all variations and instructions as to the expenditure of provisional sums	(16.1)
If the sub-contractor quoted a tender sum subject to complete remeasurement, to value all work executed	(17.1)
If the sub-contractor quoted a sub-contract sum, to prepare a statement of the final valuation of all variations under clause 16 (valuation of variations and provisional sum work), and	(21.10.1.2)
If the sub-contractor's employment has been determined by the contractor, and if instructed by the architect, to ascertain the amount of expenses properly incurred by the employer and the amount of direct loss and/or damage caused to the employer by the determination.	(29.4)

The sub-contracts also provide:

That if fluctuation clause 35 (contributions, levy and tax fluctuations) or 36 (labour and materials cost and tax fluctuations) applies the quantity surveyor and the sub-contractor may agree the net amount of the adjustment in respect of any of the events referred to in the relevant clause, and (35.4.3 or 36.5.3)

That if fluctuation clause 37 (formula adjustment) applies the contractor on behalf of and with the consent of the sub-contractor may agree with the quantity surveyor any alteration to the methods and procedures provided that the alteration is not expected to significantly vary the result. (37.5)

Appendix

Example of build-up of contractor's entitlement to reimbursement of direct loss and/or expense under JCT 1980, clause 26

INTRODUCTION

The authors have had some difficulty in devising a suitable example of a 'claim' under the 1980 JCT Contract for two reasons. First, at the time of writing even of this second edition there has been so little experience of the use of the form in practice that there is virtually no historical data available. Second, and more important, the terms of clause 26 of the form are such that, as has already been explained in the text, a contractor's entitlement to reimbursement under the clause should, if properly handled by all concerned, be dealt with almost on a monthly basis during the course of the contract; there should therefore be no need for a single consolidated 'claim' of the kind we have grown to know, but not to love, under the 1963 Edition.

We have therefore decided to give not a 'sample claim', but a final build-up of a contractor's entitlement under a hypothetical contract as it might be done by the architect or quantity surveyor at the end of the job, based upon information given to him by the contractor. It is to be assumed, of course, that payments on a provisional basis have been made to the contractor from time to time under interim certificates during the course of the contract, and that only a small balance will be left to be paid to him after this exercise.

DETAILS OF THE CONTRACT

The contract is for the construction of a speculative office development. The essential details for purposes of this exercise are: a reinforced concrete structure (no basement) supported upon bored piles; cladding is curtain walling with tinted anti-sun glass; full air-conditioning; marble flooring and wall and column linings to the prestige entrance hall; piling, cladding, air-conditioning and marble by nominated sub-contractors.

Contract Sum £2,840,380
Date of Possession .... 1 September 1980
Date for Completion .... 30 September 1982
Liquidated and ascertained damages .... £15,000 per week
Fluctuations .... clause 40

Major delays have occurred during the course of the Works as follows:

(1) Sub-soil problems led to a major re-design of the piling together with the reinforced concrete pile caps and ground beams;

(2) The consulting engineer, through the architect, was late in providing reinforcement details for the first floor structure;

(3) Sharp frosts in April and May 1981 caused delays to the reinforced concrete work;

(4) The intended nominated sub-contractor for the air-conditioning went into liquidation after the architect had issued his preliminary notice of nomination under clause 35.7; there was then a 4 week delay while the next firm on the tender list was approached and agreed to take over;

(5) The building inspector objected to the fixings for the curtain walling; there was a 6 week delay while new fixings were designed and agreed and a further delay while alterations were made to the fixing slots in the structure;

(6) A strike of quarry workers in Italy caused a 3 month delay in delivery of the marble for the entrance hall.

In other words, a fairly typical contract.

The contractor has given all the proper notices of delay etc., and the architect, having granted extensions of time during the course of the Works, has now made his final decision under clause 25.3.3 giving a total extension of $33\frac{1}{2}$ weeks, giving the completion date of 24 May 1983. In his own records the architect has the following break-down of the overall extension:

	Delay to progress (weeks)	Delay to completion (weeks)
(1) *Sub-soil problems*		
1. Work virtually suspended during the whole period of re-design	3	3
2. Extra period for additional work (some of which was not critical to overall progress)	2	$1\frac{1}{2}$
(2) *Late reinforcement details*		
The details should have been delivered on 1 February 1981, but were actually delivered on 22 February, 3 weeks late; however it was apparent from his Master Programme that the contractor had allowed a 1 week float in his request for the information, and the activity of reinforcement to the first floor was not fully critical	2	1
(3) *Frost*		
Concreting was impossible for 5 working days during a period when frost could not be anticipated – but other work continued un-impeded	1	–
(4) *Nomination for air-conditioning*		
Although there was a 4 week delay in making the new nomination, plenty of time had been allowed and there was only a small delay to progress of the Works overall	1	1

	Delay to progress (weeks)	Delay to completion (weeks)
(5) *Fixings for curtain walling*		
This effectively prevented the building being weather-proofed and had a serious effect on all following trades. The air-conditioning was not seriously affected at the time but final installations were delayed	10	9
(6) *Quarry workers' strike*		
The strike started 1 month before the revised programme date for delivery of the marble for working in UK. By the time production was back to normal some 15 weeks had been lost. The employer refused to allow the work to be omitted from the contract, or to take possession of the otherwise completed building, on the grounds that the building was useless for letting purposes with the prestige entrance hall unfinished	15	15
(7) These delays meant that construction work now extended over the Christmas/New Year 1982/83 and Easter 1983 holidays	3	3
	Total extension	33½ weeks

BUILD-UP OF ENTITLEMENT

The following are the quantity surveyor's notes showing his build-up of the contractor's total entitlement to reimbursement under clause 26 of the contract, based upon the architect's break-down of delays as given above and upon information on costs etc. provided by the contractor during the course of and at the end of the contract. As the figures used here are made up entirely out of the authors' heads they are *not* reliable and are *not* to be used in the build-up of any real-life entitlement.

(1) *Sub-soil problems*   £

   1. *Period of re-design*   £

Work was almost totally suspended during the period of re-design. The contractor's civil engineering supervisor was retained on site almost wholly unproductively during that time, although for some 25% of the time he was able to assist in connection with a problem on another contract. The contractor had brought his cement silo and concrete-mixing plant onto the site in anticipation of starting on the pile caps and ground beams.

	£	£
Civil engineering supervisor –		
3 weeks at £225 per week × 75%	506	
Other incidental labour on site and largely unproductive –		

2 Gangers – per week	£180	
5 Labourers – per week	£400	
	£580	

	£	£
3 weeks at £580 per week × 60%	1,044	
Silo and mixing plant wholly unproductive –		
3 weeks at £750 per week	2,250	3,800

At the end of the contract the contractor was detained upon the site for a period of 3 weeks and incurred running costs as follows:

	per week
On site	£
Site Agent	190
3 Sub-agents	450
4 Supervisors etc.	560
3 General staff	300
Site compound (own huts etc. – depreciation, electrical and water supply, rates, etc.)	450
Safety, health, welfare, general site plant and other general running costs (staff costs included above)	300
Off site	
Contract manager	275
2 Assistants	350
Other staff involvement, running costs directly related to this contract etc.	250
Total costs per week	£3,125

3 weeks at £3,125 per week	9,375

2. *Additional work*

The additional involvement of the civil engineering supervisor and other staff costs have already been taken into account in the valuation of the additional work in accordance with clause 13.5.3.3. of the contract. The contractor's entitlement under clause 26.1 is therefore confined to the effect of the over-run at the end of the contract period.

$1\frac{1}{2}$ weeks at £3,125 per week as (1)1 above	4,688

Total entitlement in respect of sub-soil problems	£17,863

Note: The entitlement of the nominated piling sub-

contractor to reimbursement of direct loss and/
or expense under clause 13.1 of the sub-contract
has been ascertained, certified and paid under
clause 35.17 of the main contract.

(2) *Late reinforcement details*   £

The delay in progress of the reinforced concrete
work has been stated by the architect to be 2 weeks
but, the activity not being fully critical, the architect has fixed the overall effect upon contract
completion at only 1 week.

1. *Costs at the time of the delay*

The following were detained upon the site for
a period of 2 weeks: Per week

	£
Civil engineering supervisor	225
Concreting gang; reinforcement fixers, car- penters for formwork, labourers – 15 men in all	1,350
Silo and mixing plant	750
Total costs per week	£2,325

2 Weeks at £2,325 per week	4,650
Other labour on site at the time rendered unproductive to the extent of the 1 week overall delay in completion – say	2,500

2. *Costs during over-run period*

1 Week at £3,125 per week as (1) 1 above	3,125

*Total entitlement in respect of late reinforcement
details*   £10,275

(3) *Frost*   £
No entitlement.   Nil

(4) *Nomination for air-conditioning*

Labour generally on the site was rendered unproductive to the extent of the 1 week delay to progress and completion. However the contractor was able to mitigate the effect of this to a large extent by re-deployment – say	1,000
1 week running costs during the over-run period at £3,125 per week as (1)1 above	3,125

Total entitlement in respect of delayed nomination   £4,125

(5) *Fixings for curtain walling*   £

This had a very serious effect on productivity since virtually no
work was possible until the problem had been solved; the
contractor was therefore not only involved in men standing idle,

	£
but had actually to lay off a substantial number of his workforce and re-engage when work was possible again. The total additional labour cost has been calculated and substantiated by the contractor [calculation not shown]	17,250
Standing time of scaffolding – 10 weeks at £4,800 per week	48,000
Standing time of tower crane – 10 weeks at £1,750 per week	17,500
Standing time of other general plant – 10 weeks at £1,500 per week	15,000
Running costs during the over-run period – 9 weeks at £3,125 per week as (1)1 above	28,125
Total entitlement in respect of incorrect design of fixings for curtain walling	£97,750

(6) *Quarry workers' strike*   Nil
No entitlement

(7) *Public holidays*
The delays in completion for which the contractor is entitled to reimbursement would have resulted in completion being delayed beyond the Christmas/New Year holiday 1982/83, but would not have delayed it beyond Easter 1983.

Running costs during the over-run period – 2 weeks at £3,125 per week as (1)1 above	6,250
Total entitlement in respect of public holidays	£6,250

Summary

(1)	Sub-soil problems	17,863
(2)	Late reinforcement details	10,275
(3)	Frost	Nil
(4)	Delayed nomination for air-conditioning	4,125
(5)	Fixings for curtain walling	97,750
(6)	Quarry workers' strike	Nil
(7)	Public holidays	6,250

Total entitlement of the contractor to reimbursement of direct loss and/or expense under clause 26.1 of the contract	£136,263

NOTES

Generally

The authors are very conscious that, in putting forward an exercise of this kind, they are offering themselves as hostages and may expect the slings and arrows, if not of outrageous fortune, then certainly of outraged commentators and critics. We must emphasise that this exercise is intended only to show the principles which we believe should be applied in making such an ascertainment.

In particular we say again that the figures used, like the whole exercise, are entirely fictitious, and we will accept no criticism on the grounds that they are unrelated to reality; we simply ask the reader to accept that these are the figures substantiated by this particular fictitious contractor on this particular fictitious contract. In actual practice, of course, the figures would be carefully ascertained from the contractor's cost records and would certainly not be in the round terms used here for ease of calculation.

Again, we are very conscious that other specialists in this field, and ordinary practitioners, will be able to pick large holes in the actual items we have used in the build-up of the ascertainment. We have no doubt that others will be able to point out many items which should have included but have not, and many items which we have included but should not. We can only repeat: this is not intended to be a 'model ascertainment' and we would be horrified if, for instance, a particular item of cost put forward by a real contractor on a real contract were disallowed on the grounds that 'it doesn't appear in Powell-Smith and Sims's example so you can't have it'.

There are two general points we should make.

(1) We have made life a bit easier for ourselves by making this contract subject to formula price adjustment under clause 40 of JCT 1980. The effects of inflation are therefore theoretically taken into account by the application of the formula and do not feature as an element of 'direct loss and/or expense' since the contractor is already being reimbursed under another provision of the contract. The contractor would, of course, have an entitlement if he were able to show that the effects of inflation during the extended period ranking for reimbursement were not fully covered by formula price adjustment, and we must just assume that this is not the case here.

(2) We have not included any finance costs under the principles established in the case of *F. G. Minter Ltd* v. *Welsh Health Technical Services Organisation* (1980). As we have explained in the text (see page 147), in our view the substantial differences in wording between clause 24 of JCT 1963 and clause 26 of the 1980 Edition virtually rule out any such entitlement in practice (although in theory it still exists) because, if properly administered, the contract should now ensure that the contractor's loss and/or expense is largely reimbursed to him from month to month as he incurs it; finance charges therefore should be minimal. Nevertheless, it *may* be possible for a contractor to establish such an entitlement, and we would certainly not rule it out altogether.

Comments on individual items

(1) As with other following items, the ascertainment here has been divided into those items of cost which arose at the time the delay occurred and those which only arose when the contract completion was delayed. The ascertainment of each would, of course, be on the basis of costs prevailing at the time. Regarding the delay due to extra work, the direct 'preliminary' costs incurred at the time have been included by the quantity surveyor in his valuation of the variation.

(2) The 'loss of productivity' element here is taken straightforwardly as the time the supervisor and concreting labour have been detained on site, doing no extra work. In the case of item (1) this was mitigated somewhat by the supervisor helping out on another contract and by the labour doing other productive work; one must assume this was not possible for this item.

(3) No comment.

(4) If the sub-contractor had been nominated before becoming insolvent it is probable that the contractor would have had no entitlement (see *Percy Bilton Ltd* v. *GLC* (1982)). However, as in this case the insolvency occurred before the formal nomination had been made, the architect's nomination instruction in relation to the replacement sub-contractor has not been made in 'due time', and we therefore consider the contractor entitled to an extension of time under clause 25.4.6 and reimbursement under clause 26.2.1.

(5) Someone is in for a claim for professional negligence over this one! Presumably the architect and/or consulting engineer and/or the curtain walling sub-contractor have omitted to submit the design of the fixings for approval and the building inspector has spotted them during a site visit. It shows what can be the quite horrifying effects of such an error in design and procedure at this critical stage in a contract.

(6) The contractor will no doubt argue that he should be entitled to reimbursement as the strike would not have affected delivery of the marble had the other preceding delays not occurred. For reasons given in the text (see page 127) we consider this to be erroneous due to the lack of any direct causal link and of 'foreseeability'.

(7) Some might approach this by proportioning the additional delay to the reimbursable and non-reimbursable delays generally, but we believe ours to be the more correct approach. The contractor might be able to establish a claim for payments to his workpeople during the holiday; on the other hand the architect and quantity surveyor might argue that the contractor should not recover his staff salaries during the holiday as he presumably would not lay them off at the end of the contract and would therefore have been paying them anyway! We think our way of dealing with it is fair.

Table of Cases

Note

The following abbreviations of Reports are used:

AC – Law Reports Appeal Cases Series
All ER – All England Law Reports
Ch – Law Reports Chancery Series
KB – Law Reports King's Bench Series
QB – Law Reports Queen's Bench Series
WLR – Weekly Law Reports

Other Reports cited are listed without abbreviation.

355

Table of standard form contract clauses

Page numbers in *italics* indicate where a clause is quoted in whole or part.

Index